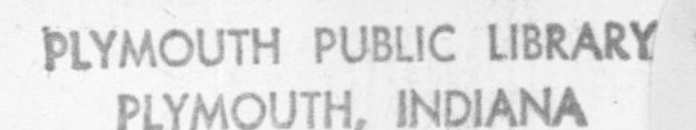

THE GATLING GUN

THE GATLING GUN

By

Paul Wahl and Donald R. Toppel

ARCO PUBLISHING COMPANY, Inc.
New York

Published by ARCO PUBLISHING COMPANY, Inc.
219 Park Avenue South, New York, N.Y. 10003

Library of Congress Catalog Card Number 64-16612

Arco Catalog Number 1196

Printed in the United States of America

Book designed by Fred Honig

PREFACE

CONCEIVED—Richard Jordan Gatling maintained—with humanitarian motives as "a labor-saving device for warfare," the prototype Gatling Gun, capable of firing at the then unheard-of rate of 200 shots per minute, made its appearance during the first year of the War Between the States, 1861-1865. Subsequently adopted almost universally by the world's armies and navies, Gatlings saw action in nearly every conflict for the next half-century. After the Spanish-American War of 1898, in which Gatlings supported the famed charge of Roosevelt's Rough Riders at San Juan Hill, this pioneer machine gun drifted into the limbo of obsolescence. In 1946, U.S. ordnance engineers dusted off the old Gatling principle and adapted it to create the 6,000-shots-per-minute Vulcan Gun that now arms supersonic military aircraft.

Telling the story of this fabulous weapon's hundred years, *The Gatling Gun* is the product of nearly a decade of research, involving intensive study of archival material such as the correspondence of Gatling and his associates, the extant records of the Gatling Gun Company, patents, official reports of tests and trials, etc., as well as rare nineteenth-century books, newspapers, and other periodicals. From such sources,* the history of the Gatling Gun, its evolution and use in warfare, has been gleaned.

A complete survey of Gatling Gun development is provided and representative models are pictured and described in detail. In making this study, the authors had the unique advantages of first-hand experience with 38 specimens of this weapon in the Toppel Collection.

* Referential footnotes have been virtually eliminated in this work, since most of the source materials are archival and not readily accessible to the average reader. There is, however, a bibliography of some principal references—books and periodicals—which might serve as a collateral reading list. With a few exceptions, these are rare publications and likely to be found only in major libraries.

In most instances, stories of battles, in which the Gatling figured, are based on eyewitness accounts and are illustrated by fine old woodcuts made from sketches done by artists sent to the war fronts by the pictorial journals of the day. Each such conflict has been put in its proper historical perspective by a brief background of that war—some of these campaigns were minor and even the more scholarly reader may be unfamiliar with them.

Interwoven with the history of the gun is that of its inventor, a remarkable man. Although best known as "Father of the Machine Gun," Richard Jordan Gatling, a nonpracticing doctor of medicine, was the patentee of many and various other inventions that made and lost millions for him. He lived 85 years and was active to the day he died.

No book of this kind can be produced without the help of others and the authors acknowledge their indebtedness to many.

Without access to the great resources of the New York Public Library, *The Gatling Gun* might not have been written. Our thanks are due the many anonymous members of the Library staff for their willing assistance, and especially to the Photographic Service personnel who made the hundreds of photocopies we required.

We are very grateful to the Connecticut State Library, at Hartford, for making available to us the wealth of Gatling material in their Colt archives. On our several visits to the Library, we were fortunate in having the invaluable assistance of Arline G. Maver, Museum Curator, in our researches. There, too, we met veteran Colt man, Charles H. Coles, whose personal recollections provided an insight to Gatling Gun manufacture not otherwise obtainable.

Our special thanks go to Mark Aziz for putting at our disposal his fine collection of Gatling documents.

The authors also wish to express their appreciation to Norm Flayderman, Val Forgett, and Herb

Glass for the use of books from their extensive arms libraries. Also to: Georgia H. Faison, Reference Librarian, North Carolina State Library; T. E. Hall, Curator, Winchester Gun Museum; Richard L. Maxon, Editor, Product Information, General Electric Company—Missile and Armament Department; Ray Riling; R. K. Smith, Associate Editor, *Ordnance;* Thomas J. Wallace, Curator, Springfield Armory Museum. There are many others who aided us; unfortunately, there isn't space available to mention each by name. To all of these helpers, our heartfelt thanks—you did much toward making this book possible.

PAUL WAHL
DONALD R. TOPPEL

PICTURE CREDITS

Page 5, Mark Aziz Collection; pages 10, 12, 13, U.S. Army; page 29, Mark Aziz Collection; page 30, National Archives; page 76, Mark Aziz Collection; page 77, Charles Hollander Collection; page 120, Connecticut State Library; page 124, Smithsonian Institution; page 142, U.S. Army (painting by H. Charles McBarron Jr.); page 145, U.S. Navy; page 153, Mark Aziz Collection; page 154, U.S. Navy; page 157, Winchester Gun Museum; page 158, U.S. Army; page 159, General Electric Company; page 160, top, General Electric Company; page 160, bottom left, U.S. Air Force; page 160, bottom right, General Dynamics Corporation; pages 161, 162, 163, 164, General Electric Company.

CONTENTS

ONE: 1818-1861

THE EARLY YEARS

A LOG CABIN in North Carolina's piney woods was the birthplace of Richard Jordan Gatling. Third son and fourth of the seven children of Jordan Gatling and his wife, Mary (nee Barnes), he was born on September 12, 1818, at the family homestead in Maney's Neck, Hertford County.

During the early nineteenth century, the log cabin was the prevailing architectural style in rural North Carolina and not an index of poverty, as some biographical sketches of Richard Jordan Gatling suggest. Descendants of English and Scotch-Irish farmers who, attracted by the availability of cheap land, emigrated to Carolina circa 1700, the Gatlings were a family of rather well-to-do small planters.

Hertford (locally pronounced "Hartford") County, where the family settled, is in the upper coastal plain region of North Carolina. It is bounded on the north by the State of Virginia, on the east by the Chowan River, separating it from Gates and Chowan Counties, on the south by Bertie County, and on the west by Northampton County. The generally mild climate and abundant, well-distributed rainfall adapted Hertford County to agriculture, still the principal source of income in the area. Early settlers engaged in subsistence farming, producing most of their needs right on the family farm and selling the surplus. From this self-sufficient economy evolved the plantation system, made profitable by the employment of slave labor.

Jordan Gatling was born May 14, 1783, the son of James Gatling and his wife, Mary (nee Cowper). He had a brother, William Cowper, and two sisters, Elizabeth (Mrs. Charles Gay) and Polly. According to the records of the Census of 1790 (the first taken in the United States), the household of James Gatling, in that year, consisted of "one free white male over 16 years, two free white males under 16 years, three free white females, and two Negro slaves." Ownership of slaves, it should be noted, is an indication of the family's economic status—the average price of a prime, young African male, suitable as a field hand, was $300, a not inconsiderable sum in 1790. Although quite probably unlettered, James Gatling, who died in 1822, was nevertheless a successful planter. In his youth—and in that of his son, Jordan—opportunities for schooling virtually did not exist in rural North Carolina. The vast majority of the Old North State's population, in the early 1800's, was illiterate. Mrs. James Gatling's family, the Cowpers, were prominent residents of Hertford County; her nephew, Lewis M. Cowper, of Murfreesboro, held the office of Clerk of the Court of Common Pleas and Common Sessions for many years.

Prior to his marriage to Mary Barnes, Jordan Gatling bought 80 acres of good, well-drained land along the Meherrin River, at Maney's Neck, not far from the site of an ancient village of the Meherrin Indians, after whom the river was named. The land was virgin forest; he cleared the acreage needed for farming and built his family's first home, the log cabin in which Richard was born. A structure 20 by 16 feet, the cabin was used as a kitchen after the "great house" was built. The typical log cabin of the period had two rooms and a loft above; the better sort, although primitive, provided reasonably comfortable frontier housing.

An experienced and shrewd farmer, Jordan Gatling was unusually skilled, though self-taught, at carpentry and blacksmithing—trades in which he instructed some of his slaves, not only increasing their usefulness but also doubling their monetary value. In 1835, patents were issued to Jordan Gatling for a cotton planter and a cotton thinner. These were the first machines invented and patented in the United States for opening the ridge, sowing and covering cotton seed, and chopping out cotton plants. Richard Jordan Gatling, it would seem, inherited his talent for invention from his father.

By virtue of patient, hard work and frugality, Jordan Gatling gradually added to his holdings in land and slaves, becoming one of the leading planters of Hertford County. During Richard's youth, the "great house" was built. A two-story frame structure 36 by 30 feet, with a T of about 20 feet, it was a veritable mansion by early nineteenth-century North Carolina standards. The house, surrounded by an ample lawn, planted with numerous shade trees, stood at the end of a quarter-mile avenue, leading from the old Petersburg road; it was flanked by a number of outbuildings, including a slave quarter. The Gatling plantation boasted one of the largest gin houses in the state. Although the family was celebrated locally for its wine and brandy, the "gin house" had nothing to do with liquor—it housed machinery for separating cotton fibers from the seeds, the cotton gin. When Jordan Gatling died in 1848, he left an estate of considerable value: a fine house and 1,200 acres of good land, much of it in timber, together with a number of other tracts, farms, and plantations; he also owned some twenty Negro slaves. An idea of the importance of the patrimony left by Jordan Gatling is provided by the U.S. Census of 1860, which indicates that of 67,022 farms in North Carolina, only 311 consisted of more than 1,000 acres. His slave holdings, too, were of consequence: with an average value of $1,000 each, twenty slaves represented, in those days, a fortune in themselves. Consider the comparative value of the dollar in times when a laborer received about 50¢ for a day's work. For a man who started out with 80 acres in the wilderness, Jordan Gatling had done well.

The boyhood of Richard Jordan Gatling was not unlike that of the average son of a North Carolina planter in that era. He attended schools in the neighborhood of his home, had his regular farm chores to do and, sharing his father's interest in things mechanical, often assisted him in carpentry and blacksmithing. His pleasures were rustic: hunting small game in the pine woods that formed a large part of his father's property, fishing for shad and herring, in the nearby river, from the dugout canoe he fashioned from a log.

Like most boys of rural North Carolina, Richard's education began with instruction in the "Three R's" at an "old field school." There being no public schools nearby, it was customary to organize a subscription school to provide rudimentary education for the children of the neighborhood. Frequently, the schoolteacher would solicit pupils, having arranged for the use of a room or building for the school. Since the schoolhouse often was a converted outbuilding in an "old field" (the Carolinian term for land no longer fertile), these rustic academies were referred to as "old field schools." In most instances, the term was short, perhaps only the three winter months when the children's services were not needed on the farm. The course consisted of instruction in spelling, reading, writing, and arithmetic; sometimes, geography was an added subject. In 1820, Samuel Nicholson, of Maney's Neck, es-

Birthplace of Richard Jordan Gatling.

tablished there Buckhorn Academy, a high school which earned a statewide reputation as a first-class institution of learning. It provided classical instruction in mathematics, Greek, Latin, philosophy, and science. Although occasionally rather extreme disciplinarians, its teachers were well educated and capable. Many of the leading men of Hertford County were alumni of Buckhorn Academy—Richard Jordan Gatling was among them.

At the age of fifteen or sixteen, his schooling apparently completed, Richard took a position in the office of his great-uncle, Lewis Cowper, Clerk of the Court of Common Pleas and Common Sessions. A good penman, the boy was assigned the work of copying records and was thus engaged for about a year.

During this period, Richard became interested in the problem of propelling water craft. While on a business trip for his father, to Norfolk, Virginia, the youth learned that the government had offered a reward to the inventor of a practical system of powering warships, having the propelling device under water and as invulnerable as possible to projectiles. A trial of the invention of a naval officer was being held and young Gatling went to see it. The experimental vessel was built after the old-fashioned "goose" or "duck" style, and the trial was a failure. Richard, on his return home, gave much thought to an idea that occurred to him while observing the tests in Norfolk. After a few months, he had made a small boat with a screw propeller and operated it successfully on the ice pond of his family's plantation. It was then fall, probably of the year 1835, and Richard was not able to go to Washington to apply for a patent until the following spring. As soon as he could, the seventeen-year-old inventor set out for the capital, a considerable journey in those days, by horseback and stage coach. Arriving in Washington City, he went directly to the Patent Office, carrying his precious model wrapped in a counter and explained his mission to the clerk, who asked him to be seated and took the model to an inner office. After a while, the Commissioner of Patents came out and asked who had brought in the ship model. He was surprised when a tall country boy rose and came forward. The commissioner invited Richard into his private office and there, side by side on the desk, were Gatling's model and another almost identical. As gently as he could, the commissioner explained to the youth that John red kerchief. At the office, he put his model on the Ericsson had anticipated him in claiming invention of the screw propeller for ships. Although Ericsson had filed his claim shortly before Richard's arrival in Washington, it was learned later that his discovery of the principle involved actually was antedated by Gatling's by several months. If only Richard hadn't waited until spring! It is unlikely that the boy, disappointed as he was, then fully realized how much he had lost; in later years, it became more apparent, with the general use of the screw propeller in steamships, that delay in filing a claim had cost Gatling a fortune.

Richard spent the next two years working on the plantation. At nineteen, he spent a term as the teacher of an "old field school" in the vicinity of Maney's Neck. In 1838, he went into business for himself, operating a country store at Frazier's Cross Roads, Hertford County, and was thus engaged for several years. Then only twenty years old, Richard Jordan Gatling probably was one of the younger storekeepers of that region. Since it was not uncommon for a planter to own such a store, it may be that Jordan Gatling had an interest in his son's business venture. In rural North Carolina, the crossroads store served not only as the neighborhood trading center (much of the business was barter), but also as the general meeting place for the folk of the surrounding countryside, who came for miles away to learn the latest news of the world, swap yarns and local gossip, and get a drink of grog. Militia musters, elections, and many holiday celebrations were held at the crossroads, which was also the customary site of such rustic sporting events as ball games, shooting matches, wrestling bouts, and horse races.

In 1839, while still engaged as a country storekeeper, Richard Jordan Gatling invented a seed-sowing machine, which he patented as a rice planter. Later, he adapted this machine to use as a wheat drill. At twenty-six, in 1844, Richard left home, moving to Saint Louis, Missouri, where he took a job as a clerk in William Adriance's dry goods store. This position provided a living while he continued to work on the development of his wheat drill. The device perfected, he engaged a skilled mechanic to make these machines for him and, by 1845, the wheat-drill business had become so successful that he quit his clerking job to devote full time to the promotion and sale of this agricultural machine.

The advantages of drilling wheat over broadcast sowing, Gatling's sales pitch argued, were that his drill method used less seed and insured a greater yield because sowing in drills protected the young wheat from the killing frost of the winter and early spring months.

Displaying a business acumen more Yankee than Southern, Gatling acted as his own salesman, dealing direct with the farmers. His standard proposition to the wheat grower was this: a portion of the farmer's land would be set aside for testing the wheat drill—one half to be hand-planted, the other half machine-planted; the inventor would receive, as down payment on a wheat drill, wheat produced in the machine-planted half which was in excess of the yield of the hand-planted half. This attractive proposition and the efficacy of the wheat drill brought Gatling his first taste of fame and fortune. The wheat drill was eminently successful, being widely used by farmers in the United States and abroad. Gatling received many awards for this invention, including a medal and diploma from the Crystal Palace, London, in 1851, and a gold medal from the American Institute, New York City. Profits earned by the wheat drill were considerable and, eventually, the British rights to this invention were sold by Gatling for what has been described as a "fortune."

While on a steam packet en route from Cincinnati to Pittsburgh, in the winter of 1845–1846, Gatling was stricken with smallpox. The ship was icebound for almost two weeks, during which time he lay isolated in his cabin, without any medical attention and almost without food. When the steamboat broke free of the ice and finally arrived at its destination, Pittsburgh, Gatling was believed to be near death and was removed to a pesthouse. The place probably was as awful as its name, a rude term then applied to a hospital for the isolation of persons stricken with contagious, especially epidemic, diseases—a place where the sick were taken and, in effect, left to die. As a result of neglect during the earlier stages of his sickness, it is likely that Gatling was, by then, also suffering from pneumonia, a not infrequent complication of smallpox. However, medical therapy in the mid-nineteenth century was rather primitive and, in many instances, the patient actually may have benefited from the lack of a doctor's attention. This possibly was true in Gatling's case; anyway, after languishing three months within the confines of the Pittsburgh pesthouse, he somehow recovered.

It has been said that this bitter and near-fatal experience prompted Gatling to study medicine. In July, 1846, shortly after his recovery, Martha, his seventeen-year-old sister, passed away. It has been suggested that this and the early deaths of his other two sisters—Mary at twenty-five years, Caroline at twenty-nine days—may have contributed to his determination to become a physician.

In 1847, Richard Jordan Gatling attended a course of lectures at Indiana Medical College at LaPorte. During the two years that followed, he studied at Ohio Medical College in Cincinnati. It has been assumed, quite generally, that he graduated in medicine in 1849. From that time on, he was known as "Doctor Gatling." However, according to Arthur Clayton McCarty, M.D., writing in *Annals of Medical History,* September, 1940: "Considerable difference of opinion exists as to whether Dr. Gatling graduated in medicine and how well he practiced. . . . Careful search of the records at Indiana and Ohio Universities show that Dr. Gatling did not graduate, and many contend he never practiced."

While his son was studying medicine in Cincinnati, Jordan Gatling died, April 13, 1848, at the age of sixty-four years, survived by his wife, Mary, and four sons, Thomas B., James Henry, Richard Jordan, and William J. Gatling. His epitaph on the monument in the family burying ground reads, "He was a kind Father."

Although much of his time during the years 1847–1849 was devoted to the study of medicine, Richard Jordan Gatling continued to work on his various inventions. On April 14, 1847, he was granted U.S. Patent No. 5073 for a hemp brake, a device for beating hemp so that the fiber could be separated. About 1849–1850, he developed a system for the distribution, by pipeline, of compressed air, generated by means of steam or water power at a distant main source, and conveyed to numerous small engines, etc., at scattered locations. His attempts to patent this power system failed; the Patent Office ruled that it was not an "invention" but, rather, a "discovery" and, as such, could not be patented.

Upon completion of his medical education, Gatling made his home in Indianapolis, Indiana. By then quite well-to-do, he was interested primarily in speculations in real estate and railroads and, during the 1850's, such activities occupied most of his time. As far as is known, Gatling never hung out his shingle as an M.D. Indeed, it appears that it was never his intention to do so; he seems to have studied medicine because of an interest in the subject and to be prepared to care for himself and his family should the need arise. Of Gatling, the *Indiana Medical Journal* said, in 1903:

> A narrow escape from death caused him to study medicine and to take a degree in that science. Diligent in this as in all things, he soon became a most skillful practitioner, but continued to devote much time to inventions. When he was married, a few years before the war, to the reigning belle and beauty of Indianapolis, and a near relative of Governor Wallace, the gossips gravely nodded their heads and said to one another, "Well, we hope she will make the doctor stick to his profession and not go frittering his time away on these trifling inventions." He didn't follow their advice, however, but changed from the profession of curing to that of killing, or, as his enemies might have said, the physician simply changed his method of killing.

The reference in the foregoing to Gatling's "trifling inventions" is amusing apocrypha. Surely no one who knew him well enough to gossip about him would have considered his inventions "trifling." By the early 1850's, his wheat drill and other agricultural machines had made him, if not a millionaire, the nineteenth-century equivalent thereof at today's prices. He was, even then, a world-famous inventor.

In 1854, Richard Jordan Gatling, then thirty-six years old, married Jemima T. Sanders, youngest daughter of Dr. John H. Sanders, a prominent Indianapolis physician. "Governor Wallace," mentioned in the preceding quotation from the *Indiana Medical Journal* as a near relative of the Sanders family, was David Wallace (1799–1859), who served as governor of Indiana from 1837 to 1840. He was the father of Maj. Gen. Lew Wallace, who served with distinction in the Union Army during the Civil War and, later, as governor of the New Mexico Territory and minister to Turkey. Lew Wallace was, of course, the author of the novel, *Ben Hur,* which brought him more fame than his careers in military service and public office—notwithstanding his much-publicized encounter with outlaw Billy the Kid.

Thomas B. Gatling, the inventor's elder brother, died May 14, 1857; he was forty-five years old. Of Jordan and Mary Gatling's seven children, three sons survived. James Henry Gatling, a bachelor, lived with his mother at Maney's Neck. William J. Gatling, the younger brother, was engaged in silver-mining operations in Canada.

After his marriage in 1854, Richard Gatling lived in Indianapolis, Indiana. Although also active as a speculator in railroads and real estate, he continued to devote much time to inventions. In 1857, he devised a steam plow, said to have the power of eight men and twelve horses. Designed for operation by combined animal and steam power, this earth-pulverizing machine consisted of a portable steam engine mounted on a massive wagon bed; the engine rotated a shaft bearing blades, adjustable to permit pulverizing the soil to the required depth. The wheeled machine was intended to use horses or oxen to guide it and to turn it around at the end of the furrow. The steam plow was not fully developed and exploited because of the inventor's poor health at the time and because the low grain prices then prevailing diminished farmers' interest in costly agricultural machinery. In 1860, Gatling was granted patents on five inventions: a rotary plow, a cultivator for cotton plants, a lath-making machine, an improved hemp brake, and a rubber washer for tightening gears.

The dramatic events of 1861 had profound effects on the lives of a great many Americans. In the case of Richard Jordan Gatling, the outbreak of the Civil War suggested the invention that was to make him an immortal: the famous gun that bears his name.

TWO: 1861-1865

WAR BETWEEN THE STATES

ON APRIL 15, 1861, when President Abraham Lincoln, proclaiming the existence of "insurrection," gave the call to arms to the states' militia, the Union was woefully unprepared to fight the offensive war to which it had been committed. Commanded by a sick septuagenarian, Lieut. Gen. Winfield Scott, the U.S. Army, that spring, consisted of a mere 16,367 officers and men in widely scattered units. The Navy, with a total personnel of about 8,000, had only forty-two vessels in commission, of which the home squadron had but thirteen ships. While enlisted men of the Regular Army and Navy, regardless of their sentiments as to the war, could leave the Federal service only by desertion (less than fifty did so), officers could resign their commissions and, thus, the Union lost about 25 percent of its Army and Navy officers to the Confederacy, giving the South some of its ablest leaders.

At the outbreak of the war, there were some three million militiamen on the rolls, subject to call —with the approval of their state governors—for service limited by law to a three-month tour of duty. This figure includes militia of the seceded states; these men joined the Confederate Army. For the most part, the militia were virtually untrained, their activities generally limited to a one-day annual muster devoted to getting drunk together. By the time President Lincoln had called upon the states to furnish 75,000 militia to augment the Federal troops for three months, the Confederacy already had 35,000 men under arms and Jefferson Davis had been authorized by his congress to call for 100,000 volunteers to serve for one year.

The North expected a short war, although a careful appraisal of the situation should have indicated otherwise. Its manpower reserves and industrial capacity exceeded those of the South but, in 1861, these were potential, not present, advantages. In the beginning, the opponents were about evenly matched. Fighting essentially a defensive war, the Confederates had the strategic advantage over the Union, whose armies had to invade enemy territory at a greater cost in men and matériel. Furthermore, the Southern citizenry were almost 100 percent behind their government's war effort, while the Lincoln Administration enjoyed no such support—a large segment of the U.S. population was in opposition.

The stunning Confederate victory at Bull Run, July 21, 1861, put a damper on Union optimism that the conflict would be a brief one and spurred the North to greater effort.

War always provides a great stimulus to invention. This was the case in 1861: the din of ploughshares being beaten into swords reached the workshops of inventors, genius and crackpot alike, who turned their efforts toward devising more efficient means of killing. Although all professed patriotic motives, it seems unrealistic to deny the presence of some admixture of avarice—after all, war is most profitable to the weapon-makers, and the inventors usually share in the profits.

During the early days of the Civil War, when Union forces often got the worst of it, Northern newspapers were suggesting, hopefully, that Yankee ingenuity would produce an *absolute weapon* to end the rebellion quickly. The *Philadelphia Enquirer* optimistically promised its readers: "Take our word for it, these geniuses will yet produce some patent Secession-Excavator, some Traitor-Annihilator, some Rebel-Thrasher, some Confederate-States-Milling-Machine, which will grind through, shell out, or slice up this war, as if it were a bushel of wheat or an ear of corn, or a big apple." Encouragingly, the *Scientific American* advised would-be inventors: "There is an enormous demand for improved firearms, cannon, shells, projectiles, explosive grenades and military accouterments of all kinds." To the contrary, Col. James Wolfe Ripley, Chief of Army Ordnance, stated in a memorandum dated June 11, 1861:

> A great evil now specially prevalent in regard to arms for the military service is the vast variety of the new inventions, each having, of course, its advocates, insisting on the superiority of his favorite arm over all others and urging its adoption by the Government. The influence thus exercised has already introduced into the service many kinds and calibers of arms, some, in my opinion, unfit for use as military weapons, and none as good as the U.S. musket, producing confusion in the manufacture, the issue, and the use of ammunition, and very injurious to the efficiency of troops. This evil can only be stopped by positively refusing to answer any requisitions for or propositions to sell new and untried arms, and steadily adhering to the rule of uniformity of arms for all troops of the same kind, such as cavalry, artillery, infantry.

The Chief of Ordnance was inflexible in holding to this policy, to the exasperation of legions of inventors and their politician-patrons, the latter including the President of the United States.

Abraham Lincoln, finding that his generals were unable to give him the quick victory for which he had hoped, was seeking a *deus ex machina* in some new weapon that would bring the Confederates to their knees in short order. His great interest in mechanical devices made the President readily accessible to inventors of tools of war. This predilection for military gadgetry led Lincoln to sponsor a number of inventions which, in the view of professional ordnancemen like Colonel Ripley, were wholly impracticable for a nation at war.

Although not infrequently portrayed as an obstructionist, James Wolfe Ripley was, in fact, a capable officer, whose considerable experience included fourteen years served with distinction as superintendent of the National Armory at Springfield, Massachusetts. A graduate of West Point, Class of 1814, Ripley had spent more than half a century in the United States' service when he retired, a brigadier general, in 1863. In defense of his policy of opposing consideration of innovations in weaponry, it can be said that, at the time of his appointment in 1861, the Chief of Ordnance was faced with a desperate situation. The Union was involved in a war for which it was woefully unprepared. Its army had soldiers without weapons. The need was not for some "super-weapon," but for an adequate supply of the unsophisticated hardware that the Army had on the shelf when the war began. Obviously, this was no time for putting into manufacture new and untried weapons, however promising these might seem, at the expense of production of standard arms. Multiplying the problem of weapon shortage were the appalling losses of matériel to the enemy. Largely officered by men whose qualifications for rank were political rather than military, the unseasoned volunteers of the Union Army had the habit of abandoning their small arms, as well as artillery, when in retreat. As one of its officers sarcastically put it: the U.S. Ordnance Department had to supply both sides in this conflict.

From his memorandum of June 11, 1861, it is clear that the Chief of Ordnance was painfully aware of the logistic problems created by a multiplicity of weapons and was attempting to standardize on proved arms and ammunition. How chaotic was this situation is pointed up by Harold L. Peterson in the précis, *Notes on Ordnance of the American Civil War, 1861–1865* (Washington, D.C.: American Ordnance Association, 1959):

> More different kinds of small arms were used during the Civil War than in any other conflict in history. The Union Army in 1863 recognized as official 79 different models of rifles and muskets, 23 different models of carbines and musketoons, and 19 models of pistols and revolvers. Almost every one required different ammunition. The Confederacy recognized almost as many varieties of guns, many of them the same as those used by the North, but many different.

In view of the problems facing the Chief of Ordnance, his position against the adoption of new weapons seems to have been well-founded.

Undaunted by—or, perhaps, unaware of—the slim prospects for official adoption of their brain children, the Union's inventors proceeded with the creation of a wide variety of revolutionary engines of war. In their ranks was Richard Jordan Gatling, nonpracticing medico and erstwhile inventor of agricultural machines. His idea was to develop a labor-saving device for killing: an effective multifiring gun.

EARLY MULTIFIRING WEAPONS

From the beginnings of weaponry, the concept of using a multifiring device to increase firepower and thus effect economy in the expense of manpower has motivated development efforts. It probably antedates recorded history by many centuries. The earliest such weapons were catapults designed to throw arrows or stones in volleys. Biblical references (II Chronicles 26:15, Ezekiel 26:9) seem to indicate that engines of war of this type were employed

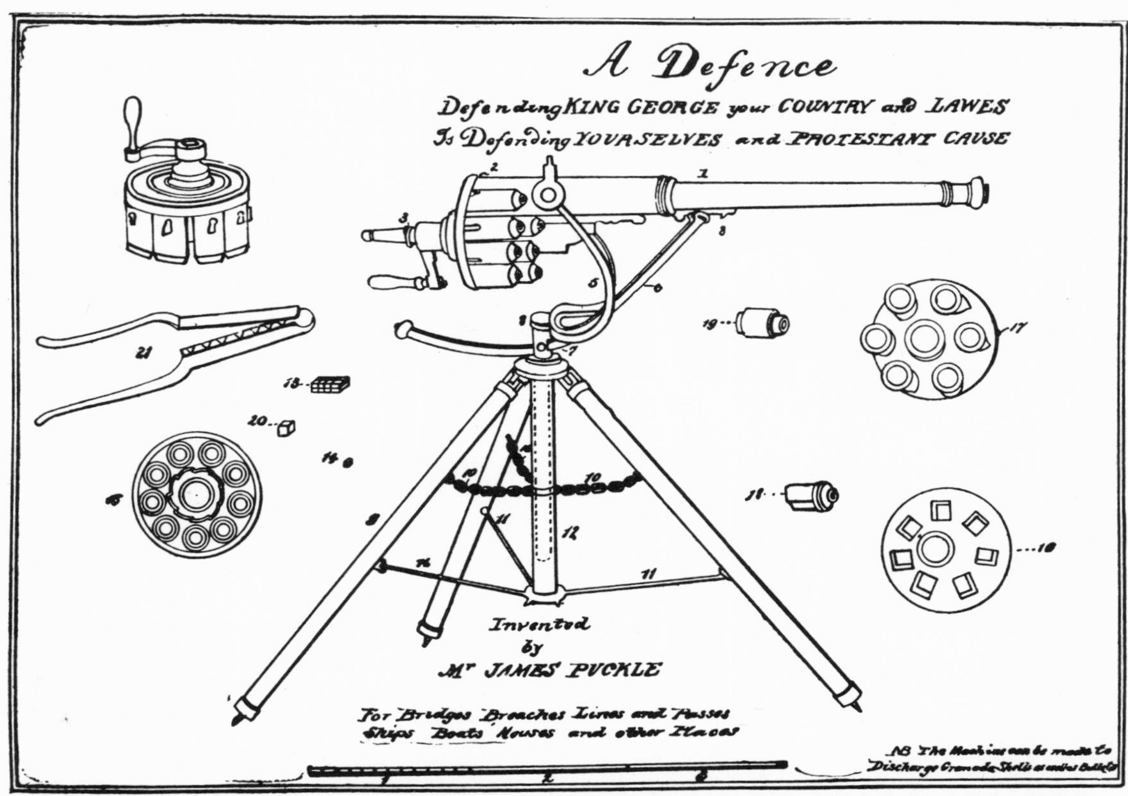

No. 1 The Barrel of the Gun
2 The Sett of Chambers Charg'd put on ready for Firing
3 The Screw upon which every Sett of Chambers play off and on
4 a Sett of Chambers ready charged to be Slip'd on when the first Sett are pull'd off to be recharg'd
5 The Crane to rise fall and Turn the Gun round
6 The Curb to Level and fix the Guns
7 The Screw to rise and fall it
8 The Screw to take out the Crane when the Gun with the Trepeid is to be folded up
9 The Trepied whereon it plays
10 The Chain to prevent the Trepieds extending too far out
11 The hooks to fix the Trepied and Unhook when the same is folded up in order to be carried with the Gun upon a Man's Shoulder
12 The Tube wherein the Pivot of the Crane turns
13 a Charge of Twenty Square Bullets
14 a single Bullet
15 The front of the Chambers of a Gun for a Boat
16 The plate of the Chambers of the Gun for a Ship shooting Square Bullets against Turks
17 For Round Bullets against Christians
18 a Single Square Chamber
19 a Single round Chamber
20 a single Bullet for a Boat
21 The Mould for Casting Single Bullets

Whereas our Soveraign Lord King George by his Letters pattents bearing date the Fifteenth day of May in the Fourth Year of his Majesties Reign was Graciously pleas'd to Give & Grant unto me James Puckle of London Gent my Exōrs Admors & Assignes the sole priviledge & Authority to Make Exercise Work & use a Portable Gun or Machine (by me lately Invented) call'd a Defence in that part of his Majesties Kingdom of Great Brittain call'd England his Dominion of Wales, Town of Berwick upon Tweed and his Majesties Kingdom of Ireland in such manner & with such Materials as should be ascertain'd to be the sd New Invention by writing under my Hand & Seal and Ircolled in the High court of Chancery within Three Calendary Months from the date of the sd pattent as in & by his Majties Letters Pattents Relacon being thereunto had Doth & may amongst other things more fully & at large appear Now I the said James Puckle Do hereby Declare that the Materials whereof the sd Machine is Made are Steel Iron & Brass and that the Trepied whereon it Stands is Wood & Iron And that in the above print (to which I hereby Refer) the said Gun or Machine by me Invented is Delienated & Described July the 25th 1718./

48/180

Ja Puckle

Puckle's Defence.

Organ Gun.

before the eighth century B.C. Among the weapons used by the armies of Dionysius the Elder, Tyrant of Syracuse 405–367 B.C., was the *Polybolos,* a repeating arrow-thrower shooting shafts, fed from a magazine, in rapid succession. Unlike the crew-served catapult, the Polybolos was an individual weapon. At the Battle of Hastings in 1066 A.D., repeating bows were used by some English archers.

By the middle of the fourteenth century, the organ gun (*Orgue des Bombardes*) had been invented (it is not known who was the originator); this consisted of a number of musket barrels mounted side by side on a cart—the forerunner of later battery guns. In 1457, Bartolommeo Colleoni, Generalissimo of Venice, used organ guns at the Battle of Piccardini. At about the same time, that most versatile Renaissance Man, Leonardo da Vinci, designed several volley-firing guns, including a breech-loader intended to use fixed ammunition!

In England, during the reign of Charles I, William Drummond was granted a patent in 1625 for his *Thunder Carriage,* an organ gun for which it was claimed that with it two men could oppose a hundred soldiers. More than 200 years later, the *Billinghurst Requa Battery Gun,* essentially an organ gun, was used for covered bridge defense in the American Civil War.

Another English inventor, James Puckle, patented in 1718 a tripod-mounted, revolver-type weapon called a *Defence.* Despite the rather bizarre provision for firing square bullets at Turks—round projectiles were to be reserved for Christian targets—the illustration of Puckle's Defence indicates that its designer was far ahead of his time.

The *Mitrailleuse,* a variation of the volley gun principle, was invented in 1851 by a Belgian Army officer, Captain Fafschamps. This gun was destined to become famous as the Montigny Mitrailleuse, named after Joseph Montigny, the Belgian engineer and armorer who, in later years, improved the design and manufactured these guns at his factory. The Mitrailleuse, France's "secret weapon" in the Franco-Prussian War, 1870–1871, was the first machine gun to be used in a modern European conflict.

Two early American machine guns, the *Ager* and the *Ripley,* appear to have influenced the design of the Gatling Gun, although Gatling never acknowledged his borrowings from these contemporary weapons. Basically, the original Gatling Gun seems to have incorporated what the inventor considered to be the better features of the Ager and Ripley guns. The barrel arrangement of the Ripley was, in effect, superimposed upon the fundamental Ager principles of operation. While it is possible that, at the time of the invention of his gun in 1861, Gatling was not familiar with either the Ager or the Ripley design, it is quite unlikely. The Ager "Coffee Mill Gun" had received a great deal of publicity, and even the less well-known Ripley Gun should have come to his attention. As an experienced inventor, Gatling certainly would have kept well-informed on all new developments in a field of his interest.

THE DEVIL'S COFFEE MILL

Did you ever see one of the Devil's Coffee-mills? I saw ten of them today, like the immemorial blackbirds, "all in a row"—the "Union Repeating Gun"—an implement that might do tremendous execution in skirmishing were it not as likely to get out of order as a lady's watch. Imagine a big rifle mounted upon a light pair of wheels, and swung easily upon an arc of a circle by a lever under the gunner's left arm so as to sweep the enemy like a broom. Fancy a coffee-mill hopper where the lock ought to be, and a crank to match. Then here is a little copper

Montigny Mitrailleuse.

box fitting the hopper. You fill it with a dozen or twenty cartridges, clap it into the hopper, and the thing is ready for business. The gunner seats himself comfortably behind the gun, elevates or depresses it with a touch, and takes sight. Before his face as he sits, and attached to the gun barrel, is a steel shield about the shape of an overgrown shovel and inclined a little toward the miller, so that a shot aimed affectionately at his head glances up and flies harmlessly away. Through the center of this shield is a narrow slit—*à la* Monitor-turret—which enables him to take sight.

Now, all things ready, the diabolical grist of bullets in the hopper, the gunner—if he is a gunner—with the rudder under his left arm, turns the crank with his right hand, and the play begins. I saw one of them work; it was tick, tick, tick, sixty to the minute, as fast as you could think; no brisk little French clock ever beat faster. When the barrel gets hot, there is another in that chest; when the grists are all out and the battle over, you pack the whole affiair in a sort of traveling-trunk, slip in a pair of shafts, with a horse between them, in a twinkling, and trundle it off as lightly as the cart of a Bowery butcher boy. But soldiers do not fancy it. Even if it were not liable to derangement, it is so foreign to the old, familiar action of battle—that sitting behind a steel blinder and turning a crank—that enthusiasm dies out; there is no play to the pulses; it does not seem like soldiers' work. Indeed, they regard it much as your genuine man-of-war's man is apt to look upon the creeping, low-lying mud turtles of Monitors, when, shut up in an iron box, he remembers with a sigh the free decks and upper air broadsides of his dear, old, stately ship-of-the-line, whose "fore-foot" lifts grandly on the waves as if she were going up a sea-green stairway, and who shakes her splendid plumage as if she were ready to fly.

— Benjamin F. Taylor,
Pictures of Life in Camp and Field

Coffee Mill Gun.

Thus, with unrestrained metaphors, was the Union Repeating Gun described by war correspondent Taylor in one of the letters he wrote during the Chattanooga Campaign, August–November 1863.

This revolver-type, hand-cranked weapon, nicknamed "the Coffee Mill Gun" by President Lincoln, often is referred to as the Ager Machine Gun, after Wilson Ager, an American who took out two British patents on this type of machine gun in 1866. No record has been found of similar U.S. patents issued to Ager. He, like Richard Jordan Gatling, was also an inventor of agricultural machinery. Who actually invented the Coffee Mill Gun is in question. In 1861, the patent rights to the Union Repeating Gun were the subject of litigation between Edward Nugent and William Palmer, both of New York City.

Sales representative for the Union Repeating Gun was J. D. Mills, who coined for it the vividly descriptive phrase, "An Army in Six Feet Square." The initial efforts of Mills and his associates to sell their gun to the Union Army ran into the stone-wall opposition of General Ripley, despite Lincoln's enthusiasm for this weapon. Mills persevered and, on October 16, 1861, made the first recorded sale of machine guns in history. On that day, President Lincoln witnessed a demonstration of the Union Repeating Gun and was so impressed that, on his own responsibility, he purchased all ten guns available, paying $1,300 apiece for them, more than twice the figure estimated by Capt. John A. B. Dahlgren (Chief of Bureau of Ordnance, U.S. Navy) as the probable cost of manufacture.

It was two of these guns, with Col. John W. Geary's 28th Pennsylvania Volunteers, that saw action in the machine gun's baptism of fire in the spring of 1862 along the Potomac River. Although accounts indicate that the Coffee Mill Guns were effective in routing a squadron of Confederate cavalry, Colonel Geary subsequently returned the weapons to Washington with the report that they were "inefficient and unsafe to the operators." Quite a number of these guns were purchased for the Union Army and saw action in various engagements. The piece illustrated here bears serial number 2; it was used at the siege of Petersburg, Virginia. Toward the end of the war, the unreliability of the Coffee Mill Gun was well established, reports of malfunctions and breakdowns being common. Because of this, most of these guns eventually were relegated to covered-bridge defense use, along with the Requa Battery, an updated organ gun.

Fifty Union Repeating Guns, ordered by General McClellan in 1861, cost the Government $735 apiece; the following year, General Fremont bought two at the steep price of $1,500 each. General Butler, who acquired his pair of Coffee Mill Guns in 1861, probably paid $1,300 or more per gun. J. D. Mills evidently was a very good salesman. On August 3, 1865, in a sale of surplus ordnance at Fortress Monroe, Virginia, thirteen Union Repeating Guns were sold at prices ranging from five to eight dollars each.

The Coffee Mill Gun employed preloaded steel chambers or tubes, closed at the rear and fitted with a nipple for a percussion cap; these chambers could be loaded with either loose powder and ball or the issue .58 caliber paper cartridge. The loaded chambers were fed to the gun through a hopper, resembling that of an old-fashioned coffee-grinder, hence the nickname. Since the piece was capable of firing about 120 rounds per minute, barrel overheating was a serious problem. For this reason, one or two spare barrels, readily interchangeable, accompanied each gun. In his 1866 British patent, Wilson Ager described an air-cooling system for his gun—it involved a fan, driven by the firing crank, intended to cool the barrel with jets of air.

Pointedly and, under the circumstances, perhaps tactlessly, Gatling informed President Lincoln, in his letter of February 18, 1864:

> I have seen an inferior arm known as the "Coffee Mill Gun" which I am informed has not given satisfaction in practical tests on the battle field. I assure you my invention is no "Coffee Mill Gun"—but is entirely a different arm, and is entirely free from the accidents and objections raised against that arm.

Despite this disclaimer of any likeness, the Model 1862 Gatling Gun has a feed system plainly copied from that of the Union Repeating Gun: similar steel chambers were used, the feed hopper was of the "coffee-mill" type, and the carrier block of the Gatling, located just behind the barrel group, was much the same in principle as the fluted cylinder of the Coffee Mill Gun, into whose flutes or troughs the steel chambers dropped.

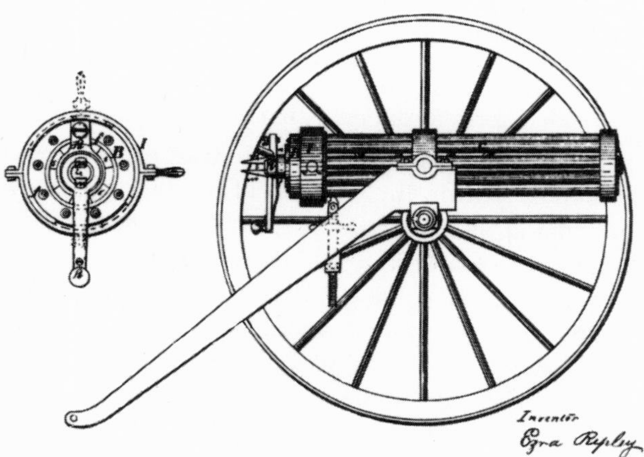

Ripley Machine Gun.

The performance of the Union Repeating Gun, when subjected to the rigors of the battlefield, was so poor as to prejudice military men against all similar weapons, including the Gatling Gun. While both the Union Repeating Gun and the Gatling Gun were ingenious designs, at their Civil War stage of development, neither possessed the reliability demanded in a combat weapon.

THE RIPLEY MACHINE GUN

Invented by Ezra Ripley, of Troy, New York, the Ripley Machine Gun was patented October 22, 1861, U.S. Patent No. 33,544. It is quite generally assumed that this weapon suggested elements of the Gatling design. Since the latter was invented during 1861 (the prototype was exhibited early in 1862), apparently the features of the Ripley Gun had become known prior to the date of its patent.

At a glance, the Ripley looks like a Gatling, having a similar barrel arrangement; however, the mechanical differences were considerable. The Ripley had a fixed, nonrotating barrel group. It was fitted with a detachable breech block, having a series of chambers mated to the rear of the barrels. In use, the chambers were loaded with paper cartridges of the regular issue type and the nipple behind each chamber was capped. Then, the breech block was locked in place behind the barrels, the loaded chambers lining up with the bores. A crank, located on the cascabel, was turned to fire the barrels, either singly or, by rapid cranking, in a volley. When the cartridges in the breech unit had been expended, it was replaced by a loaded block.

The Ripley Gun was light and mobile, had the advantage of using standard paper cartridges. Although a promising weapon in its day, the Ripley was poorly promoted and never got into production.

THE INVENTION OF THE GATLING GUN

Shortly after the outbreak of the War Between the States in April, 1861, Richard Jordan Gatling began work on his most famous invention, the Gatling Gun. According to an article in the *Scientific American* of March 30, 1889, "The idea of it originated in a conversation Dr. Gatling had in India-

First Gatling Gun (front view).

napolis in 1861 with a friend of his, Benjamin Harrison, now President." At the time of the invention of the Gatling Gun, Harrison was a colonel, commanding a regiment of the Indiana Volunteers. It has been suggested that he assisted or, at least, encouraged Gatling in the development of his battery gun. Gatling's own story of the invention of this weapon is related in his letter of June 15, 1877, to Miss Lizzie Jarvis:

> It may be interesting to you to know how I came to invent the gun which bears my name; I will tell you: In 1861, during the opening events of the war (residing at the time in Indianapolis, Ind.) I witnessed almost daily the departure of troops to the front and the return of the wounded, sick and dead. The most of the latter lost their lives, not in battle, but by sickness and exposure incident to the service. It occurred to me if I could invent a machine—a gun—which could by its rapidity of fire, enable one man to do as much battle duty as a hundred, that it would, to a great extent, supersede the necessity of large armies, and consequently, exposure to battle and disease be greatly diminished. I thought over the subject and finally this idea took practical form in the invention of the Gatling Gun.

Apparently, the idea for the Gatling Gun was conceived during the summer of 1861. A prototype gun, made late in that year, was demonstrated in Indianapolis early in 1862. Patent No. 36,836, "Improvement in Revolving Battery-Guns," was granted Gatling on November 4, 1862. Since, aside from the actual construction of the original gun, the development of this revolutionary weapon—the first practical machine gun—was a one-man project, the speed with which it was accomplished is testimony to the mechanical genius of Richard Jordan Gatling.

First Gatling Gun (rear view).

THE FIRST GATLING, MODEL 1862

Gatling's Patent No. 36,836, granted November 4, 1862, included among its specifications features found only in the earliest of the Model 1862 guns; however, two claims cover elements of the design common to all Gatling Guns: a lock cylinder, containing the strikers, which revolves with the barrels; a separate striker for each barrel. It was these claims that made close copies of the Gatling Gun unpatentable.

The earliest percussion version of the Model 1862 was quite unlike any of the later guns. As can be seen in the original patent illustration, this gun consisted of six rifled barrels arranged parallel to, and revolving around, an axis; behind each barrel was a short, open trough milled in the carrier block; at the rear of the breech, six strikers were located, one behind each barrel and loading trough. The entire central assembly—barrels, loading troughs, and strikers—rotated within the gun's frame, powered by the manually operated crank.

Instead of self-contained cartridges, this model used separate steel chambers or tubes having their closed ends fitted with nipples for percussion caps. These units were, in effect, miniature gun barrels. A paper cartridge, containing powder and .58 bullet, was inserted into the tube, which was then primed by putting a percussion cap on the nipple. A quantity of these charge tubes was placed in the feed hopper and the gun was ready to fire.

Six strikers were located behind, and turned with, the barrels. Each striker had a projecting lug and,

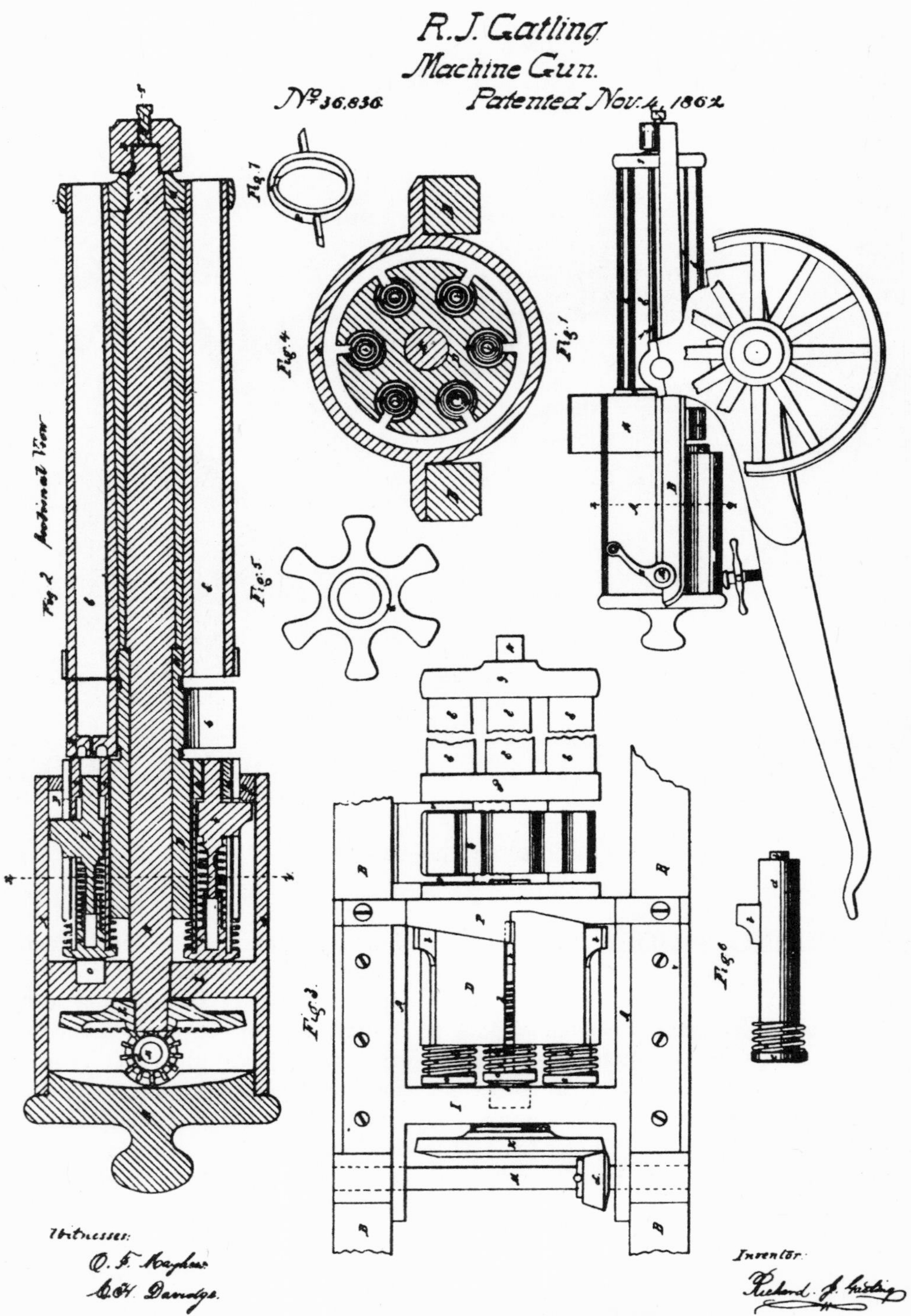

Original Gatling Gun patent.

UNITED STATES PATENT OFFICE.

RICHARD J. GATLING, OF INDIANAPOLIS, INDIANA.

IMPROVEMENT IN REVOLVING BATTERY-GUNS.

Specification forming part of Letters Patent No. **36,836**, dated November 4, 1862.

To all whom it may concern:

Be it known that I, RICHARD J. GATLING, of Indianapolis, county of Marion, and State of Indiana, have invented new and useful Improvements in Fire-Arms; and I do hereby declare that the following is a full and exact description thereof, reference being had to the accompanying drawings, making part of this specification, in which—

Figure 1 is a side elevation of the gun with the upper portion of the wheels cut away. Fig. 2 is a vertical longitudinal section through the center of the gun. Fig. 3 is a top view of the gun with the top half of the external casing, A, left off and the middle portion of the barrels cut away to shorten the drawing. Fig. 4 is a transverse section through lock-cylinder on line *x y* in Figs. 1 and 2. Fig. 5 is an end view of the grooved carrier C which receives the cartridges or cartridge-chambers. Fig. 6 is a side view of one of the tubes containing the mainspring and hammer of one of the locks. Fig. 7 is a perspective view of the ring P which surrounds the forward end of the lock-cylinder D, having inclined planes on its rear edge for cocking and drawing back the hammers to their proper position.

The object of this invention is to obtain a simple, compact, durable, and efficient fire-arm for war purposes, to be used either in attack or defence, one that is light when compared with ordinary field-artillery, that is easily transported, that may be rapidly fired, and that can be operated by few men.

The invention consists in a singularly-constructed revolving lock cylinder or breech, in combination with a grooved carrier and barrels all rigidly fixed upon the same shaft, and all of which revolve together when the gun is in operation, the locks and grooves in the carrier and the barrels all being parallel with the axis of revolution.

The invention also consists in the novel means employed in cocking and firing the gun without the use of a trigger by means of the inclined plane on the rear edge of the ring P, which surrounds the forward end of the lock-cylinder, and also in the novel use of the inner tubes (which contain the locks) to press the cartridge-chambers firmly against the rear ends of the barrels while being discharged, and in the outer casing and disk, which protects the locks from injury.

Similar letters of reference indicate corresponding parts in the several figures.

To enable others skilled in the art to make and use my invention, I will proceed to describe its construction and operation.

I construct my gun usually with six ordinary rifle-barrels, E, fixed at their rear and forward ends into circular plates F and G, which are rigidly secured to a shaft, N, upon which is also rigidly fixed the grooved carrier C and lock-cylinder D and cog-wheel K. A case or shield, A, covers and protects the lock-cylinder and cog-wheel. All of these several parts are mounted on a frame, B, and are supported by an ordinary gun-carriage. The lock-cylinder D is perforated longitudinally with six holes, (corresponding to the number of barrels,) as shown in Fig. 4, and has slots cut through from the surface of the cylinder to the holes to admit the projecting portion of the hammers *b*. In the perforations or holes in the lock-cylinder the locks (one of which is shown in elevation in Fig. 6) are placed.

The locks are constructed of the tubes *a a*, &c., having a flanged breech-pin, *c*, secured in their rear ends and provided with hammers *b* and mainsprings *d*, all formed and arranged as clearly shown in section in Fig. 2.

C is a grooved carrier for conveying the cartridge-chambers from the reservoir or hopper H up to the position in which they are fired, and thence on around until they fall out by their own weight; but that the cartridge-chambers may be removed with certainty from the grooved carrier C a comb or rake is provided and attached to the frame, as shown by the red lines in Figs. 2 and 3.

P, Figs. 2, 3, and 7, is a ring encircling the forward end of the lock-cylinder D, and is rigidly secured by lugs to the frame B. The rear edge of this ring is formed into two inclined planes, as clearly shown in Fig. 3, the greater inclined plane serving to push back or cock the hammers *b* as they are successively revolved, while the lesser inclined plane serves to push the hammers back into their proper places within the tubes *a* after they have struck the percussion-cap, so as to allow the cartridge-chambers to drop from the carrier.

The disk I forms a division in the case A, the forward portion of the case forming a shield or covering for the locks, while the rear division contains and protects the cog-wheel K and L. In the forward face of the disk I a small steel plug, O, is inserted, having its forward face rounded or swelled out slightly beyond the face of the disk. This swell is for the purpose of pressing the tubes *a* forward against the cartridge-chambers R, and thus pressing the cartridge-chambers firmly against the rear end of the barrel at the time of each and every discharge, thereby preventing the escape of gas from the ignited powder. The forward motion of the tubes *a*, caused by the swell O on disk I, also assists in compressing the mainsprings *d*, thereby increasing the force of the blow from the lock-hammers *b* upon the percussion-caps on the nipples of the cartridge-chambers.

The rounded heads of the breech-pin *c* bear against the forward face of the disk I, being kept in their position by the coiled springs *e e*, &c., which surround the rear ends of the tubes *a a*, &c., the springs *e* bearing against the rear end of the lock-cylinder and against the flange of the breech-pin *c*. By this arrangement the forward ends of the locks are kept flush with the forward face of the lock-cylinder until they are revolved opposite the swell *o*, when they are pressed forward, as before described.

The shaft N, upon which the lock-cylinder D, carrier C, barrels E, and cog-wheel K are rigidly secured, has a bearing near its rear end in disk I and a bearing at its forward end in a box on the frame B. A crank-shaft, M, runs through the rear part of case A and has fixed upon it the small cog-wheel or pinion L and crank S.

An adjusting-screw, T, is placed in the box opposite the forward end of shaft N, for regulating the pressure upon the cartridge-chambers R. The cartridge-chambers R, (any desired number of which may be used,) being loaded, are placed in the hopper or reservoir, with their nipple or cap ends toward the hammers, over the grooved carriers C, when, by rotating the crank S, which carries with it the shaft M, and pinion L, which meshes into the large cog-wheel K, thereby revolving the shaft N, lock-cylinder D, carrier C, and barrels E, the cartridges drop or rather roll into the grooves of carrier C and are carried by it up to the position in which they are discharged. The hammers, cartridge-chambers, and barrels all being on a line parallel to the axis of revolution, it is impossible for the cartridges to be out of place when discharged.

The hammers *b* are pushed back by the large inclined plane on the rear edge of the ring P, and when they have passed the highest point of the inclined plane they are driven forward against the percussion-cap on the nipple of the cartridge-chamber by the coiled mainspring *e* with sufficient force to explode the cap and discharge the cartridge, after which the cartridge-holder is carried on around until it drops out of the carrier by its own weight, when it is ready to be taken up and reloaded.

I do not claim the use of the grooved or fluted revolving carrier C, separately considered, and when the same is made to revolve separately and independently of the barrels and breech, the same being an old device; neither do I claim the direct combination thereof with an automatic revolving gear or with a device for pressing the cartridge-chamber against the barrel when used alone for that purpose; but

What I do claim as new and as my invention, and desire to secure by Letters Patent, is—

1. The combination of the lock-cylinder or breech D with the grooved carrier C, circular plate F, and barrels E E, &c., the lock-cylinder or breech, carrier, and circular plate being firmly fastened upon the main shaft N, and the locks, grooves in the carrier, and barrels being arranged on a line parallel with the axis of revolution, the whole revolving together when the gun is in operation, substantially as described.

2. In the construction of revolving fire-arms, the use of as many locks as there are barrels, said locks revolving simultaneously with the breech and barrels, and being arranged and operated substantially as set forth.

3. The stationary ring P, provided with inclined planes on its rear edge, in combination with lock-cylinder D and locks, when constructed and operated for the purposes substantially as set forth.

4. The tubes *a a*, &c., furnished with the flanged breech-pins *c c*, &c., and springs *e e*, &c., and which contain the lock-hammers *b b*, &c., and mainsprings *d d*, &c., in combination with the revolving breech D, disk I, and swell *o*, when constructed, arranged, and operated for the purposes substantially as set forth.

5. The disk I, in combination with the external breech-piece or casing, A, which forms a shield or covering for the lock-cylinder and which protects the locks and cog-wheels from injury.

RICHARD J. GATLING.

Witnesses:

A. F. MAYHEW,

W. O. ROCKWOOD.

as the striker rotated, this lug was caused to bear on an inclined plane, which first withdrew and then sharply released it, allowing the striker to fly forward and hit the percussion cap, detonating it and firing the charge.

As the geared driving mechanism, cranked by the operator, revolved the gun, loaded chambers dropped gravity-fed from the hopper into the loading troughs behind each barrel. At a certain point in the operating sequence, the striker fired the charge; at a farther point in the rotation of the barrels, the fired chamber was permitted to drop out of the gun; the chambers were recovered after firing and, at least in theory, could be reused many times. Each complete revolution of the barrels completed the loading, firing, and ejection of six rounds.

Although this first Gatling Gun achieved the remarkable cyclic rate of 200 rounds per minute, it was doomed by certain shortcomings. Tests indicated that there was considerable gas leakage at the breech due to the chambers not fitting tightly against the rear of the barrels. Gatling remedied this defect by fitting, into the breech casing, a wedgelike device designed to force the chambers more tightly into their seats at the rear ends of the barrels. This served to minimize gas leakage, but introduced another problem. The friction, resulting from the pressure of the wedge on the strikers, made the gun very hard to crank. Ordnance experts then advised Gatling to adapt his gun to handle the recently developed self-contained metallic cartridge. He followed their advice and all subsequent models were designed for such ammunition.

The second type of Model 1862 Gatling fired a copper-cased rimfire cartridge of .58 caliber. Bore size was the same as in the percussion model. Even though metallic cartridges were used, the separate steel chambers were retained and the rounds were inserted in these tubes. Great difficulty was encountered in getting the separate chambers to align properly with the bores of the barrels. In an effort to overcome this problem, Gatling resorted to tapered bores—larger diameter at the breech providing easier entry of the bullet. While this solved the feed problem, it introduced a far more serious difficulty: the bullets tumbled end-over-end in flight, often striking the target sideways ("keyholing"). Frequently, these bullets, when examined, showed little or no rifling marks because of the overly large bore.

Plagued by feed problems, Gatling directed his efforts toward the perfection of a breech system which would allow the cartridge to be inserted and withdrawn from a chamber that was an integral part of the barrel. This required a reciprocal motion on the part of the breech mechanism and led to the development of the much-improved Model 1865, forerunner of all later Gatling Guns.

The carriage of the 1862 Gatling was a far cry from the ingenious mounts of later models. It was essentially a modified cannon carriage of rather light wooden construction. Elevation was effected by means of a jackscrew set in the trail, while windage (lateral) adjustment was provided in the limited traversing movement of the yoke supporting the gun. This type of mount was probably satisfactory for purposes such as the defense of streets, bridges, and other narrow ways, but not adequate to realize the combat potential of the weapon.

EARLY SALES EFFORTS

During 1862, the prototype Gatling Gun was demonstrated to thousands of people in the vicinity of Indianapolis. As an ordnance novelty, it created a great deal of interest and evoked much comment in the press. Among those favorably impressed by the Gatling Gun was Oliver Hazard Perry Throck Morton, then Governor of Indiana. Early that year, Governor Morton appointed a committee of men of military experience to examine the Gatling Gun and advise him of its merits. They reported as follows:

> To His Excellency
> Gov. O. P. Morton,
>
> Sir, - The undersigned, agreeably to your request, have examined with much care the revolving gun of Dr. Gatling.
>
> They have also witnessed several trials of it, both with blank and ball cartridges.
>
> We are aware that nothing but actual service in the field, subject to all the casualties of war, can fully establish the utility of any arm, but in this gun, as far as we have been able to judge, everything has been anticipated to render it effective under all circumstances.
>
> The lock is certainly ingenious and simple in its construction, and fully protected from injury from any cause. The barrels are so arranged as to fire independently of each other, so that an injury to one does not effect the others. There are no complicated parts, and the common soldier can keep it in order as readily as he can his musket. It is so substantial as to endure without injury the same usage as an ordinary field-piece. The discharge can be made with all desirable accuracy as rapidly as 150 times per minute, and may be continued for hours without danger, as we think, from overheating. Two men are sufficient to work the gun, and two horses can carry it over the field with the rapidity of cavalry. The very low price at which the gun can be made, its superiority in every respect, induce us to hope that your Excellency will order enough to

be immediately constructed for a fair experiment in the field.

We are, very respectfully,
Your obedient servants,
T. A. Morris.
A. Ballweg.
D. G. Rose.

Indianapolis, July 14th, 1862.

Some months later, Governor Morton addressed the following letter to the Assistant Secretary of War:

State of Indiana,
Executive Department,
Indianapolis, Dec. 2nd, 1862.

Sir, - Allow me to call your attention to the "Gatling gun," invented by Dr. R. J. Gatling, of this city. I have been present at several trials of this gun, and without considering myself competent to judge certainly of its merits, am of the opinion that it is a valuable and useful arm. Dr. Gatling desires to bring it to the notice of your Department, with the view of having it introduced into the Service.

I cheerfully recommend him to you as a gentleman of character and attainments, and worthy in all respects of your kind consideration. Any favour you may be pleased to show him will be duly appreciated.

Very respectfully,
Your obedient servant,
O. P. Morton,
Governor of Indiana.

P. H. Watson, Esq.
Assistant Secretary of War,
Washington, D. C.

An influential politician, as well as one of the abler governors of the Civil War era, Oliver Morton was one of the organizers of the Republican Party in Indiana and a strong supporter of President Lincoln. Nevertheless, his endorsement of the Gatling Gun did little, if anything, to advance its cause. It is quite likely that this letter was referred by Secretary Watson to the Chief of Ordnance, General Ripley. Since the governor and the general had met frequently in epistolary clashes over the latter's policies, the Morton letter probably was filed and forgotten.

In November, 1862, Richard Jordan Gatling was granted a patent on his machine gun. About this time, having obtained financial backing for his project, he went to Cincinnati, Ohio, where he contracted with Miles H. Greenwood & Co. for the manufacture of six guns at their Eagle Iron Works, the largest plant of its kind in the West. As the guns were nearing completion, the factory was burned and these weapons, together with pilot models, plans, and patterns, were totally destroyed. The Eagle Iron Works was engaged almost wholly in war production for the Union and, in attempts to persuade Miles H. Greenwood & Co. to discontinue such work, Confederate saboteurs three times set fire to the plant. It was on one of these occasions that the Gatling project met with disaster. While this misfortune subjected him to a considerable financial loss, Gatling was successful in securing the necessary capital to proceed with the manufacture of thirteen guns at the Cincinnati Type Foundry Works. His principal backers were McWhinny, Rindge & Co., also of Cincinnati.

During this period, Gatling continued to demonstrate his original gun, made at Indianapolis, in that city and in Cincinnati. Observers frequently included ranking military men. Descriptions and glowing reports of the Gatling Gun were common in the newspapers and other publications of the day.

Eclectic Magazine of Foreign Literature, Science and Art, December, 1862:

TWO HUNDRED SHOTS PER MINUTE

Arrangements are now in progress in Cincinnati for the manufacture of a newly invented revolving gun, which will discharge from one hundred to two hundred shots per minute. The construction is exceedingly simple. Six rifle-barrels, of the size and caliber of the Springfield and Enfield regulation rifle, are placed in a circular frame of solid iron, in which are also placed the locks and springs which produce the explosion. The regulation cartridge of fifty-eight one-hundredths caliber is loaded into a cast-steel chamber some three inches long and capped. These chambers, to the number of fifty, are placed in a hopper, from whence they fall, one by one, into cavities prepared for them at the rear of the barrel in the same iron frame. A rotary motion is imparted by a crank, attached to a mitered gearing fixed in the breech, and the fifty charges are discharged in sixteen seconds, or at the rate of one hundred and ninety to two hundred per minute. Several hundred chambers are attached to each gun, and as the attendants can load them as fast as they are fired, thousands of shots can be made without any necessity of intermission. The recoil is entirely overcome, the point of the barrel does not fly up, and each shot is effective at more than ordinary Enfield rifle range.—Commercial Advertiser.

Indianapolis Evening Gazette:

THE GATLING GUN—A SUBSTITUTE FOR TROOPS

This valuable fire-arm can be discharged at the rate of two hundred shots per minute and is regarded as the most effective fire-arm ever invented.

It takes from three to five men to work the gun to its full capacity, and it is estimated that two of the guns are fully equal to a regiment of men. One of these guns, with its appendages ready for action, costs $1,500. A regiment of men ready for the field, costs about $50,000, and it takes $150,000 to keep a regiment in service twelve months. It will be seen from the above, that it would be great economy to use the Gatling Gun.

If to crush out the rebellion by force of arms, in the quickest possible time, is the best way to end the war, and as we think, the only way, then the Government or the War Department should at once bring into requisition a large number of Gatling guns. One of the guns, or we should say batteries (for each one has six barrels) will discharge as high as two hundred shots per minute; but say even but half that number, or a hundred and twenty per minute—and then one of them properly manned may be considered very nearly equal to a full regiment of infantry, all things considered.

They are so light, so easily handled, and require so few men to work them, and can be made so important at the critical moment—the turning point in a battle—that it does seem strange to us that the Government has not long since ordered a large number of them to be made for use of the army. Every regiment ought to have at least one of them, and it would be well in some cases if every company had one. In cases of battle, they should probably only be used as a reserve, to be brought up and turned on the enemy at the critical moment, or in case the enemy is making a charge. Three or four of them in such case would be equal to as many fresh regiments, with not one-tenth the danger of loss of life on our side.

In the spring of 1863, Gatling and his partner, Rindge, actively demonstrated the gun themselves and made numerous trips to Washington in the effort to interest the Army in adopting the Gatling Gun for the service. Toward this end, the following letter was written to the Chief of Ordnance by Maj. Gen. H. G. Wright, commander of Federal troops at Cincinnati:

Head-quarters, Department of the Ohio
Cincinnati, March 11th, 1863.

Brigadier-General J. W. Ripley
Chief of Ordnance, U.S.A.
Washington, D.C.

General,—I have examined, in company with Lieutenant Edson, Chief Ordnance Officer of this Department, the invention known as the "Gatling gun," and it seems to me to possess much merit.

As a device for obtaining a heavy fire of small arms with very few men, it seems to me admirably adapted to transport steamers plying upon the Western rivers, where infantry squads are needed for security, against guerilla and other predatory bands.

Mr. Rindge, the agent for the gun, visits Washington, and I would ask for him the opportunity to exhibit the invention to you, or some designated officer of your Department.

Very respectfully,
Your obedient servant,
H. G. Wright.
Major-General Commanding.

Gatling told the story that follows in an interview published in a New York newspaper years later:

Following this accident [fire at the Greenwood plant] I had thirteen guns made at what is now the type foundry in Cincinnati, and those I sent on by my partner, a wealthy merchant of Cincinnati, to Washington to persuade the government to introduce them. He took them to Baltimore, where he left twelve, and went with the other to Washington. The chief of the ordnance department received him coldly, told him he had no faith in his gun, and that he believed flint-lock muskets were, on the whole, the best weapons for warfare. In short he would have nothing to do with him. My partner then left Washington and returned to Baltimore. Ben Butler was there with his troops. He had heard of the guns, and he asked to see them work. As soon as he had done so he said he would buy them on his own responsibility, and did so, giving his voucher for $12,000 for them. My partner had this cashed, but at this time there was a great fall in pork, and 50,000 hogs which he had packed in Chicago with the expectation of a rise had to be sold. In a word, the break in the market ruined him, and my money went with him. So, for the first twenty guns I had made at great cost to myself, I received nothing. Ben Butler took the guns he had bought with him to the battle of Petersburg and fired them himself upon the rebels. They created great consternation and slaughter and the news of them went all over the world.

Quoted in obituary of Gatling,
Hartford Times, February 27, 1903.

General Ripley's refusal to consider the Gatling Gun occurred during his last year as Chief of Ordnance. Undoubtedly aware that his compulsory retirement was imminent, Ripley probably saw no reason for changing his attitude toward inventors at that late date. On September 15, 1863, at the age of 69, James Wolfe Ripley was retired officially from active duty.

Following the summary rejection of the Gatling Gun by the testy old Chief of Ordnance, it was the good fortune of Gatling's partner to meet, in Baltimore, the famous (or infamous, from the Southern viewpoint) Ben Butler—Maj. Gen. Benjamin Franklin Butler, of the Massachusetts Volunteers, politician-turned-general for the duration. Butler's sole qualification for his high military rank was his influence as a leading Massachusetts Democrat. The Lincoln Administration was hopeful that this favor (Butler's appointment) might prompt some members of his party to support the government's war policy. Totally lacking in military experience or even aptitude, Butler, nevertheless, fancied himself something of an ordnance expert and, being an inveterate gadgeteer, he championed all manner of military curiosa. Needless to say, Ben Butler was no more popular with General Ripley than he was with the Confederates who—because of his unchivalrous conduct toward Southern women, while military governor of New Orleans—nick-named him "Beast" Butler. Approached by Gatling's associate, Butler readily agreed to a demonstration of the gun. He was so favorably impressed with the effectiveness of the weapon that he immediately purchased twelve guns with carriages and 12,000 rounds of ammunition, at a cost of $12,000—a considerable sum in 1863!

FIRST OFFICIAL TRIAL BY THE U. S. NAVY

In addition to the success in selling General Butler, Gatling found the Navy receptive to consideration of his gun. In May and July, 1863, trials of the Gatling Gun were conducted at the Washington Navy Yard. The official report stated:

Navy Ordnance Yard,
Washington City, May 20th, 1863.

Rear-Admiral John A. Dahlgren,
Chief of Bureau of Ordnance,

Sir,—In relation to the "Gatling gun or battery," I have to report as follows:—

The gun consists of six rifle barrels, of 58/100 inch calibre; each barrel is firmly connected to a breech-piece by a screw of 1 inch in length. The breech-piece is composed of one solid piece, which is made secure to a shaft 1⅝-inch in diameter. The barrels are inserted in the breech-piece around the shaft, on a parallel line with the axes of said shaft, and held in the proper position by a muzzle-piece, bored by the same gauge as the holes for the breech-piece for the reception of the barrels. The breech-piece is also bored in the rear end, for the reception of the locks, on a parallel line with the barrels, each barrel having its own independent lock, revolving simultaneously, so that in case one lock or barrel becomes disabled, those remaining can be used effectively.

Between the locks and barrels is a receptacle for the charges on a parallel line with the locks and barrels. As the entire gun revolves, the charges find their way through a hopper, containing any given number, fed from cases, instantaneously. The breech-piece contains the locks, and is entirely protected by a heavy casting of gun-metal, made fast to a wrought-iron frame, resting on trunnions 1½ inches in diameter. It is screwed to the frame by four bolts. Inside this casing is attached an inclined ring, which the hammers of the locks ride as the gun revolves, until, coming to the point of line of fire, when the discharge takes place. The locks are composed of three pieces and one spiral spring, and are entirely protected from dust or any injury. The gun is mounted as other field-pieces, with limber attached.

. . . [the report concludes]

The gun or battery has stood the limited test given it admirably; has proved itself to be a very effective arm at short range; is well constructed, and calculated to stand the usage to which it would necessarily be subjected. It is suggested that an improvement in the manner of rifling the barrels would be advantageous.

Respectfully submitted,
J. S. Skerrett,
Lieut. Commanding, U.S.N.

A new set of barrels were made, following Lieutenant Skerrett's recommendation, and installed in the test gun. On July 17, 1863, the Gatling Gun was again fired at the Navy Yard, in the presence of a number of officers. The report of this second trial states, in part:

. . . the penetration of the Gatling battery was equal to that of the Springfield musket; . . . mechanical construction is very simple, the workmanship is well executed, and we are of the opinion that it is not liable to get out of working order.

Admiral Dahlgren, satisfied with the results of the trials, gave permission to commanders of fleets and squadrons to order Gatling Guns for their use. Very few were requisitioned, since Gatling and his partners lacked the time to acquaint sufficient numbers of Naval officers with the advantages of the gun. Futhermore, McWhinny, Rindge & Co. were unable to produce the Gatling Guns in quantity. It is, however, known that Admiral David Dixon Porter obtained a Gatling Gun for use by his Mississippi squadron.

Following a demonstration of the Gatling Gun's effectiveness at Cairo, Illinois, in 1863, this letter was published in the *Cairo Daily News:*

Editors Daily News: On Friday last I had the pleasure of witnessing the operations of a new gun, called the "Gatling Battery," brought to this city by order of the Ordnance Department, to be used in the Mississippi squadron.

I have seen many new inventions in the way of fire-arms, but nothing has been presented as yet equal to this gun for simplicity and execution. The exhibition of this gun on Friday, managed by Mr. Ringe [Rindge], convinced the bystanders that he would silence a field gun across the Ohio, in less than a minute, and that for guerrillas on the Mississippi it will prove a very valuable weapon, and do more to drive them from attacks on our boats than any other means now used. Had the Government sent out one hundred of these guns long ago, many Union lives and much property would have been saved, and business on the Mississippi been opened long ago, and double what it now is; for at this time many boats will not venture in the lower trade on account of the danger of attacks from guerrillas.

I understand from Mr. Ringe that the gun was

purchased by the Government for the Mississippi squadron, and if satisfactory to Admiral Porter, the Ordnance Department will immediately answer his requisition for a large number for transports.

These guns have many advantages over large pieces for driving guerrillas from the banks of the Mississippi river. In the first place, they can be placed upon the upper decks of our steamboats, with a shield to protect the gunners from sharpshooters. The elevation is such that they can be brought to bear on the highest bluffs where heavy pieces cannot. Again, I noticed that there was no recoil to the gun when discharged, therefore no time is lost, but a constant stream of balls flying; and I must say that I was astonished at their accuracy, and had I not seen it, I could not have believed that a gun could be invented to do such execution and with such rapid firing as I witnessed on Friday afternoon.

My opinion is, that if our government were to put 50 to 100 of these guns into the Mississippi squadron and as many more in the field, there would be no necessity for a draft to crush the present rebellion, and would save many valuable lives which under the present state of affairs must be sacrificed before this war is closed.

When I see such a weapon brought out and adopted, I feel as though we will see the end of this war, and our Union once more restored, our soldiers returned to their homes, and employed in the practical pursuits of life, which the American people were noted for previous to this rebellion.

Yours, UNION.

One cannot help but wonder as to the identity of the writer who signed himself "Union"—it has been suggested that it might have been Richard Jordan Gatling.

AN OFFER TO FRANCE

As early as 1863, Gatling had begun to look abroad for customers for his gun. The less-than-enthusiastic reception the Gatling Gun had received from the American military undoubtedly contributed to the inventor's decision to explore the possibilities of the foreign market.

On October 29, 1863, Gatling addressed a letter to Maj. R. Maldon, of the French Artillery, attached to the Ministry of War, Committee of Artillery. He enclosed a full description of his battery gun with the letter and requested that the major bring the matter to the attention of Napoleon III. While a copy of Gatling's letter is not available, the following is a translation of Maldon's reply:

Ministry of War, Committee of Artillery
Paris, November 20, 1863.

Sir: I read the letter you addressed to me on the 29th of last October, and communicated it to the private office of the Emperor.

In consequence of the answer received, I have to tell you that your cannon has excited a profound interest, and I ask of your kindness to answer the following questions that have been proposed to me:—

1st. What are the results of the tests in regard to precision at the various distances it was tried?

2d. What proofs have been made in regard to the solidity of your cannon?

3d. What is the weight of the ball, and of the charge of powder, in the combination which gives the best results?

4th. Since your cannon has been adopted by the government of the United States, there should be some official report upon the proofs which has caused its adoption. Can you send me a copy of such report?

5th. If the information which I ask you, and which, when received, will be transmitted to the Emperor, should cause His Majesty to desire that experiments be made in France with your system, under what conditions would you consent to send to France a cannon complete with all the munitions necessary to make conclusive proofs?

Do me the favor, Sir, to reply to the five questions which I have placed before you, and after I have received your reply, I will put the matter under the eyes of the Emperor, and cause you to know the decision of His Majesty.

Receive, Sir, the assurance of my very distinguished consideration,

Your servant,
R. Maldon,
Major of Artillery to the
Committee of Artillery, Paris.

Mr. Richard J. Gatling, Indianapolis, U. S.*

Gatling replied to Major Maldon's letter, giving detailed, definite answers to the questions put to him. While it would seem that he should have been delighted at the opportunity to furnish a sample gun for trials in France, Gatling's proposal to the French Government was one that no ordnance department would consider in view of the fact that this weapon was new and untried: Gatling indicated that he would not sell one gun, as suggested by Maldon, but would only consider a quantity order, proposed to furnish one hundred or more guns and stated that he could make delivery on such a contract in a reasonable period of time. The French, needless to say, declined this proposition. As it turned out, nothing was lost since shortly thereafter the United States put an embargo on exports of matériel of war, and it would not have been possible for Gatling to fulfill a foreign contract.

---

* Charles B. Norton, *American Breech-Loading Small Arms* (New York: F. W. Chistern, 1872), pp. 238–239.

"TO HIS EXCELLENCY, A. LINCOLN"

The War Between the States was about to enter its fourth year when Gatling, unsuccessful—aside from the sales of 12 guns to General Butler and one to Admiral Porter—after two years of trying to sell his gun to the Government, decided to address a plea to President Lincoln himself:

Indianapolis, Ind
Feby 18th, 1864,

To His Excellency
A. Lincoln
President of U.S.
Sir

Pardon me for the liberty I have taken in addressing you this letter.

I enclose herewith a circular giving a description of the "Gatling Gun" of which I am inventor and patentee.

The arm in question, is an invention of no ordinary character. It is regarded, by all who have seen it operate, as the most effective implement of warfare invented during the war, and it is just the thing needed to aid in crushing the present rebellion.

The gun is very simple in its construction, strong and durable and can be used effectively by men of ordinary intelligence.

The gun, was, months ago, tested at the Washton Navy Yard and gave entire satisfaction to the officers who attended the trial, and it was adopted by the Naval Bureau with the understanding that any requisitions for the guns made by Naval officers would be allowed, since which time a number of requisitions have been sent in by different Naval officers, but none of said requisitions have been granted to my knowledge.

Genl. Banks, commanding at New Orleans, has also made requisitions for a number of guns to be placed on transport vessels in his Department, where they would be found, no doubt, very serviceable. Many other Army officers are very anxious to obtain the guns.

Messrs. McWhinney & Rindge, — partners of mine in the manufacture & sale of the gun — are now in Washington with a sample gun and I hope ere long to hear of its adoption by the War Department. Its use, will, undoubtedly, be of great service to our armies now in the field.

May I ask your kindly aid and assistance in getting this gun in use? I know of a truth that it will do good & effective service.

Such an invention, at a time like the present, seems to be providential, to be used as a means in crushing the rebellion.

With very great consideration
I am your obt. sevt.
R. J. Gatling
(over)

P. S.—I have seen an inferior arm known as the "Coffee Mill Gun" which I am informed has not given satisfaction in practical tests on the battle field. I assure you my invention is no "Coffee Mill Gun"—but is entirely a different arm, and is entirely free from the accidents and objections raised against that arm.

R. J. G.

As far as is known, Lincoln never replied to this letter; at any rate, it certainly did not produce the desired effect. Gatling waited too long before approaching the President; a few years earlier, Lincoln might have been greatly interested by the Gatling Gun. In 1861 and 1862, he actively championed a number of ordnance innovations, usually against the spirited opposition of General Ripley. Among the weapons, whose adoption was supported by Lincoln, was Wilson Ager's Union Repeating Gun, which the President nicknamed the "Coffee Mill Gun"—the machine gun mentioned disparagingly in Gatling's letter. By 1864, Abraham Lincoln had lost his enthusiasm for new inventions. He had too many other problems with which to contend. Not only was he faced with the problems of government and the conduct of the war, but he was buffeted by criticisms of his administration and charges of dictatorship; with the Election of 1864 impending, it seemed for a time that the leaders of his own Republican Party would desert him and nominate another candidate for the Presidency. It is understandable that Lincoln had no time to aid in securing the adoption of the Gatling Gun. Futhermore, Gatling was then under suspicion of disloyalty and this charge may have been brought to the attention of the President.

GATLING BRANDED A COPPERHEAD

The War Between the States was not universally supported by the North. A considerable body of loyal Americans, most of them Democrats, were bitterly opposed to the Lincoln Administration, feeling that the Civil War was a terrible mistake and fearing the increasing power of the Federal Government as a trend toward tyranny. These people sought peace, not victory for the Confederacy. They did not engage in treasonable activities. There was, however, a radical minority in the North, who were Southern sympathizers. Many of this group joined the secret order known as the Knights of the Golden Circle. Its founder, Dr. George W. L. Bickley, a Virginian, organized the first "castle" (local branch) in Cincinnati in 1854. With the outbreak of the Civil War in 1861, the order spread to the states of Indiana, Illinois, Kentucky, and Missouri. In 1862, it was broken up by the Federal authorities and its leaders jailed. Soon, the Knights of the Golden Circle were reorganized as the Order of American Knights. By late 1863, the O.A.K. suffered the same fate as its predecessor. Early in 1864, the former "knights" banded together in the Order of the Sons of Liberty, with Clement Laird Vallandigham as commander. A prominent Copperhead, Vallandigham had been banished to the Confederate States in 1863 and had returned to his native Ohio via Canada. At its maximum, membership in the Sons of Liberty is estimated to have been between 200,000 and 300,000. By the end of 1864, the successive Union victories heralding the conclusion of the war, the order dissolved. Actually, these Copperhead groups accomplished little of real aid to the Confederate cause. In the border states, most of the members were Peace Democrats, who could not be classed as militant Southern sympathizers. A minority of the membership—the more radical element—did engage in subversive activities to some extent, but when Confederate raider John Hunt Morgan invaded Kentucky, Indiana, and Ohio during the summer of 1863, he failed to receive the expected support of the O.A.K. councils in these states.

The Copperhead organizations were secret societies, complete with terrible oaths and sophomoric rituals. Members were sworn to keep secret their own and others' membership, as well as all details of the society's activities. Even years after the war, these secrets were well kept and eventually buried with the former members. Most of the information on these politico-military secret societies and on their members and activities is derived from the reports of spies planted in their councils by the Federal authorities.

By late 1862, Federal agents had reported that Gatling was a member of the Knights of the Golden Circle. Subsequently, he was said to be active in the Order of American Knights and Sons of Liberty councils in Indianapolis. The chief source of information on Gatling's Copperhead activities seems to have been one Felix G. Stidger, a Federal spy who attended O.A.K. and Sons of Liberty meetings in Indiana and Kentucky. According to Stidger, at one meeting in Louisville, Gatling, whom he described as "a leader in the Copperhead movement in Indiana," proposed the use of "Greek fire" bombs, presumably against Federal troops. He was also accused of having offered to turn over the Gatling Gun to the Confederacy.

Armed with the Stidger report and possibly those of other spies, Brig. Gen. Henry Beebee Carrington, who commanded the District of Indiana, attempted to establish the basis for a case against Richard Jordan Gatling, with the intent of bringing him before a military commission for trial as a conspirator against the United States. The specific charge, it seems, would have been that, having sold his machine gun to the Union Army, he subsequently had given it to the Confederacy.

A letter of inquiry from Carrington, as to the purchase of Gatling Guns by the War Department, elicited this reply dated July 13, 1863, from Col. James A. Hardie, Inspector General, Office of the Secretary of War: "I am directed to inform you that the Ordnance Department have never purchased any of the 'Gatling guns' and that only very few are in use in our Navy. The gun does not enjoy a high reputation."

Evidently, it then was decided that there was not sufficient basis for charges against Gatling and the matter was dropped. However, to this day, references are made to his alleged disloyalty, such as calling him a "Copperhead doctor."

The charge that Gatling was a Southern sympathizer seems to have first been suggested by his North Carolina origin. This supposition, obviously based on prejudice, disregarded the fact that he emigrated from North Carolina in 1844 and, thereafter, for the rest of his life, made his home in the North. While it was only natural that he would retain some affection for the state where he was born and spent his earlier years, to brand him as disloyal because he was born in the South is ridiculous. Many Southerners fought for the Union and many Northerners espoused the Confederate cause.

Among Gatling's friends in Indianapolis, during the war, were Brig. Gen. Benjamin Harrison, of the Indiana Volunteers, later to become President of the United States, and Oliver Perry Morton, Governor of Indiana, both Republican politicians. It was largely through the efforts of Governor Morton, a staunch supporter of the Lincoln administration and the archenemy of the Copperheads in Indiana, that the Sons of Liberty movement was stamped out in the border states. Incidentally, Gatling's wife was a relative of Maj. Gen. Lew Wallace, Adjutant General of Indiana at the outbreak of the war.

It was alleged that Gatling joined the Knights of the Golden Circle in 1862 and, from that time, was under suspicion of being a subversive. Certainly, Governor Morton would have been aware of this and yet, in December, 1862, he addressed a letter to the Assistant Secretary of War, urging the consideration of the Gatling Gun for adoption by the Army and recommending Gatling as "a gentleman of character and attainments, and worthy in all respects of your kind consideration." Would he have so endorsed a suspected traitor?

In the spring of 1863, Maj. Gen. H. G. Wright, commanding the Department of the Ohio, interceded in behalf of Gatling in a letter addressed to the Chief of Ordnance. It seems unlikely that he would have done so knowing that the inventor was a Copperhead, and equally unlikely that General Wright would have been unaware that Gatling was under surveillance by Federal agents.

Gatling, it has been suggested, was disgruntled by the Army's refusal to conduct trials of the Gatling Gun and, for this reason, became disaffected to the Union cause, joining the Copperhead movement with the view of making his gun available to the Confederacy. However, if he joined the Knights of the Golden Circle in 1862, he did so *before* he ever offered the gun to the War Department. It was not until the fall of 1862, probably after the patent had been granted, that he contracted with Miles H. Greenwood & Co. to manufacture the first six "production model" guns. These pieces were destroyed when the Greenwood plant was burned by Confederate saboteurs (Gatling's "fellow Copperheads"?).

One particularly fascinating story—often repeated —has it that "Southern sympathizer" Gatling located his place of manufacture in Cincinnati, right across the Ohio River from "the South," for convenience in supplying both sides. The Confederate customers, according to this legend, were to take delivery by hitting the works in a sudden raid and seizing the purchased Gatling Guns. Reference to a map will show that "the South" across the river from Cincinnati is Kentucky—this border state remained in the Union. It was strongly defended by Federal troops and, after 1862, there was no major fighting in Kentucky, although guerrilla bands were active in the eastern mountains and Morgan's Raiders made occasional forays. It is improbable, however, that even the daring General Morgan would have attempted a commando operation within the city of Cincinnati, especially with his getaway encumbered by Gatling Guns.

It was well known that Gatling and his partners, McWhinny and Rindge, were making an all-out effort to sell Gatling Guns to the Union Army and Navy—for use against the Confederacy "as a means in crushing the rebellion," as he wrote in his letter to Lincoln. In 1863, twelve Gatling Guns were sold to the infamous "Beast" Butler, who had earned the bitterest hatred of Southerners. It is difficult to believe that a Southern sympathizer would have sold guns to General Butler. Imagine how Gatling would have been welcomed in Copperhead circles after it had become known that he had done business with Butler!

It is the authors' considered opinion, after much investigation, that Richard Jordan Gatling was not a Copperhead, but simply the unfortunate victim of calumniators. There is every evidence that he was a man of high principles and utterly incapable of the sort of double-dealing of which he was accused.

THE GATLING GUN IN ACTION

By 1863, the ranks of the Union Army had thinned to a critical point and voluntary enlistments were too few to maintain the fighting strength needed. Something had to be done and the Congressional solution to the problem was resort to conscription by national law for the first time in the history of the United States. The Conscription Act of March 3, 1863, was bitterly opposed by a large segment of the population, chiefly because of exemption clauses that made it possible for the more affluent draftee to buy his way out of the army for $300. In the 1860's, this sum was more than the average working man could earn in six months and so, as opponents of the draft declared, it had become "a rich man's war and a poor man's fight." Enforcement of the unpopular draft was met with disturbances all over the nation, but none compared with New York City's bloody four days of near anarchy—July 13–16, 1863—during which the mob, which grew to 50,000, caused at least 1,000 deaths and did close to $2,000,000 in property damage.

While others cowered in fear of mob violence, Henry Jarvis Raymond, editor of the *New York Times* and a prominent Republican politician, was prepared to fight. Daily, he blasted the mob in flaming editorials in the *Times*. Brightly illuminated by night, its plate glass windows gleaming a challenge to the mob, the imposing Times Building, an arrogant symbol of wealth, seemed to dare the rioters to attack. Raymond, who advised "Give them grape [shot], and plenty of it," was quite ready to do so. Inside the two northern windows, commanding the most likely avenues of attack were mounted Gatling Guns, manned by Raymond himself and Leonard Walter Jerome, a major stockholder of the *New York Times* (and future grandfather of Winston Churchill). A third Gatling was on the roof of the building, in position to sweep the streets below. The entire staff of the newspaper had been equipped with rifles and stood ready for the attack that might have come at any moment. The *Times* was waiting for the mob—Messrs. Raymond and Jerome probably would have liked nothing better than a chance to play Gatling music for the rioters' edification—but the attack never came. Learning that the *Times*men were well armed, the mob directed its attentions elsewhere. As it was to do many times in future years, the Gatling Gun had served well—without firing a shot.

Where the Gatling Guns, used to defend the *New York Times* offices, came from is a mystery. Tradition of the newspaper has it that President Lincoln arranged that the guns be sent to his friend, Editor Raymond, but this is improbable. As far as is known, the War Department had no Gatlings at that time. These may have been sample guns, in New York for demonstration purposes, made available by Dr. Gatling or his associates.

While it seems fairly certain that at least a few Gatling Guns were sold to the U.S. Navy after Admiral Dahlgren gave his approval in 1863, diligent research has failed to turn up a single report of a Civil War naval engagement in which a Gatling was used. Admiral Porter's Mississippi squadron appears to have had one or more, and other Gatlings are supposed to have been used to protect boats plying the Western rivers from guerrilla attacks.

As far as is known, the only Gatling Guns in Army Service were those sold to General Butler late in 1863. According to Gatling, "Some of them, however, did get into service before the close of the American war, and were used effectively in repelling rebel attacks upon the Union forces, under command of General Butler, near Richmond, Virginia."

In 1867, Case, Lockwood and Company, of Hartford, Connecticut, published (presumably for Colt's, by then manufacturing the Gatling Gun) a promotional brochure entitled *Gatling's Battery Gun.* This contains the following quotation from the *Indianapolis Journal:*

THE GATLING GUN

> Our dispatches to-day state that the "Gatling gun" was used with terrible effect upon the rebels in repelling a recent assault upon our works on James river. So far as we know this is the first time this formidable invention has ever had a chance to exhibit its power, though it has been tested and approved fifty times. No one who has seen it has doubted that in destructive energy it would prove equal to a regiment of men, and that its lightness and facility of handling would enable it to be used where a regiment could not be placed, and be moved with a rapidity that no regiment, not even of cavalry, could equal.

No date is given for this excerpt and the original could not be found.

With Grant and Lee engaged in the bloody Wilderness campaign, in May, 1864, General Butler, commanding the Army of the James, advanced on the Confederate capital, Richmond, Virginia. On May 16, his army was defeated at Drewrys Bluff by a much smaller Confederate force under General Beauregard. Butler retreated to Bermuda Hundred, a fishing village on the peninsula at the confluence of the Appomattox and James rivers, north-northeast of Petersburg, Virginia. Here he was bottled up by Beauregard and earned a new nickname, "Bottled-up" Butler (perhaps an improvement over "Beast," but under the circumstances just as unflattering). Butler remained at Bermuda Hundred until Grant crossed the James and advanced on Petersburg June 12–16. This campaign, in which Ben Butler hardly covered himself with glory, is the one in which the Gatlings were used—apparently without causing Beauregard much trouble.

It is interesting to note that, in the autobiographical *Butler's Book,* no mention whatever is made of the Gatling Guns, for which Butler spent $12,000. We have, however, an eyewitness account of an instance of the employment of the Gatling by General Butler in Virginia. In the unpublished "Personal Recollections" of Capt. Gustavus S. Dana, Signal Corps (Regular Army), attached to the staff of Maj. Gen. Quincy A. Gillmore, commanding the X Army Corps, Army of the James, is the following account:

> The entrenchments we had erected were from the Appomattox to the James across the neck of land at its narrowest part west of Bermuda Hundred, and the position was described by General Grant as being "corked up in a bottle." Beauregard had entrenched across the front of us and our salients were at one point only thirty yards apart. My signal party were stationed at these batteries to direct each others' fire and to communicate with the Navy and our various headquarters. Nearly every day there would be a fierce attack from one side or the other, sometimes the Rebels getting over our works and sometimes we over theirs. I saw General Butler testing the Gatling gun, which was a new thing then, upon some unarmed and unsuspecting Rebels who were strolling up and down the top of their earthworks talking to our men in the rifle pits during one of those mutually agreed upon armistices the enlisted men used to have. It brought on quite an artillery duel . . .*

This incident, from its context, must have occurred during the latter part of May, 1864, after Butler's defeat at Drewrys Bluff and his retreat to Bermuda Hundred.

* From "The Machine Gun—Its Early Applications," Part II, by Lt. Col. Calvin Goddard, *Army Ordnance,* Nov-Dec. 1941, p. 407 (". . . I have had the extreme good fortune to receive from Lester L. Swift, of Cleveland Heights, Ohio, citation of an instance of the employment of the Gatling by General Butler in Virginia.")

THE CIVIL WAR DRAWS TO A CLOSE

After his successes in the West, Ulysses S. Grant was made commander-in-chief of the Union Armies in March, 1864. That May, General Grant took personal command of the offensive in Virginia. After the abortive Wilderness campaign, in which he lost 60,000 men, Grant moved southward and, in mid-June, crossed the James River and advanced on Petersburg, which guarded the southern approach to his prime objective, the Confederate capital, Richmond. Unable to take Petersburg by assault, Grant invested the city, a siege that lasted almost a year. Butler's Gatlings, as well as Coffee Mill Guns, saw action with the Union forces during the siege of Petersburg.

Meanwhile, General Sherman successfully concluded his Atlanta campaign and subsequent "March to the Sea." On April 1, 1865, after General Sheridan's victory at Five Forks, Robert E. Lee abandoned the defense of Petersburg and Richmond, and retreated westward. Two days later, Grant took Richmond. Sheridan cut off the retreat of Lee's Army of Northern Virginia at Appomattox Courthouse and there, on April 9, 1865, General Lee, recognizing the futility of continuing to fight, surrendered to General Grant. It was just three days short of four years since the War Between the States began with the bombardment of Fort Sumter. Five days later, President Lincoln was assassinated. Jefferson Davis, President of the Confederate States of America, who fled Richmond on the day of its capture, was taken prisoner the following month. By June 1865, the last diehard rebel bands had given up and the Civil War finally had run its bloody course. The cost was more than 800,000 lives and untold billions of dollars.

THE WAR IN RETROSPECT

Unquestionably, the War Between the States had a profound effect on the military and political thought of the late nineteenth century, despite the opinion of the great Prussian general, Graf von Moltke, who characterized the conflict as "two armed mobs chasing each other around the country, from which nothing could be learned." Actually, quite a lot was learned from the experiences of this major war.

Of great interest to the world's military leaders were the many innovations in ordnance devised during our Civil War, among these the breech-loading repeating rifle and the Gatling Gun. The latter, which its inventor hoped would materially assist in securing an early Union victory, played such a minor role that most of the vast legion of Civil War historians have overlooked its part entirely. Aside from its bloodless effectiveness in the defense of the *New York Times* building during the 1863 Draft Riots in New York and its limited use by General Butler and Admiral Porter, instances of its use have gone unrecorded. For nearly a century, the legend has persisted that Gatling's agents gave battlefield demonstrations of the Battery Gun's effectiveness in actual combat with Confederate troops. The authors have found no documentary evidence to corroborate these stories.

Like many another invention, earlier and later, in the field of ordnance, the Gatling Gun was "born too soon"—the military mind wasn't ready for it yet. In 1862, there was no tactical need for a machine gun, since the Army did not know how to employ such a weapon effectively. Used as artillery, the Gatling Gun was unimpressive, being out of its class, and the concept of using close-support machine guns in an infantry attack—now an important principle of fire and maneuver—was not to be demonstrated by the U.S. Army until 1898, at San Juan Hill.

There were, of course, other reasons why the Gatling Gun did not find the military acceptance, during the War Between the States, that its inventor expected. It was a revolver-type weapon, as was Ager's "Coffee Mill Gun." After the Army's bad experience with the Model 1855 Colt Revolving Rifle, all weapons on this general principle were suspect. The Colt rifles blew up with such frequency that their use in the service was discontinued and, declared surplus, they were sold, to the highest bidder, for 42¢ each. Both the Billinghurst Requa Battery Gun and the Union Repeating Gun (Ager) had proved unsatisfactory in the field and this hurt the Gatling Gun, which was considered a weapon of the same type. Actually, neither the Gatling nor the Ager gun was a sufficiently reliable weapon, at the time of the Civil War, to warrant official adoption. It is quite probable that, while amateurs at arms like President Lincoln and General Butler were impressed by such military novelties, the professionals in the Ordnance Department recognized these guns' shortcomings. Furthermore, it must be realized that the logistic problem presented by a gun capable of firing 200 rounds per minute was well nigh staggering in 1862. It is likely that these factors, more than General Ripley's obstructionism or Gatling's alleged espousal of the Copperhead movement, contributed to the non-acceptance of the Gatling Gun during the War Between the States.

THREE: 1865-1870

A TIME FOR PEACE

WITH THE CIVIL WAR in the United States over, American munitions makers began to look abroad for markets for their deadly wares and found plenty of customers waiting—especially in Europe, but also in the Middle East, the Far East, and in Latin America. It was then a time of uneasy peace marked by vigorous saber-rattling in various quarters and a general girding for war. Richard Jordan Gatling, whose business acumen had parlayed his wheat drill into a substantial fortune, recognized that the time was right for promoting world-wide sales of the Gatling Gun.

During the early 1860's, Gatling arranged for many public demonstrations of the gun, which were enthusiastically reported in the press. He succeeded also in getting the leading military journals, American and foreign, to publish detailed descriptions and illustrations of the Gatling Gun. While such publicity was valuable in arousing interest abroad, the weapon lacked what it needed most of all—acceptance by the United States Government. The Gatling Gun had been tested officially only by the U.S. Navy, in 1863, and had seen only token use during the War Between the States.

FIRST TRIALS BY THE U.S. ARMY

In January, 1865, Maj. Gen. John Love,* acting as Gatling's agent, submitted an improved model of the gun for consideration by the U.S. Army Ordnance Department. It is interesting to note that this test gun, unlike all previous and subsequent Gatlings, had only four barrels. A trial of the weapon was ordered made at once at Washington Arsenal. Second Lieut. I. W. Maclay, who conducted the tests, reported as follows:

Experiments on Cannon, (Class I.)
First Report on Gatling's Improved Battery Gun made by Lt. I. W. Maclay, 1st Art'y. at Washington Arsenal 1865.

January 20th 1865.

Major J. G. Benton,
Com'd'g Arsenal,

Major,

In accordance with orders I have examined and tested for accuracy, rapidity and penetration, "Gatling's Improved Battery Gun," presented for trial by General Love, and have the honor to submit the following report.

Description.

This gun consists of four rifled steel barrels secured to an iron breech-piece with a shaft through their centre, revolving in an iron frame to which trunnions are attached, and supported on a light wooden carriage of similar pattern but smaller than that for a 6 Pdr. field gun.

Four brass collars preserve the parallelism of the barrels; the front collar being a plate pierced with holes for two barrels, and attached to the shaft, the rear collar has corresponding holes into which the barrels are secured.

The lock chamber is a cylindrical iron box attached to the rear of the shaft, revolves with it and is so arranged as to contain a lock bolt for each barrel.

The lock bolts are simple pieces of mechanism, comprising the lock (which is a spiral spring encircling the centre of the bolt), igniting pin, and ejector, and are operated by two iron cam rings.

These rings form circular inclined planes, one of which surrounds the front end of the lock chamber, and is fastened by bolts to an external iron casing which covers the lock chamber. This casing is divided inside by a partition through which the shaft passes.

The other cam ring is located immediately in rear of the lock chamber and is secured by a screw bolt through the partition of the casing. The front

* Love, a graduate of the U. S. Military Academy and a veteran of the Mexican War, served as major general of the Indiana Legion (militia), 1861–1863.

ring carries back the lock frame until the highest point of the inclined plane is passed, when the charge is ignited by the action of the spiral spring. The rear ring by a similar operation draws back the entire lock bolt, and ejects the old case.

Between the lock chamber and rear collar is an iron casting with grooves for cartridges, and is so arranged as to act as a carrier. It is covered by a hopper of brass which has an opening so that tin cases containing cartridges may be fitted to it.

The barrels, carrier and cartridges, and lock cylinder, are all rotated by means of a crank and cog gear. The cog wheels are in the rear of the external casing, attached to the shaft, and covered by an iron breech and cascable.

The operation of loading is as follows, viz: The cartridges are placed in tin cases which will contain 20 cartridges, their cap ends in one direction; the tin case or feeder is then inserted in the hopper, and as the gun rotates the cartridges drop one by one into the grooves of the carrier and are shoved into the barrel by the lock, which is pushed by the inclined plane, up which it travels as the gun rotates.

The gun is elevated and depressed by means of the ordinary elevating screw for field pieces. The front sight is similar to that of a field piece, and the rear sight is one taken from an English musket.

Trial.

This gun was tried for accuracy by firing 20 rounds at target with a range of 100 yards—the copper case primed cartridge was used. As the rear sight did not correspond at all to this piece, it was necessary to aim at the top of the bull's eye. (See Target Record.)

At 300 yards 20 rounds were fired—the gun aimed one foot above the top of the target, which was 10 ft. square. The balls for barrel No. 2 did not take the grooves well. (See Target Record.)

20 more rounds were fired at 500 yards—the gun being sighted 5 ft. above the top of the target and the rear sight adjusted for 650 yards. (See Target Record.)

For rapidity 20 shots were fired in 8 seconds.

The gun was then fired to make up 300 shots in all, and after 220 shots barrel No. 2 burst. It broke 9 inches from the rear end—a section of its length 3 inches long was broken out, and this section was split, in the direction of its length, into 3 pieces. The centre of the section was bulged out—the fracture showed no defect in the metal.

The trial was continued with the remaining barrels—the lock piece of the barrel that burst having been taken out. After 300 shots had been fired, it was tried without cleaning for accuracy at 300 yards, 20 more shots being fired at this distance. (See Target Record.)

The penetration was ascertained to be 11 inches.

Total weight of gun exclusive of carriage	224 lbs.
" " " Carriage	202 "
" " " Limber	200 "

Conclusions.

The advantages claimed for this gun are—

1st. There is no escape of gas.

2d. There is no recoil.

3d. It performs the operations of loading, firing, and extracting the case by simply revolving the crank.

4th. Accuracy.

5th. Rapidity of fire.

The gun certainly possesses the advantages of rapidity, accuracy, and loads, fires, &c. while the barrels are revolving.—There is no escape of gas, but like all fire arms, there is a recoil. It has one lock for each barrel, so that in the event of one barrel or lock becoming disabled, the gun is still sufficient. This was proved by continuing the trial after the barrel had burst.

The objections that I find with this arm are—

1st. There is no sufficient preponderance.

2d. There is too much twist to the rifling and the grooves are too shallow.

3d. The rear sight is not adapted for this gun.

4th. The carriage might be made lighter and the frame and trunnions heavier.

With regard to the bursting of barrel No. 2—from the appearance of fracture &c. it must have been occasioned by the lodging of a ball, as the material was good American steel.

All the parts worked well, but there was no test for their endurance.

Respectfully submitted,
I. W. Maclay,
2d Lt. 1st. U.S. Art'y.

Respectfully forwarded to the Chief of Ordnance in accordance with his instructions.

Gatling's gun seems to possess all the good qualities claimed for it; it is therefore merely a question of whether such a piece would be of use in actual service.

H. Stockton, 2d Lt. Ord. Com'd'g.

After this test of the Gatling Gun at Washington Arsenal, General Dyer, Chief of Ordnance, suggested the development of a larger version of the weapon, to be chambered for a 1-inch caliber metallic cartridge. The gun tested in 1865 was .58 caliber. Gatling immediately proceeded to design an improved model to handle the large 1-inch round. Eight caliber 1-inch Gatlings were manufactured at the plant of Cooper Fire Arms Mfg. Co., Philadelphia, under the personal supervision of the inventor. Meanwhile, Frankford Arsenal, in Philadelphia, tooled up for production of the ammunition.

Upon completion of the arms, they were delivered to Col. S. V. Benet, commandant of Frankford Arsenal, who had been ordered by the Chief of Ordnance to conduct extensive trials of the new 1-inch Gatling Guns. During 1866, a prolonged series of tests were made at Frankford Arsenal, and Colonel Benet reported: "The gun worked smoothly in all its parts, and the cartridges were fed and thrown out after firing, with ease and certainty. The cartridge also worked well, and no more difficulty is to be experienced with it than with any other metallic cartridge of similar construction, if indeed so much."

GATLING'S
IMPROVED BATTERY GUN.

The main characteristic of this invention is, a gun having a series of barrels, with a carrier and lock cylinder rigidly fastened to the main shaft, and rotating simultaneously and continuously, by means of a crank, the cartridges being fed into the cavities of the carrier from feed boxes, thence driven endwise into the rear ends of the barrels, then exploded, and the empty cartridge cases withdrawn, without any pause in the operation.

It is not necessary to describe the construction and operation of the invention in detail; suffice it to say, the foregoing practical results – of loading and firing incessantly – are produced by the simplest kind of mechanism, there being less parts about the gun than in the Springfield Musket.

The gun can be discharged at the rate of *two hundred shots per minute*, and it bears the same relation to other fire arms that McCormack's Reaper does to the sickle, or the Sewing Machine to the common needle. It will, no doubt, be the means of producing a great revolution in the art of warfare, from the fact, that a few men with it, can perform the work of a regiment.

One of the valuable features of this arm is, there is no recoil which can effect the accuracy of its aim. When the gun is once sighted at a given object, say at the battery of an enemy, the same can be maintained at the will of the operator, until thousands of discharges take place. This is a matter of great practical importance, inasmuch as it supercedes, in a great degree, that random shooting which ordinarily occurs in the smoke and excitement of battle. A lateral train motion of the gun may be kept up, if desired, while the same is being discharged, so that a perfect sheet of balls, as it were, can be made to sweep a section of a circle within its range.

There is no escape of gas at the breech of the gun; all the force of the powder is, therefore, expended in giving velocity to the ball; hence the initial velocity and penetration of balls discharged from this gun are greater than that of most arms of the same calibre. A consideration of the very first importance in this improvement is, that every cartridge must be either discharged or withdrawn from the barrels, precluding the possibility of such results as were shown on the battle field at Gettysburg, where of the 27,574 muskets collected after the battle, 24,000 were found loaded; 12,000 of which contained two loads, and 6,000, (or 20 per cent.) were charged with from three to ten loads each, the cartridges often times being loaded without breaking them, and many inserted with the ball down first.

The gun is light and easily transported; is simple in its construction, strong and durable, and not at all liable to get out of order from use.

Two sizes of the gun are now being manufactured by the Cooper Fire Arms Manufacturing Company, Frankford, Philadelphia, Pa. One size discharges 58-100 inch calibre balls, and weighs 225 pounds, and the other one inch calibre leaden balls of 9 oz. in weight. The smaller size gun has a range of about one mile, and the larger size upwards of two miles.

R. J. GATLING, Patentee,

INDIANAPOLIS, IND.

August 17th, 1865.

Gatling advertising broadside, 1865.

1" Gatling Guns, Washington trials, May 8, 1866.

On March 16, 1866, Bvt. Lt. Col. D. H. Buel conducted firings of a 1-inch *smooth-bore* Gatling at Frankford Arsenal. The gun was fired at ranges of 100, 150, 200, and 250 yards; the target, made of 1-inch pine boards, measured 35-1/2 x 15 feet. Twelve rounds, canister, were fired from each distance. Since each cartridge contained 16 canister shot, a total of 192 projectiles were discharged in each stage of the test. At 100 yards, 180 out of a possible 192 balls hit the target; at 150 yards, 123 hits were scored. Only 64 hits were made at 200 yards; of these, 25 percent failed to penetrate the boards. At 250 yards, 34 projectiles reached the target, but half did not penetrate.

During these tests, it was observed that out of 342 cartridges fired, there were only four defective rounds. Throughout the trials the gun functioned perfectly.

Subsequently, three of the 1-inch Gatlings were shipped to Washington, D.C. and, in the course of many demonstrations in the presence of high-ranking civil and military officials, were fired many hundreds of times. Among those attending these Gatling exhibitions were Gen. Ulysses S. Grant, Maj. Gen. Winfield Scott Hancock, Bvt. Maj. Gen. Alexander B. Dyer, Chief of Ordnance, Bvt. Brig. Gen. P. V. Hagner of Watervliet Arsenal, and Capt. Henry Augustus Wise, Chief of the Bureau of Ordnance, U.S.N. So impressed was General Hancock that he promptly ordered twelve Gatlings for his corps.

Early in the summer of 1866, General Dyer ordered that one of the 1-inch Gatlings be taken to Fortress Monroe, Virginia, for further testing. The gun was to be fired in comparison with the 24-pounder flank defense howitzer. Unlike the smooth-bored 1-inch gun tested by Colonel Buel at Frankford Arsenal in March 1866, this Gatling had rifled barrels. The gun was fired, with canister, at ranges of 100, 150, and 200 yards; with solid shot, at 800, 1,000, and 1,200 yards. Bvt. Col. T. G. Baylor submitted the following report to the Chief of Ordnance:

Fort Monroe Arsenal, Virginia, July 14, 1866
Major-General A. B. Dyer, Chief of Ordnance:
Sir: I have the honor to state that in obedience to your letter of May 31st, 1866, I have tested Gatling's rifle gun, in comparison with the 24-pounder flank defence Howitzer, and I have also fired it with ball cartridges at targets.

The results of the experiments are herewith forwarded.

I consider it a superior arm to the 24-pounder Howitzer, for flank defence, as from 80 to 100 buck and ball cartridges can easily be fired from it in one minute, being a discharge 1,200 to 1,600 projectiles, while from the 24-pounder flank defence Howitzer only four rounds can be fired in the same time, giving for canister 192 projectiles, and for case shot about 700.

The moral effect of the Gatling gun would be very great in repelling an assault, as there is not a second of time for the assailants to advance between the discharges.

The machinery of this gun is simple and strong, and I do not think it likely to get out of order. I had the oil rubbed off this gun, drenched it with water, and then exposed it for two nights and a day to the rain and weather, but though it was quite rusty, it was fired 97 times in a minute and a-half, one man turning at the crank.

In my opinion this arm could be used to advantage in the military service, as a flank defence gun, and mounted on a field carriage, to defend a bridge, causeway, or ford.

The size of the bore might be increased to advantage, which would allow the buck and ball cartridges to contain a greater number of, and larger sized balls.

Respectfully your obedient servant,
T. G. Baylor
Captain of Ordnance,
and Brevet-Colonel U.S.A.,
Commanding

Many years later, Gatling related an anecote of the 1866 Fortress Monroe trials, which was published in *Scientific American,* March 30, 1889:

I went to Fortress Monroe and tested them, and made a great success. The young officers at the fort tried to play a trick on me. At their old howitzers they had trained artillerists. To me they assigned three old negroes. I saw through the game, and asked Col. Baylor, who was in command, to give me an hour in which to instruct my men how to use the gun. This he readily assented to, and I began drilling my "recruits." They learned very quickly, and in an hour, I was ready. The firing was a competitive examination and with my three old negroes I fired and made about three hits to one on the target to those made by the old guns.

After these trials, the United States Government officially adopted the Gatling Gun and, on August 24, 1866, a contract was awarded for fifty guns of 1-inch caliber and fifty chambered for the .50 caliber centerfire infantry rifle cartridge. These hundred guns, the first major government order, were manufactured at Colt's Armory in Hartford, Connecticut, and delivery was made in 1867.

Since the military regarded the Gatling Gun as artillery, it was decided to mount these guns on altered cannon carriages. There being no provision for lateral adjustment, when the gunners desired to shoot the piece to either side of the point at which it had been aimed, it was necessary to move the entire carriage, as with a cannon. This style of mounting restricted the use of the Gatling Gun to

The following is copied from the official Target Record of firing with Gatling's Breech-loading Repeating Gun, made at Fort Monroe Arsenal, Va., from June 21st to July 7th, 1866, to test its merits with 24 Pdr. Howitzer for flank defence.

No. of Trials.	No. of Fires.	Time, 1866.		Powder.			Projectiles.	Elevation, in degrees.	Wind, Strength and Direction.	No. of hits on Target.	Time occupied in firing.	SPECIAL REMARKS.
		Month.	Day.	Kind.	Wt. Lbs.	Wt. Ozs.						
1	73	June	21	Musket.		$\frac{3}{4}$	Buck-shot Cartridges.	0° 55′	M Rto F.	278	1′ 30″	
2	74	,,	22	,,		$\frac{3}{4}$	,,	,,	,,	322	1′ 30″	Gun oiled and cleaned before firing.
3	101	,,	26	,,		$\frac{3}{4}$	,,	0° 50′	C.	691	1′ 30″	
4	29	,,	30	,,		$\frac{5}{4}$	,,	0° 30′	M.F. & L.	291	0′ $22\frac{1}{2}$″	3 or 4 seconds lost by reason of defective case.

Kind of Cannon - - - Gatling's Breech Loading Repeating Gun.
Diameter of Bore - - 1 inch—6 Barrels.
Weight of piece in lbs. - 800.
Character of Rifling - - Uniform.
Kind of Carriage - - Wooden Field Carriage.

GENERAL REMARKS.

Target 4 8 6 feet, in 4 sections of 12 × 6 feet each, placed 200 yards distant from gun. Ground rolling between gun and target.
At third trial, target placed 150 yards from gun.
At fourth trial, target placed 100 yards from gun.

DESCRIPTION OF CARTRIDGE.

15 bullets, ·48 and ·50 of an inch in diameter.
$2\frac{1}{2}$ oz. lead in one point ball, making in all 7 oz. of lead.
Cases made of No. 18 sheet copper.
Length of case 4.2 inches.
Diameter of case, 1 ,,
,, of head, 1·15 ,,
Weight of case 1 oz., 272 grains.

CHARGE.

Powder, 3-4 oz. Musket Powder.
Entire weight of cartridge, $9\frac{1}{2}$ oz.

(Signed) T. G. BAYLOR,
Capt. of Ordnance, and Bvt. Col. U. S. A., Commanding.

Table of Results, 1866 Fort Monroe Trials.

long-range flank defense, where distance would provide some dispersion of shots.

Not long after the Army's Gatlings were delivered, a serious defect in the design was discovered. When the gun was cranked at top speed, the timing of the firing mechanism was altered and the point of discharge of the firing barrel was changed; shots occasionally struck the cross bar at the front of the frame, spattering the gun crew with fragments of metal. To eliminate this dangerous occurrence, Gatling redesigned the frame, curving the front cross bars so that there was more clearance between the muzzle of the firing barrel and the frame. Evidently, guns in service were never altered and, more than 30 years later during the Spanish-American War, units in the field, armed with the early 1865 Gatlings, reported the same type of accident.

Sale of 100 guns to the United States Government proved to foreign governments that the Gatling was good enough to be adopted by a major world power. As a result, European countries began ordering trials and a number of small, but important, sales were made abroad.

GATLING MODELS OF 1865 AND 1866

Feed problems inherent in the original 1862 Gatling system, which employed separate chambers or loading tubes, necessitated extensive redesign of the basic mechanism of the weapon. These improvements, covered by U.S. Patent No. 47,631 granted May 9, 1865, were incorporated in the Model 1865 and all later Gatling Guns.

In the improved models, as the breech bolts revolved with the barrels, the former also moved forward and backward, feeding rounds into chambers integral with the barrels and, after firing, extracting the empty cases. Elimination of the separate chamber removed the cause of gas leakage and the need for taper boring, which had contributed to inaccuracy.

Reciprocation of the breech bolts was achieved rather ingeniously: a deep, helical groove was cut in the inside surface of the breech casing; each bolt had a projecting lug that rode in this groove; as the bolt revolved with its barrel, it moved forward and backward, guided by its lug, completing one firing cycle with each revolution of the barrel unit.

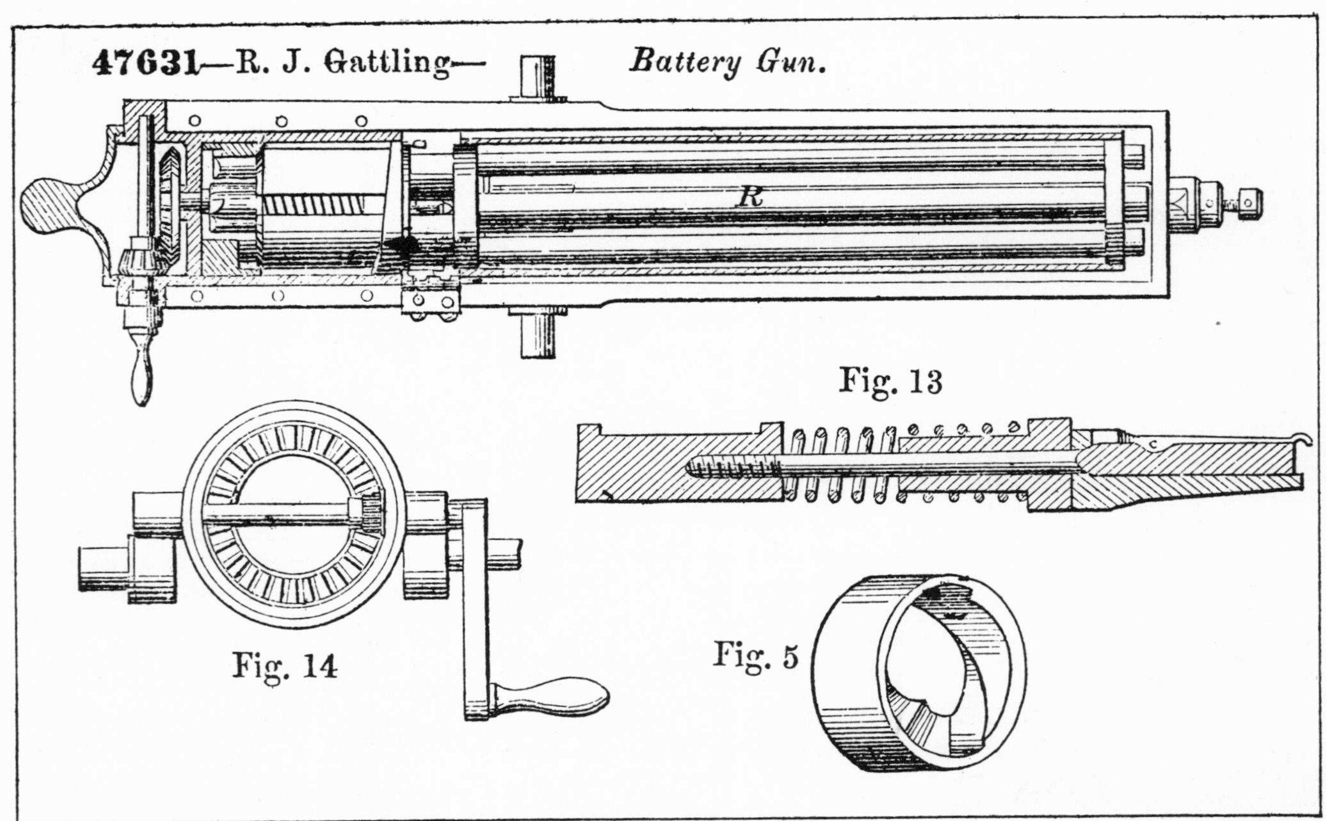

Model 1865 Gatling Gun, as illustrated in patent drawings. Fig. 5 shows details of camming sleeve, liner inside breech casing; spiral grooves caused breech bolts to move back and forth as they revolved. Set screw at front of frame operated on main shaft to adjust headspace.

Model 1865 Gatling Gun, caliber 1-inch. Since this model had no provision for lateral movement, canister shot was used to obtain dispersal of fire.

Operating sequence of the 1865 and 1866 Gatling was as follows. Assume that you are viewing the weapon from the front, facing the muzzles. At the 12 o'clock position, the bolt was drawn fully to the rear; the magazine then deposited a live cartridge in the loading trough of the carrier block, just ahead of the bolt. As the crank was turned, the barrel unit revolved counterclockwise; at 10 o'clock, the bolt began to move forward and chambered the round. At 7 o'clock, the bolt was closed fully and locked, and the cartridge was fired. By the time the bolt reached the 5 o'clock position, it was unlocked and moving rearward, extracting the fired case from the chamber. At 2 o'clock, the bolt was again in its full-rearward position and the empty case was ejected. Completion of this operating cycle was very rapid—the four-barrel Gatling, used in the 1865 Washington Trial, was capable of a cyclic rate of 200 rounds per minute.

Early in 1865, Gatling severed relations with his Cincinnati partners, McWhinny and Rindge, and entered into a contract with the Cooper Fire Arms Manufacturing Company, of Philadelphia, Pennsylvania. Well known as the manufacturer of James Maslin Cooper's percussion revolvers, this firm enjoyed a good reputation in the arms industry for precision workmanship—for the first time, the Gatling Gun was produced by specialists in gunmaking. The last of the .58 rimfire Gatlings and the first of the huge caliber 1-inch guns were made by Cooper.

After award of the 1866 U.S. contract for 100 guns, production was transferred to Colt's Armory, Hartford, Connecticut, where Gatling Guns were made for the next four decades. The Colt-manufactured Improved Model of 1866, furnished the U.S. Army on this initial contract, was the first Gatling Gun bought in quantity by any government. Fifty guns in .50 and fifty in 1-inch caliber were ordered.

Chambered for the .50/70/450 centerfire infantry cartridge, this gun had six barrels (a few were made with ten), weighed 224 pounds (without carriage and limber, which added 202 and 200 pounds respectively). Ammunition was gravity-fed from a tin box-magazine, rectangular in shape, with an open bottom that fitted into the mouth of the feed hopper. Steel breech housing was topped with a bronze plate bearing Colt markings and Gatling patent dates. Open sights were centrally located on the breech housing; when not in use, the rear sight retracted into the casing. Mounted in a yoke on a wheeled artillery carriage, the gun was traversed by turning a wheel at the left rear of the piece and elevated by means of a jackscrew in the trail. Model

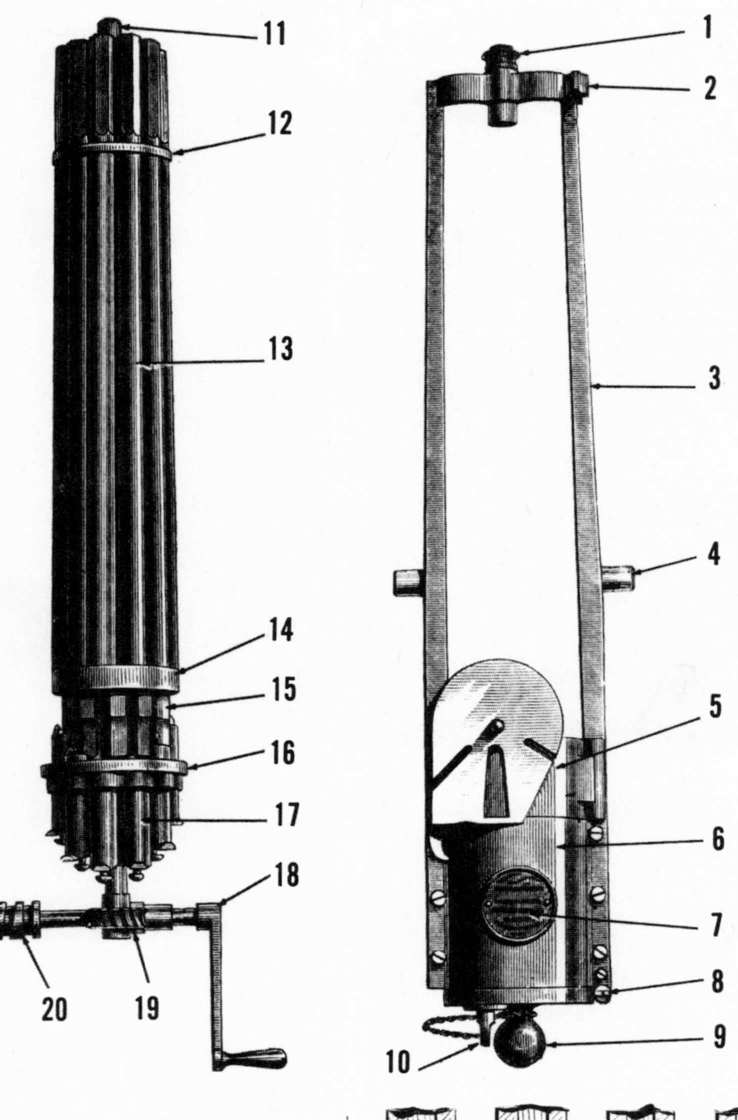

GATLING GUN NOMENCLATURE

1. Headspace adjusting screw.
2. Front sight.
3. Frame.
4. Trunnion.
5. Feed hopper (with base for Broadwell drum magazine).
6. Breech housing.
7. Name plate.
8. Rear sight.
9. Cascabel knob.
10. Plug, breech bolt access port.
11. Axle or shaft on which barrel assembly revolves.
12. Front barrel-retaining plate.
13. Barrels.
14. Rear barrel-retaining plate.
15. Carrier block with loading troughs.
16. Breech bolt guide plate.
17. Breech bolts.
18. Crank shaft with handle.
19. Drive gears.
20. Oscillator cam.

ACTION OF THE BREECH BOLTS IN RELATION TO THE BARRELS

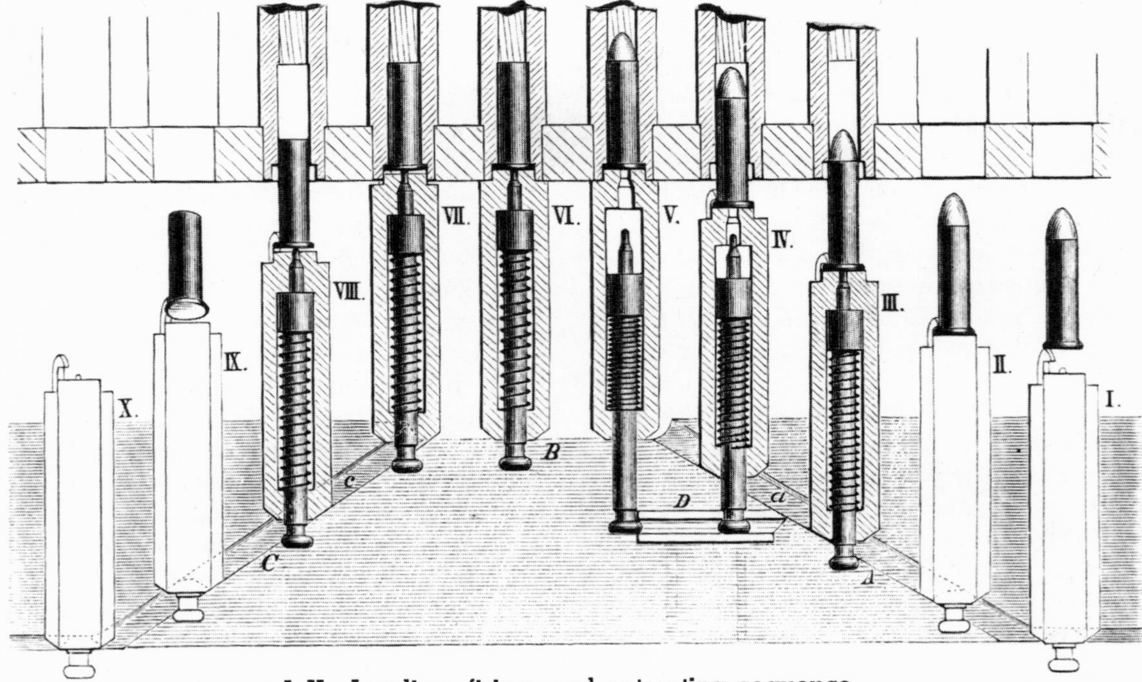

I–X—Loading, firing, and extracting sequence

1866 .50 caliber Gatlings purchased by the U.S. Government bore these serial numbers: 1-32, 34-44, 46-48, 50, 51, 53-55. Guns numbered 1-3, 5-8, 12-17, 19-26 were assigned to the U.S. Navy. All but numbers 3, 13, 15, 16 and 17 eventually were recalled and converted to caliber .45/70.

The 1-inch Gatling Gun cartridge, produced at Frankford Arsenal in Philadelphia, was an inside-primed centerfire with a 2 5/32 inch copper case, a charge of 3/4-ounce of mortar powder, and an 8-ounce conical lead bullet; over-all length of this round was 3 7/8 inches.

Although similar in general appearance and characteristics to the .50 caliber Model 1866 Gatling, the 1-inch gun was much larger. It measured 68 inches over-all and weighed 1,008 pounds without carriage or limber. Mounted on cheeks like a cannon, the 1-inch Gatling had no provision for lateral aiming adjustment, but there was a jackscrew in the trail for changing elevation. Model 1866 1-inch Gatlings were numbered in a different series from the .50 caliber; serial numbers of guns furnished on U.S. contract: 1-23, 26-35, 37-52.

Close-up of Gatling Gun with hopper open. Lower bolt has just extracted fired case. Next three bolts, having received cartridges from hopper, are pushing them forward, progressively, into chambers.

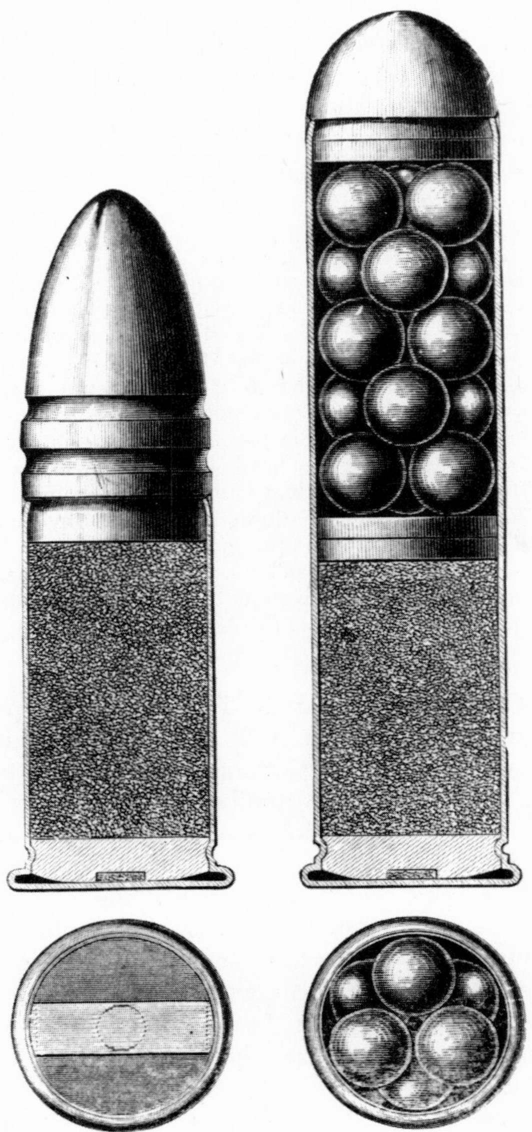

One-inch cartridges for Model 1865 (actual size).

THE WORLD MARKET

During the late 1860's, Gatling traveled extensively in Europe, promoting his gun through demonstrations and official trials, while securing additional foreign patent protection for this invention.

The Paris Universal Exhibition of 1867 provided an international showcase for the Gatling Gun, two examples of which were on display in the American section of the exposition. These guns, a 1-inch and a .50 caliber, were improved models of the lot of 100 produced for the United States Government order of 1866.

Among the many distinguished visitors to the Paris Exhibition, who viewed the Gatlings with more than passing interest, was the Emperor of France, Napoleon III. Since, like his famous uncle, Napoleon I, Louis Napoleon Bonaparte had been an artillery officer before he became an emperor, his

Tin-plated box magazines for Model 1865, caliber 1-inch (left), .50 (right). This type of magazine has no latch or other device to retain cartridges, hence the detachable cover.

interest in the Gatling Gun was a professional one. On one of his several visits to the Gatling Gun Company stand at the exposition, Napoleon III was accompanied by his consort, Eugénie, who regarded as one of the great beauties of her day. The empress is said to have taken childlike amusement in turning the crank of one of the Gatlings—an action attended by a loud, rattling noise.

Apparently much impressed by the Gatling Gun, the emperor directed that one of these weapons be removed from exhibit and taken to Versailles for testing. Salesman Gatling, optimistic as to the import of this imperial interest in his gun, felt that he now had his foot in the French door. From Paris, on January 10, 1868, he wrote to Colt's General Franklin:*

> . . . All trials here, have been a success so far & after a few private trials are made—at which the Emperor has promised to be present—I hope a respectable order for the guns will be given, & if so, they will have to be made & delivered in the shortest possible time. If order is given, by the French govt. I will telegraph you briefly—which you will understand—"200 large & 200 small,"—as the case may be, of guns to be furnished.—By sending a dispatch some 10 or 15 days time will be saved.—All Europe is arming & if France gives an order (as I feel confident she will) they will, as stated, want the guns in as short a time as possible.—I have had an interview, since my last, with the Chief of Ordnance & the Secretary of War & Genl Fave, & prospects seems to bid fair for getting an order soon. . . .

Although the gun's capabilities were successfully demonstrated in the trials at Versailles, Gatling did not receive the big order he expected. Two large, ten-barreled Gatlings were ordered by the French Ministry of Marine, presumably for further testing, but no additional orders were forthcoming. Unable to learn France's decision on the adoption of his gun, a worried Gatling wrote General Franklin on April 26, 1868:

> . . . The trials of my guns have been a perfect success, & Genl Le Bouf the chairman of the committee says his Report has been made out & sent to the Minister of War, & that it is strongly in favor of the gun—but strange to say, the Minister of War has not as yet given an order, & it is whispered around (with what truth I know not) that it is the intention of the French Gov't to go to making my guns, from the samples they have, without leave or license from me or the Gatling Gun Co.—and I must say I have fears they may do so, notwithstanding I have 2 French patents for the gun.
>
> The way the French Gov't has acted towards other inventions as well as to my gun, has caused much talk here among the Americans now living, or sojourning in Paris. . . .

Gatling's fears that the French would copy his gun were unfounded. As it later developed, at the very time when the Gatling Gun was being tested at Versailles, the Mitrailleuse, which had been adopted earlier in 1867, was already in production at France's Meudon Arsenal. The development of the French Government never had any intention of official secrecy and, quite possibly, Gatling knew nothing of it at this time. It seems very likely that the French Government never had any intention of adopting the Gatling, but was just interested in testing it for purposes of comparison with the Mitrailleuse.

Subsequently, Gatling maintained that the Mitrailleuse system was "borrowed" from his patent. This claim was groundless: aside from the fact that

* Maj. Gen. William Buel Franklin, a distinguished soldier and engineer, served Colt's Patent Fire Arms Mfg. Co. as general agent and vice president from November 15, 1865, to April 1, 1888, directing arms-making activities, including production of Gatling Guns.

Richard Jordan Gatling. Portrait made in 1868.

the systems are basically dissimilar, the Mitrailleuse antedated the Gatling Gun by more than a decade.

A factor undoubtedly contributing to France's interest in the Gatling was that her archenemy, Prussia, had the weapon under consideration. A contract was entered into, October 9, 1867, by the Kingdom of Prussia and the Gatling Gun Company represented by Maj. Gen. John Love, agent. Under the terms of this agreement, Prussia was to purchase three Gatling Guns—six-barrel 1-inch, six-barrel .50 caliber, and ten-barrel .50 caliber—for purposes of trial. It was provided in the contract that an additional 97 guns would be bought if, after testing, the Prussian military decided to adopt the Gatling. Prussia did not purchase the additional guns.

During 1867 and 1868, the Gatling Gun was officially tested in England, Holland, Denmark, Sweden, Bavaria, Austria, Russia, and Turkey, as well as in France and Prussia. In addition, several guns were sold to Japan.

Gatling's letters of this period, written from various European capitals to General Franklin of Colt's indicated that, while the gun generally performed well, ammunition presented a considerable problem. Like all machine guns, the Gatling, because of its high rate of fire and precise operation, required reliable ammunition of greater uniformity than necessary for infantry rifles. Unfortunately, at this time, the metallic cartridge was still in its infancy and the usual run of military ammunition was poor, often totally lacking in uniformity and anything but reliable.

Frequently, it was required that trials be conducted with Gatlings chambering the testing nation's issue rifle cartridge. Quality of ammunition could "make or break" the gun in these tests—with poor cartridges, rounds might jam, burst in the weapon, or cause other malfunction. Even though such mishaps were plainly due to defects in the ammunition and not the result of any inherent fault of the Gatling Gun, the typical chauvinism of European ordnance officers and government officials conducting trials would not permit them to admit that their ammunition was at fault—it had to be blamed on the foreigner's gun.

Constantly plagued by the cartridge problem, Gatling was forced to have ammunition specially made, to high standards, which would permit efficient operation of his gun. Although American metallic cartridges were of better quality than obtainable abroad, these too lacked the requisite uniformity in many instances.

EARLY TRIALS IN ENGLAND AND FRANCE

In 1867, the Gatling Gun was tried before the Ordnance Select Committee at Shoeburyness, England. The following account, which appeared in the British *Army and Navy Gazette,* is included in *Report to the Government of the United States on the Munitions of War Exhibited at the Paris Universal Exhibition, 1867* by Charles B. Norton and W. J. Valentine:

> The specimen of this gun now brought over to Europe is one of the first made, and is not as perfect and as good in material and workmanship as those which are now being made by the Colt's Company for the American Government. Nevertheless, it is sufficient to demonstrate the value of the invention. At the trial, which took place on the 7th instant, before the Ordnance Select Committee, the gun was fired at the range of 150 yards with case shot, and 800 yards with solid shot, giving a good target in both cases. At 150 yards the gun disposed of ninety-six cartridges in one minute and twenty seconds, but as, owing to an accident, one of the barrels could not be fired, twenty of the cartridges dropped out unexploded. The seventy-six effective rounds discharged 1,216 bullets, 668 of which were counted on the target. The strong wind blowing at the time no doubt drove a great many of the

light bullets to the right of the target. A second trial of the gun took place at Shoeburyness, last Tuesday, before the Egyptian Commander-in-Chief his Excellency Chanine Pasha, who wished to acquaint himself with the construction and performance of the gun. One of the barrels being still unable to explode the cartridges, the fire of the gun was materially impeded thereby. The large bore Gatling gun, if fired with solid ball, is said to make a good target up to 2,000 yards.

In an appendix to the Norton and Valentine Report, there is published a significant statement by Richard Jordan Gatling:

The Gatling Battery

The inventor of this weapon, referring to the guns tested in France and England during 1867, says: "I wish to state that the Gatling Battery guns of six barrels exhibited in the Paris Exhibition, and tried at Versailles, as well as those used in the trials at Shoeburyness, and at Fortress Monroe, have, together with the ammunition, been greatly improved since these trials were made. Improved Gatling guns, of one inch calibre with ten barrels, are now being constructed at Colt's Armory in Hartford, which can be fired at the rate of 200 rounds per minute. These guns discharge half pound solid lead-balls, and have an effective range of 2,500 metres or say one and a half English miles. Another class of the same weapons, also with ten barrels and of half-inch calibre, are now making at the same Armory; these have been fired at the rate of over 300 shots per minute. The trials of the Gatling gun at Shoeburyness were made under the most unfavorable conditions. The gun used on that occasion was very imperfect both in material and workmanship, the firing pins were made of hard steel, and one of them was broken before the commencement of the trial. Thus the gun was tested in a disabled condition against an Armstrong gun, and that too by men who were unacquainted with its use, and who were quite familiar with the Armstrong. The ammunition was also very defective. Two of the six barrel, and one of the ten barrel improved guns with new ammunition have been tried lately at the target grounds at Versailles. At one of these trials the Emperor attended, accompanied by the minister of War and several distinguished officers of the French army. On this occasion the president of the Artillery Commission reported that, the service of the one-inch gun was excellent at 2,400 metres, and indeed exceeded his expectations."

A SECOND TRIAL BY THE U. S. NAVY

Early in 1868, General Love wrote to the U.S. Navy Department, proposing trials of the improved models of the Gatling Gun. In answer to this letter, he was informed by the Chief of the Bureau of Ordnance: "The Department has no objection to the gun being tried provided it can be done without the detail of additional officers and without any expense to the Government for powder or anything else." The Gatling Gun Company decided that trial by a naval board, even at the firm's expense, would be worth while and proceeded to make arrangements with the Bureau of Ordnance for proving guns at the Washington, D.C., Navy Yard.

Trials of both caliber .50 and 1-inch Gatlings were conducted in May, 1868, and the board of officers reported to Secretary of the Navy Gideon Welles:

. . . the board is of the opinion that, as an auxiliary arm for special service, to be used from top-gallant, forecastle, poop deck, and tops of vessels of war, and in boat operations against the enemy, either in passing open land works or clearing beaches and other proposed places for landing from boats, &c., if opposing infantry and cavalry, it has no known superior.

Its great merit consists in its accuracy within the limits of its range; the certainty, and, if need be, rapidity of fire, with additional merit of only requiring three persons to load, direct, and fire each piece, when suitably mounted, afloat or ashore. . . . The mechanism is simple, and not likely to get out of order; but in such event it could be repaired on board ship. Spare pieces, as in musket locks, could be part of the outfit.

The report further states that, at the close of the trials, ten shots were fired at an elevation of 10° 40′, giving an average distance, by the plane table, of 2,800 yards. None of the cartridges missed fire.

The favorable conclusions of the Naval Board must have been most heartening to Gatling, as the U.S. Navy Bureau of Ordnance, headed by Capt. Henry A. Wise, an experienced professional ordnance officer, who had served under Admiral Dahlgren during the Civil War, was notably hard to sell. Guns submitted to the Navy for trial often were subjected to rigorous testing, as in this incident related in Gatling's obituary in the *Indianapolis Sentinel*, March 2, 1903:

It was contended by naval officers that the gun could not stand any exposure incident to such service. He was invited to come to Fortress Monroe to make a test of his invention, and he took with him a beautifully polished specimen of his gun. It was taken out of the casement and to his surprise instead of being tested, it was sunk in salt water, where it remained overnight. The next morning it was fished up, and dripping with salt water, it was tested and worked perfectly.

Even though an order for Gatling Guns for the U.S. Navy was not immediately forthcoming, a successful trial such as this was of great value to Gatling: it was a step in the direction of general adoption by the Navy, and provided "ammunition" for his sales talks to other governments.

GATLING GUNS FOR RUSSIA

Shortly after the end of the American Civil War, the Russian Government procured two Gatling Guns of the 1862 model for experimental trials. After exhaustive testing by the Russian Army and Navy, the Gatling Gun Company was awarded a contract for twenty guns in .42 caliber, which were manufactured at Colt's Armory in 1868 and delivered in Russia early in 1869. Thus, Russia became the first major European power to adopt the Gatling Gun and, when this became known in England, was editorially criticized by the *London Times* for "making haste to adopt American inventions whether good or bad." This comment reflected the then-current British military view of the Gatling, one that was soon to be changed with England following suit in the adoption of this weapon.

Col. A. Gorloff, of the Imperial Russian Artillery, arrived in the United States in 1868, assigned to serve as chief inspector of ordnance being manufactured for Russia. During the years of his tour of duty in America, Gorloff acquired a reputation for setting almost impossibly high standards and then spending many long hours personally inspecting and testing matériel to make sure that his specifications were being met to the letter. There was a very sound reason for the Russian officer's zeal. As Gorloff once explained, in—for him—a moment of rare candor, he would be held personally responsible to the Czar himself for any failure of matériel produced under his supervision and, in the unhappy event of such failure, his best course would be to take a revolver and blow out his brains. Although an able and trusted officer—"trusted" to the extent that an autocrat can trust any of his servants—while in the United States, Gorloff was under constant surveillance by the Czar's spies, sent to make sure that he performed as was expected of him. The colonel undoubtedly knew that he was being watched. Fortunately, there were no failures and no need for suicide. In 1870, Gorloff was rewarded for his dedication to duty, when his master in St. Petersburg elevated him to the rank of major general.

Gorloff spent much time, in 1868 and 1869, at the Colt plant in Hartford, conducting tests of the Gatling and making improvements in its design, preliminary to ordering additional guns. No foreign officer contributed as much to the development of the Gatling Gun as did this talented Russian engineer. By the spring of 1869, the meticulous Gorloff, finally satisfied with the Gatling, was ready to order more guns for the Russian armed forces. On May 13, 1869, W. H. Talbott, president of Gatling Gun Company, wrote Colonel Gorloff:

> We propose to furnish to the Russian Government Seventy (70) forty-two inch Caliber Gatling guns—to be of ten (10) barrels each and of the same material and finish as the twenty guns just furnished to the said Government of Russia—the work on said guns to be commenced at once and finished as rapidly as possible, these guns to be in every respect after the model of the twenty guns above referred to;
>
> Although these guns are finished in a higher state of workmanship and are in some of their parts of more expensive material than the guns furnished the Government of the United States, and will cost us largely in excess of those furnished said Government of the United States—Yet in consideration of the modifications and changes made by yourself in the gun, bringing it as we think to a high state of perfection—We will furnish these seventy (70) guns at the same price charged for the twenty just completed for your Government, and which is the same price paid by the Government of the United States, "to wit" Fifteen hundred dollars ($1,500.00) each in United States currency, payable on inspection and acceptance—in installments of not less than twenty guns,—at Colts Patent Fire Arms Manufacturing Co. in Hartford Connecticut.

Colonel Gorloff promptly ordered seventy guns, agreeing to these terms. On May 14th, General Franklin submitted to the Gatling Gun Company a quotation of $710 per gun; attached to this letter from Colt's is a cost sheet indicating that, on January 1, 1868, the Gatling Gun Company's cost for guns of the type of the twenty pieces furnished Russia was $665 each. Modifications in the design, as requierd by Gorloff, increased the cost per gun by $45 for extra labor and contribution toward the cost of extra tools. Thus, the Gatling Gun Company made a gross profit of $790 on each gun sold to Russia for $1,500.

The fact that Gatling Guns were made in Russian arsenals after 1870 appears to have given rise to the false allegation that Russia stole the Gatling design and proceeded to manufacture such guns, calling them "Gorloffs." Actually, Russia had the legal right to make Gatling Guns in its own plants for its own use, without payment of royalty. This right was granted by a paper signed November 16, 1869, by W. H. Talbott, President, Gatling Gun Company—given in consideration of Russia increasing its order of May 13, 1869, to 100 guns. Capt. E. Rogers ("The Gatling Gun; Its Place In Tactics," *Journal of the Royal United Service Institution*, Vol. XIX, 1876, pp. 423–424) explains the use of the name Gorloff:

> Why the Gatlings in Russia were named "Gorloff's" had better be explained, and indeed I have been requested by General Gorloff to disclaim, on

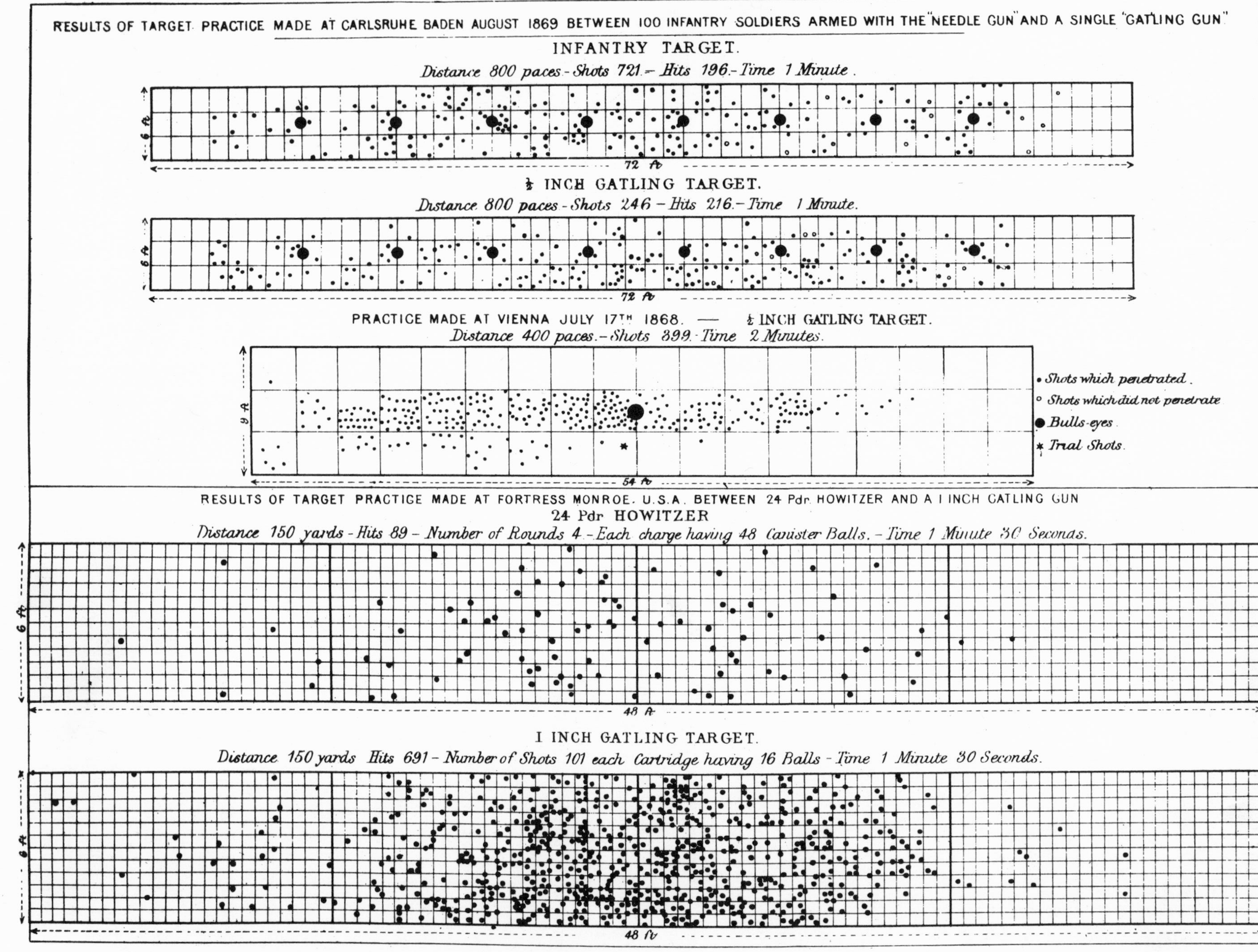
RESULTS OF TARGET PRACTICE MADE AT CARLSRUHE BADEN AUGUST 1869 BETWEEN 100 INFANTRY SOLDIERS ARMED WITH THE "NEEDLE GUN" AND A SINGLE "GATLING GUN"
INFANTRY TARGET.
Distance 800 paces - Shots 721. - Hits 196. - Time 1 Minute.
6 ft
72 ft
½ INCH GATLING TARGET.
Distance 800 paces - Shots 246 - Hits 216. - Time 1 Minute.
6 ft
72 ft
PRACTICE MADE AT VIENNA JULY 17TH 1868. — ½ INCH GATLING TARGET.
Distance 400 paces. - Shots 399. Time 2 Minutes.
9 ft
54 ft
• Shots which penetrated.
○ Shots which did not penetrate
● Bulls-eyes.
* Trial Shots.
RESULTS OF TARGET PRACTICE MADE AT FORTRESS MONROE. U.S.A. BETWEEN 24 Pdr. HOWITZER AND A I INCH GATLING GUN
24 Pdr. HOWITZER
Distance 150 yards - Hits 89 - Number of Rounds 4 - Each charge having 48 Canister Balls. - Time 1 Minute 30 Seconds.
6 ft
48 ft
I INCH GATLING TARGET.
Distance 150 yards Hits 691 - Number of Shots 101 each Cartridge having 16 Balls - Time 1 Minute 30 Seconds.
6 ft
48 ft

his part, any pretentions to the title of inventor. There is a rule in the Russian service that the name of any official superintending the casting or construction of a gun must be engraved on it. Hence the erroneous notion that General Gorloff altered in any way the mechanism of the Gatling. While at Hartford (United States of America) superintending the construction of the Gatlings for his Government, he experimented largely with the cartridges of the Berdan rifle (which is in partial use in Russia), and he succeeded in effecting an assimilation of ammunition (an important and economic provision which we would do well to imitate), but he did not tamper with the gun. Considerable changes, but no radical one, have been introduced in the construction of the Russian Gatling at the instance of a mechanical genius in St. Petersburgh, named Barononski, in whose service are the Nobel brothers (*par nobile fratrum*), whose names have, in like manner, been given to the so-called improved Gatling.

The idea of giving General Gorloff credit for the development of the Gatling Gun probably was the work of some ultra-chauvinist Russian military journalist, seeking to curry favor by claiming this important ordnance invention for his motherland. In the issue of March 9, 1872, *Army & Navy Journal* (U.S.) commented:

> An attempt was made by Russian Journals some months since, to claim the invention of the Gatling batteries now being made in St. Petersburg and even a lot of them made in this country, for General Gorloff, an officer of too high ideals of professional honor to be flattered by this attempt to ascribe to him credit which belonged to another.

TRIALS AT VIENNA AND KARLSRUHE

Hoping to interest Austria-Hungary in purchasing his gun, Gatling arranged for a trial at Vienna on July 9, 1869. A ten-barreled .50 caliber gun was fired from distances of 800 to 1,200 paces, ranges that might be encountered in flank defense, at a target 54 feet wide by 9 feet high, intended to simulate a body of infantry.

Firing was begun at 800 paces. After three sighting shots, a volley of 216 rounds was discharged—213 shots hit the mark. In effect, the "troops" represented by the target were almost decimated by this one Gatling volley. The gun was then moved back to 1,200 paces from the target. After firing "sighters," a volley of 191 shots was fired, of which 152 were effective. This trial demonstrated that the Gatling Gun's performance greatly surpassed that which might be expected from a fieldpiece of that era, firing explosive shells, under the same conditions.

Shortly after the Vienna trial, a contest was held at Karlsruhe, Grand Duchy of Baden, in which one ten-barreled .50 caliber Gatling Gun was pitted against a hundred picked infantrymen armed with the celebrated needle-gun. Range was 800 paces. In one minute's firing, the Gatling discharged 246 rounds, scored 216 hits on the target, while the 100 marksmen fired 721 rounds for only 196 hits. These results proved the Gatling's superiority over massed infantry small arms fire.

TURKISH CONTRACT

Ever since the sixth century B.C., Russians and Turks had been fighting each other periodically. During the late 1860's, Russian eastward expansion made it obvious that another Russo-Turkish war was inevitable, although it didn't come until a decade later. In this period between wars, the Ottoman Empire engaged in an extensive preparedness program and its purchasing agents became well-known figures in U.S. armsmaking centers, as well as in those of Europe. Among the weapons that especially interested the Turks was the Gatling Gun—if it was good enough for the Russians, then Turkey had to have the Gatling too.

In July, 1870, a contract was signed between Halil Pasha, Grand Master of Artillery, acting for the Ottoman Empire, and L. W. Broadwell, agent of the Gatling Gun Company, by which the Turks agreed to purchase 200 ten-barreled Gatlings chambered for the .58 Turkish Snider cartridge, without carriage or feed, at a price of $950 each. Under the terms of an agreement made with Ed. A. Paget & Co., of Vienna, August 12, 1870, the Turkish contract was transferred to the Austrian firm. Later the same year, Gatling Gun Company received another order from the Imperial Ottoman Government—thirty of the same guns for the Turkish Navy—which also was assigned to Paget. On both contracts, Ed. A. Paget & Co. was to receive 1,100 Austrian florins (about $530) for each gun, with the difference between that sum and $950 to be paid to the Gatling Gun Company.

GATLING PRODUCTION ABROAD

By an agreement signed in 1869 and renewed in 1881, R. J. Gatling licensed Sir William G. Armstrong & Co. to make and vend Gatling Guns in the United Kingdom of Great Britain, Ireland, the Channel Islands, and the Isle of Man. At a some-

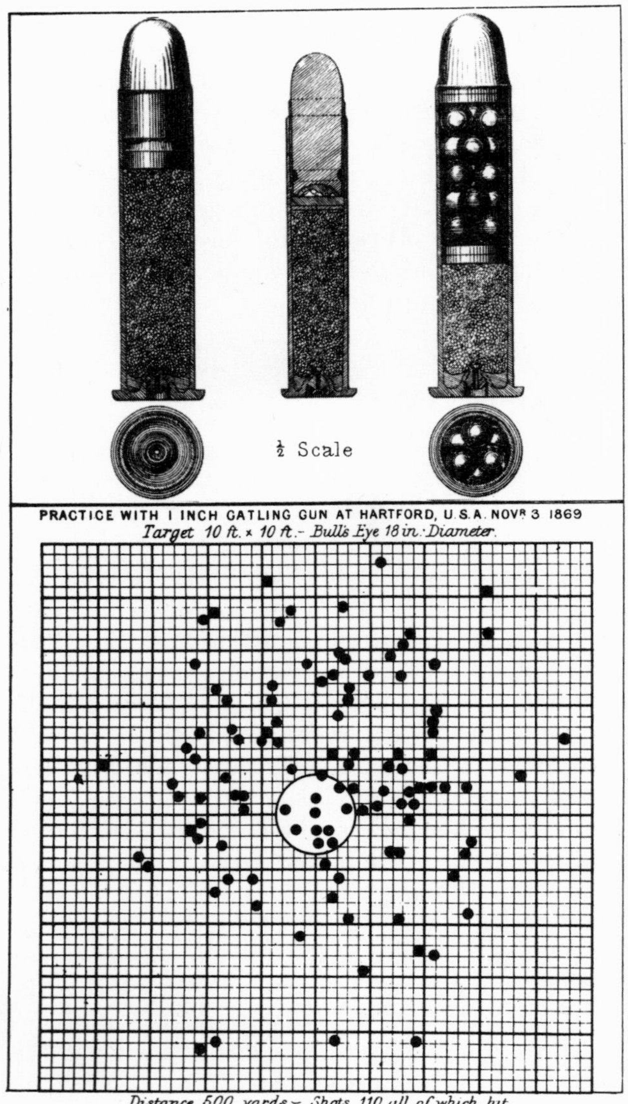

what earlier date, arrangements were made with Ed. A. Paget & Co., Vienna, to manufacture the gun at their plant. L. W. Broadwell, Gatling's European sales agent, was a partner in the Paget operation.

Provisions for production outside the United States evidently were deemed desirable by the Gatling Gun Company, and their association with both Armstrong and the Nobel brothers in Russia proved satisfactory, unlike that with Paget, which eventually was terminated.

In 1871, W. H. Talbott, president of the Gatling Gun Company, visited Austria and found the Paget firm on the verge of dissolution as the result of mismanagement and disunity in the partnership. It was also found that the guns produced by Paget were not up to the high standards of those manufactured by Colt, Armstrong, and Nobel. For a time, Gatling management considered purchasing the Paget works, as proposed by Paget to Talbott, but as it turned out they did not buy this Vienna plant for reasons unknown.

GATLING FAMILY MOVES TO CONNECTICUT

In 1870, returning from his second tour of Europe, Richard Jordan Gatling moved his family from Indianapolis, Indiana, their home for many years, to Hartford, Connecticut, where the Gatling Gun was manufactured at Colt's Armory. The Gatling home, in Hartford, was on Charter Oak Place, not far from the spot where the Charter Oak once grew.

Hartford was home to the Gatlings for 27 years, until 1897, when Mr. and Mrs. Gatling moved to New York City to live with their daughter, Ida, and her husband, Hugh O. Pentecost, an attorney. During his more than 25 years as a resident of Hartford, Gatling took an active interest in local affairs, and was a charter member of the Hartford Club. The Gatling family attended the South Baptist Church; their son-in-law, Hugh Pentecost, prior to giving up the cloth for the bar, served as pastor of this church.

Judging from correspondence of the early 1870's, the headquarters of the Gatling Gun Company remained in Indianapolis until 1874, although the guns had been made in Hartford since 1866. By act of the General Assembly of the State of Connecticut, in 1874, the Gatling Gun Company was incorporated under the laws of that state. Mentioned in the resolution as incorporators: Richard J. Gatling, James Goodwin, Henry Keney, and Edgar T. Welles.

FOUR: 1870-1880

A TIME FOR WAR

BY 1870, sabers that had rattled in the preceding decade began to be drawn. Compared with the American Civil War and World Wars I and II, the conflicts of the late nineteenth century may seem minor, yet most of these "little wars" significantly affected world history.

The first major European power to adopt the Gatling Gun was Russia, in 1867, a year after the weapon's adoption by the United States. Quite a number of other countries soon followed in equipping their armed forces with Gatlings; England, however, waited until 1874. Ten years later, there were few nations without Gatling guns in their armament. Until superseded by the automatic machine gun, the Gatling was the most widely used weapon of its type. It saw action in nearly every war of that era.

FRANCE'S SECRET WEAPON

The resounding defeat of Austria by the Prussians in the Seven Weeks War of 1866 was credited to a great extent to the effectiveness of the Dreyse *Zündnadelgewehr* (needle gun) in the hands of well-trained German infantrymen, who had been using this bolt-action breechloader since 1842. With the needle gun, a soldier could deliver five or more aimed shots per minute, giving considerable superiority of fire over an enemy equipped with muzzleloading muskets. Publicity given the conspicuous successes of this rifle in combat had served to damage the morale of French troops, who expected to have to face it soon.

France did have a counterweapon in the similar *Chassepot,* adopted in 1866, but it had not been produced in sufficient quantity for general issue. Napoleon III, feverishly preparing France for the inevitable and seemingly imminent war with Prussia, began to look about for an "equalizer" in a multifiring weapon and seized upon the Mitrailleuse, a kind of volley gun. As far back as 1863, the Emperor had displayed interest in the Gatling but, by the time he saw and tested it during the fall of 1867, the Mitrailleuse had already been adopted. By imperial order, manufacture of this gun was begun, with highest priority, at Meudon Arsenal under the direction of Commandant de Reffye.

Production of the French Mitrailleuse was cloaked in darkest official secrecy. Only those actually concerned with its manufacture were allowed to see the gun. When a finished piece left the factory, it was enveloped in tarpaulins and heavily guarded. As France's secret weapon, the Mitrailleuse was the subject of a good deal of propaganda designed to demoralize the enemy (who probably were laughing over their intelligence reports) and to bolster the flagging fighting spirit of French armed forces. Stories that the French had a terrible new weapon that would decimate her enemies appeared with regularity in the Gallic press. The gun was never described or even mentioned by name.

Subject of all this secrecy was the twenty-five-year-old Fafschamps-Montigny Mitrailleuse, warmed over by De Reffye. This weapon was invented in 1851, ten years before the advent of the Gatling Gun, by Captain Fafschamps of the Belgian Army. Some years after its invention, two Belgian ordnance engineers, Joseph Montigny and Louis Christophe, improved the Mitrailleuse and the former subsequently produced several such guns at his plant at Fontaine l'Evêque; these were employed in arming Belgian forts. The Mitrailleuse manufactured in France after 1867 incorporated some changes made in its design by De Reffye, but was essentially the same as the Montigny version. The De Reffye Mitrailleuse had 25 barrels instead of 37, employed the Metford system of rifling, and was chambered for the standard Chassepot cartridge.

WAR
MILITARY GLORY.
Th. Nast

While France jealously guarded her "great military secret," any ordnance man who was not already familiar with the Mitrailleuse could read all about it in the British *Journal of the Royal United Service Institution* which, in 1869, published a paper, "On Mitrailleurs, and Their Place in the Wars of the Future," by Maj. G. V. Fosbery. In it, the Montigny Mitrailleuse, almost identical to France's De Reffye gun, was illustrated and described in detail:

> The Montigny mitrailleur consists of an assemblage of barrels contained in a wrought-iron tube, mounted much on the same principle as an ordinary field gun, which, indeed, it somewhat resembles in form. To this a massive breech action is attached sliding between heavy iron plates. This is controlled by a jointed lever, and contains a simple contrivance for the separate and successive ignition of the cartridges. The cartridges are carried in steel plates perforated with holes, corresponding in number and position to the chambers of the barrel, of which, indeed, these holes form portions, being bored and finished with the same tools, and at the same time as the chambers themselves. These plates are about eleven millimetres in thickness, and when the cartridges (which are central fire) are dropped into them they stand out at right angles in proper position for introduction into the chambers of the gun. Grooves formed on the face of the breech-block receive the plate, which, being dropped into them, advances or retires with the breech-block itself.
>
> A plate of cartridges being introduced into the gun, the gunner would depress the lever, which he holds in his left hand, the breech-block would advance, pushing each cartridge into its appropriate barrel, and finally becoming secured in its place beyond chance of accidental disturbance by recoil or otherwise. The contrivance which effects this is a very simple and perfect one. At the same time and by the same motion the whole weapon is set at full cock, ready for firing.
>
> The gunner now quits the loading lever, and grasping the firing handle at the right side of the gun awaits the order to fire. One second of time is sufficient to give a complete revolution of the handle and discharge the whole of the thirty-seven barrels, of which the weapon consists, but each may be fired separately and at any intervals of time. When the last barrel has been discharged, he raises the loading lever, thereby opening the breech, and withdraws the empty cases by means of the plate, which now performs the office of an extractor, or rather of thirty-seven extractors in one. The plate is lifted from its groove, carrying with it the empty cases,

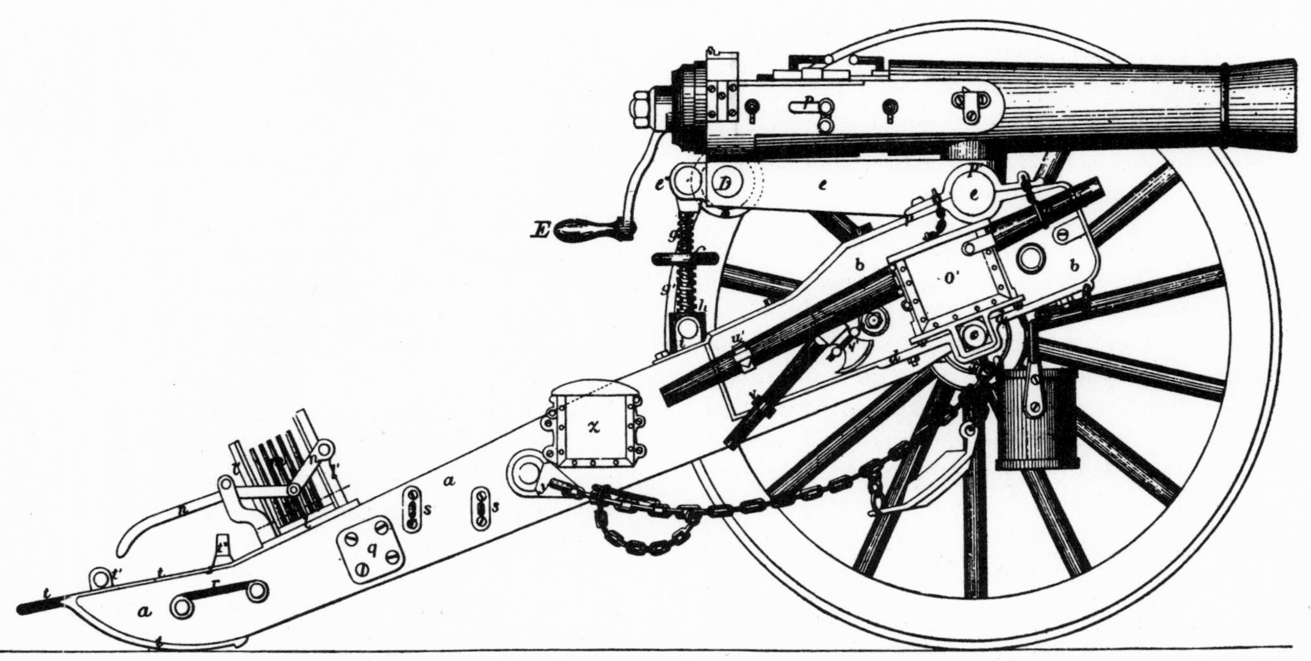

French Mitrailleuse of 1870, 25 barrels, caliber 13mm.

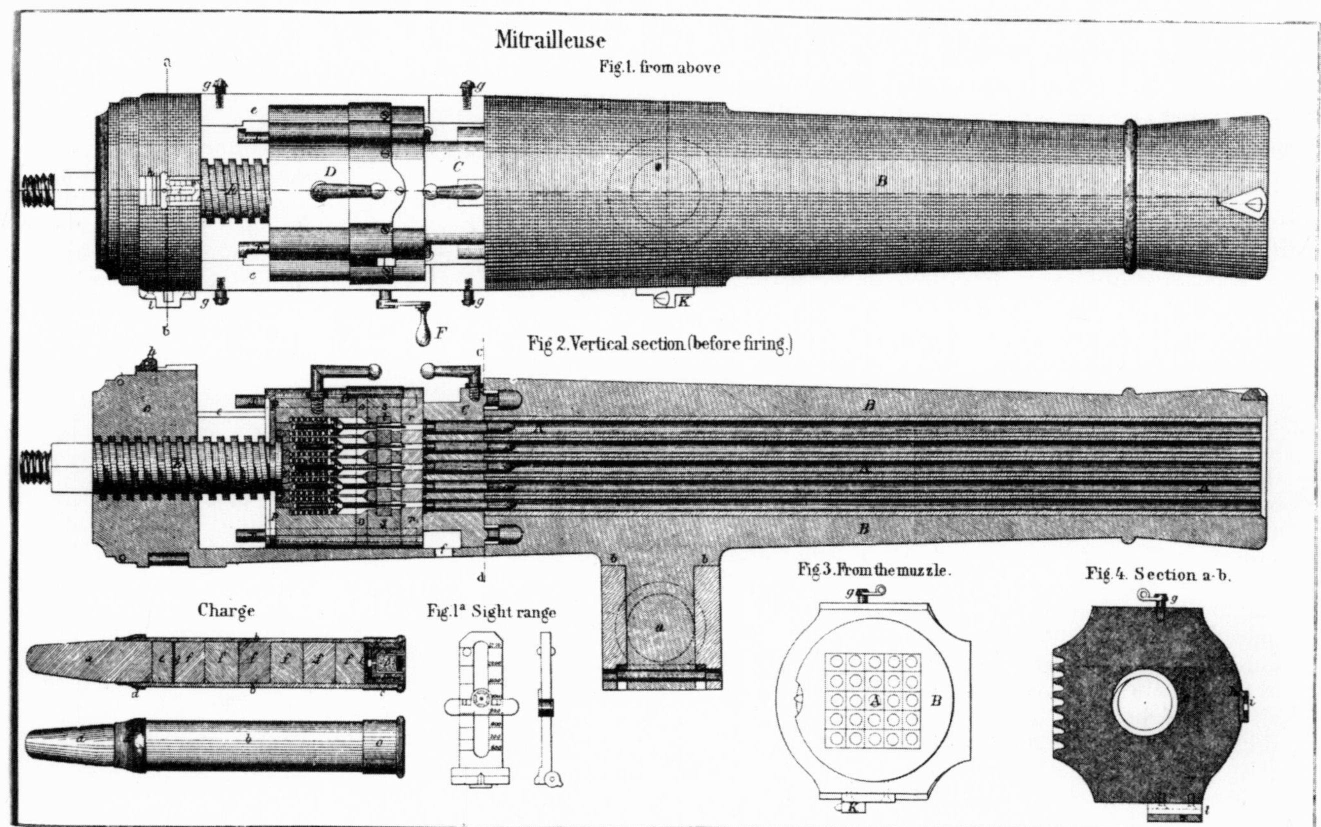

Mechanism of 1870 Mitrailleuse.

and replaced by one filled with loaded cartridges, and the operation is repeated. To open the gun, remove the empty plate, insert a full one, and reclose ready for firing takes somewhat less than four seconds. It has thus been found possible to fire this weapon twelve times per minute, throwing therefore 444 rifle shots in that time. This I believe to be the largest number ever yet thrown by a machine of like weight, though others pretend to the possession of greater powers in this particular.*

Thus, it would appear that the great secrecy about France's Mitrailleuse applied only to those who would be expected to serve it in battle. These guns were not given to the troops until the eve of the war with Prussia, denying them the opportunity to become familiar with a new weapon before actual combat. This typified the inefficiency and lack of sound planning that characterized France's military preparations in 1870.

* The very high rate of fire—12 volleys or 444 shots per minute—claimed for the Montigny Mitrailleuse in Major Fosbery's paper is at variance with other reports on this weapon. These indicate that, under ideal conditions, operated at top speed, it could be loaded and discharged only five times per minute at the most, giving a volley fire of 175 rounds. In the 1870 British trials, a Montigny Mitrailleuse, fired at maximum speed for *two* minutes, delivered eight volleys or 296 shots.

FRANCO-PRUSSIAN WAR

Maneuvered by the wily Bismarck into a position where she had no alternative but to declare war on Prussia, France became the victim of the first blitzkrieg in history. From the beginning, things went badly for the French, unprepared for war against a united Germany that was superior in arms, as well as in organization and leadership. During the first few weeks following her declaration of war, July 19, 1870, it became obvious that France's defeat was only a matter of time and the neutral nations, which might have aided Napoleon III, decided to let him fight alone.

On August 4, the Germans invaded Alsace; they proceeded to defeat the French at Wissembourg, forced Marshal MacMahon to Châlons-sur-Marne, drove a wedge between his army and that of Marshal Bazaine at Metz. Bazaine, in an attempt to join forces with MacMahon, was defeated at Vionville, August 16, and at Gravelotte, August 18, and retreated to Metz. On September 1, the effort of Napoleon and MacMahon to relieve Bazaine resulted in the disaster of Sedan, in which the Emperor and 100,000 French troops were captured. When news of Napoleon's capitulation reached Paris, there was a bloodless revolution and, the Emperor deposed, a provisional government formed under Favre, Gambetta, and Trochu. The new republic continued the fight against the invaders, but the German victory was a *fait accompli* at Sedan. On September 19, the German troops began the siege of Paris, which lasted until the armistice of January 28, 1871.

Defeat of the French, pioneers in the use of the machine gun in this war, constituted in the eyes of many military men a defeat for this type of weapon. To the contrary, Lieut. John H. Parker, U.S.A., in his book *Tactical Organization and Uses of Machine Guns in the Field* (1899) states:

> Summing up the use of machine guns in the Franco-Prussian War, it may be said that the French were defeated in the campaign, not because they used machine guns, but because they blundered in every other possible way. Their artillery was inefficient, their cavalry worthless, and their generalship conspicuous by its absence. Powerful as the imperfect mitrailleuse was, it was unable to rescue the doomed nation from the fate it had prepared for itself by gross military incompetence in every other part of the war.

The ineffectiveness of the Mitrailleuse in this conflict was due chiefly to the way in which it was employed by the French. Since it looked like a field gun, the Mitrailleuse was organized into batteries as artillery and used against enemy field guns at the effective range of the latter. While the Mitrailleuse was not really effective at more than 400 yards, the range of opposing Krupp guns was 4,000 yards. Knocking out the Mitrailleuse at long and safe range became a favorite sport of German gunners, who repeatedly put the French guns out of action. On a few occasions, the Mitrailleuse was used intelligently and with good effect in support of infantry, instead of being put in line with field guns and exposed to long-range shelling. In these instances, it scored impressively, although not decisively, in enemy casualties.

In *Colburn's United Service Magazine,* October 1894, Lieutenant Pratt, R.A., says: "At Gravelotte, when taking the offensive, 94 per cent of the German killed and wounded were due to mitrailleuse and small-arm fire, and but 5 per cent to artillery fire."

The official German account of the action of the

Effect of the Mitrailleuse, Battle of Gravelotte.

38th Prussian Infantry Brigade in the bloody battle at Marș-la-Tour says:

> The brave battalions are forced to fall back into the valley beneath, and the fire of the adversaries from mitrailleuses advancing to the crest increases the losses almost to annihilation. Cavalry were then pushed forward by the Prussians to protect the shattered remnant, but in consequence of the violent mitrailleuse fire the leader was unable to deliver home his attack.

According to *Colburn's United Service Magazine,* October 1881, German losses here were 72 officers, 2,542 men, killed, wounded, and missing, of 95 officers and 4,546 men engaged; proportion of killed to wounded was 3 to 4.

After Sedan, where many of their Mitrailleuses were captured, the rest being bottled up in Metz with Bazaine's army, the French obtained a few Gatlings as replacements. In January, 1871, at Le-Mans, Gatling batteries successfully defended the plateau of Anvours and the crossings of the River Huisne. Kept out of sight in trenches, the Gatlings served to check the advance of German infantry with unexpected bursts of fire. In *The Gatling Guns, For Service Ashore and Afloat,* a Gatling Gun Company promotional booklet published (undated) in England by Sheppard & St. John, London, the following incident is cited:

> In the late Prussian war, the Gatling Gun was used by the French, conjointly with the mitrailleuse. From the London *Journal* we clip a correspondent's description of its efficacious use in action:—
>
> "Up to this time we had not seen any Prussians, beyond a few skirmishers in the plain, though our battery of Gatlings had kept blazing away at nothing in particular all the while; but now an opportunity of its being in use occurred. A column of troops appeared in the valley below us, coming from the right—a mere dark streak upon the white snow; but no one in the battery could tell whether they were friends or foes, and the commander hesitated about opening fire. But now an aide-de-camp came dashing down the hill with orders for us to pound at them at once—a French journalist having, it seems, discovered them to be enemies, when the general and all his staff were as puzzled as ourselves. *Rr-rr-a* go our Gatlings, the deadly hail of bullets crashes into the thick of them, and slowly back into the woods the dark mass retires, leaving, however, a trace of black dots upon the white snow behind it. This, their famous and historical four o'clock effort, and its failure, has decided the day. That one discharge was enough."

Model 1871 Gatling on all-metal Broadwell carriage.

GATLING MODELS OF 1871-1873

Frequently, despite exhaustive testing in prototype, it is only after a weapon has been in actual service for some time that certain of its shortcomings are revealed. This was the case with the Model 1865 Gatling and, as a result, Gatling redesigned his gun, incorporating a number of improvements, which he patented February 28, 1871. The improved gun—Model 1871—looked much like its predecessors, but was quite superior to them.

Model 1865 breech bolts, cylindrical in cross section, were smaller in diameter at the front section, which was unsupported. In the Model 1871, the bolts were more heavily constructed and uniform in diameter throughout the length, with a supporting rib on the bottom.

To remove the breech bolts of the earlier Gatlings, it was necessary to disassemble completely the rear breech housing and remove a number of parts, including much of the geared driving mechanism. This really was a job for a skilled armorer and, when attempted by troops in the field, often resulted in extensive damage, costly to repair. In the Model 1871, a port, fitted with a latched plug closure, was provided in the cascabel plate (rear cover of the breech housing). Through this port, bolts could be removed easily and without tools. Since the need for removal of bolts for cleaning or repair was not infrequent, this was an important improvement and, with minor variations, was incorporated in all succeeding models.

In the Model 1871 Gatling, the simple tin box used to hold cartridges in the Model 1865 was replaced by a curved magazine, better suited to handling the broad-rimmed cartridges used, and fitted with a heavy brass weight to help feed the column of rounds into the gun.

Additional improvements, patented April 9, 1872, included a new type of hopper to accept a drum feed. This unusual magazine, known as the Broadwell drum—after L. M. Broadwell, a Gatling Gun Company employee, who evidently devised it, consisted of a circular cluster of twenty vertical magazines, each containing twenty cartridges. In use, it was attached to the top of a special hopper on the gun. As each magazine was exhausted, the gunner manually rotated the drum to the next position, bringing a full magazine over the mouth of the hopper, until all twenty magazines were emptied—a total of 400 rounds.

Another of the improvements covered by this patent was the automatic oscillating device. Actuated by a rotating multitracked cam at the end of the crank shaft, the oscillator, when engaged into the cam, caused the gun to swing from side to side automatically. Traverse could be adjusted by the gunner to give a sweep of up to 12°; at 1,200 yards, a target area 62 feet wide was covered. A U.S. Board of Officers reported (*Ordnance Memorandum No. 17*) after testing the oscillator:

> Although the advantages, for target practice, where hits cannot be seen even with a glass, of an automatic oscillator adjustable at pleasure for any sector from zero to 10 or 12 degrees are plainly obvious, it does not follow that such a mechanism is equally necessary under all circumstances, when operating against troops, for the reason that in the latter case the points reached by the projectiles (unless the firing is very bad) and the effects produced can generally be observed from the gun, and the direction and elevation of the piece adjusted and varied, from time to time, as circumstances require. But in order to leave as little as possible to the judgement of the enlisted men, by whom in actual service the gun will be served, and thereby secure the best results, an adjustable automatic oscillator is considered desirable.

Model 1871 magazines: (left) early type with lid as in Model 1865 magazine; (right) magazine with spring catch, manually released, to retain cartridges.

3 Sheets—Sheet 3.

R. J. GATLING.

REVOLVING BATTERY GUN.

No. 112,138. Patented Feb. 28, 1871.

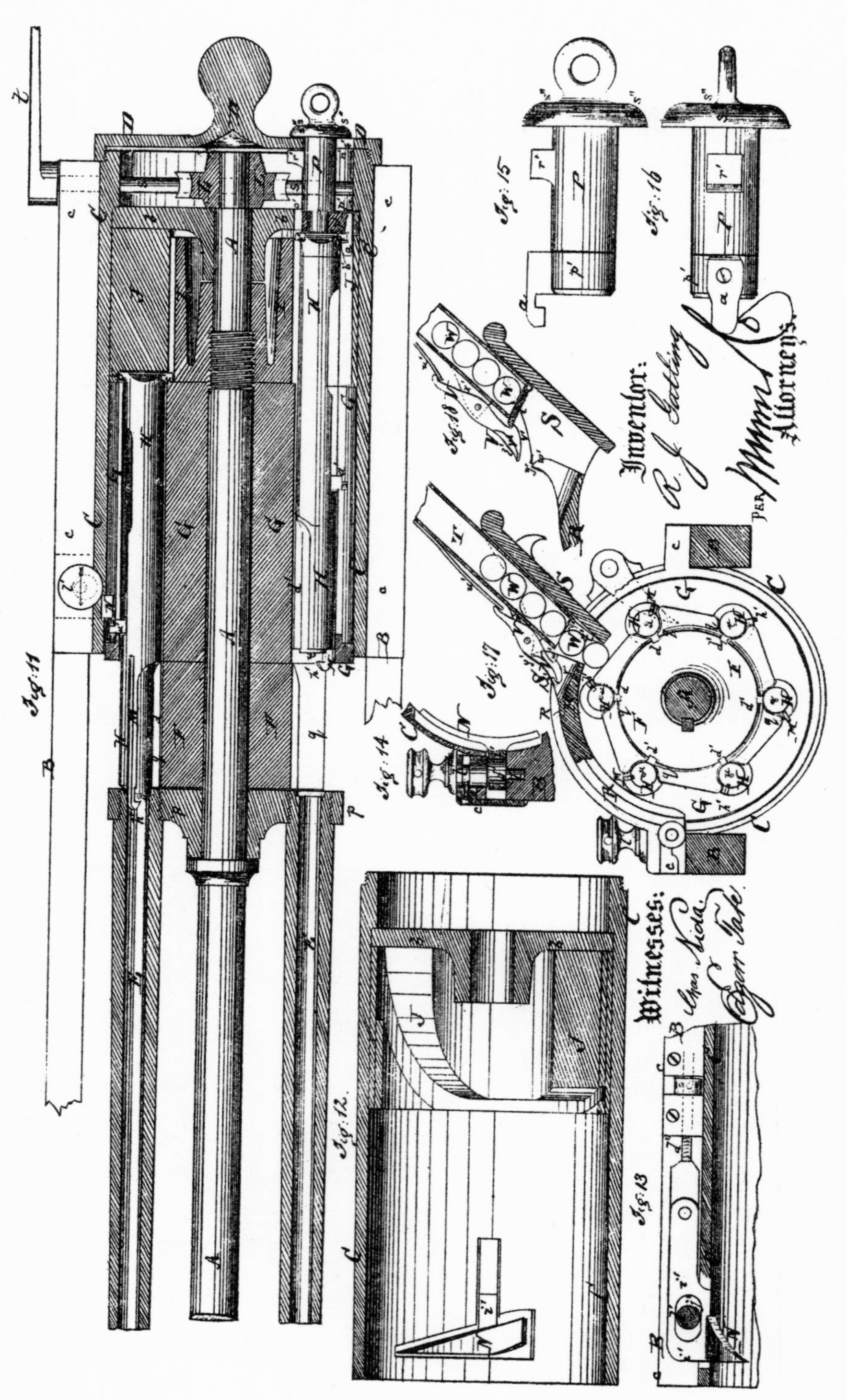

Detail drawing, Model 1871 Gatling. Note access port in cascabel plate through which breech bolts were removed (Fig. 11); plug (Fig. 11, 15, 16), was provided to close port.

3 Sheets—Sheet 2.

R. J. GATLING.

REVOLVING BATTERY GUN.

No. 112,138. Patented Feb. 28, 1871.

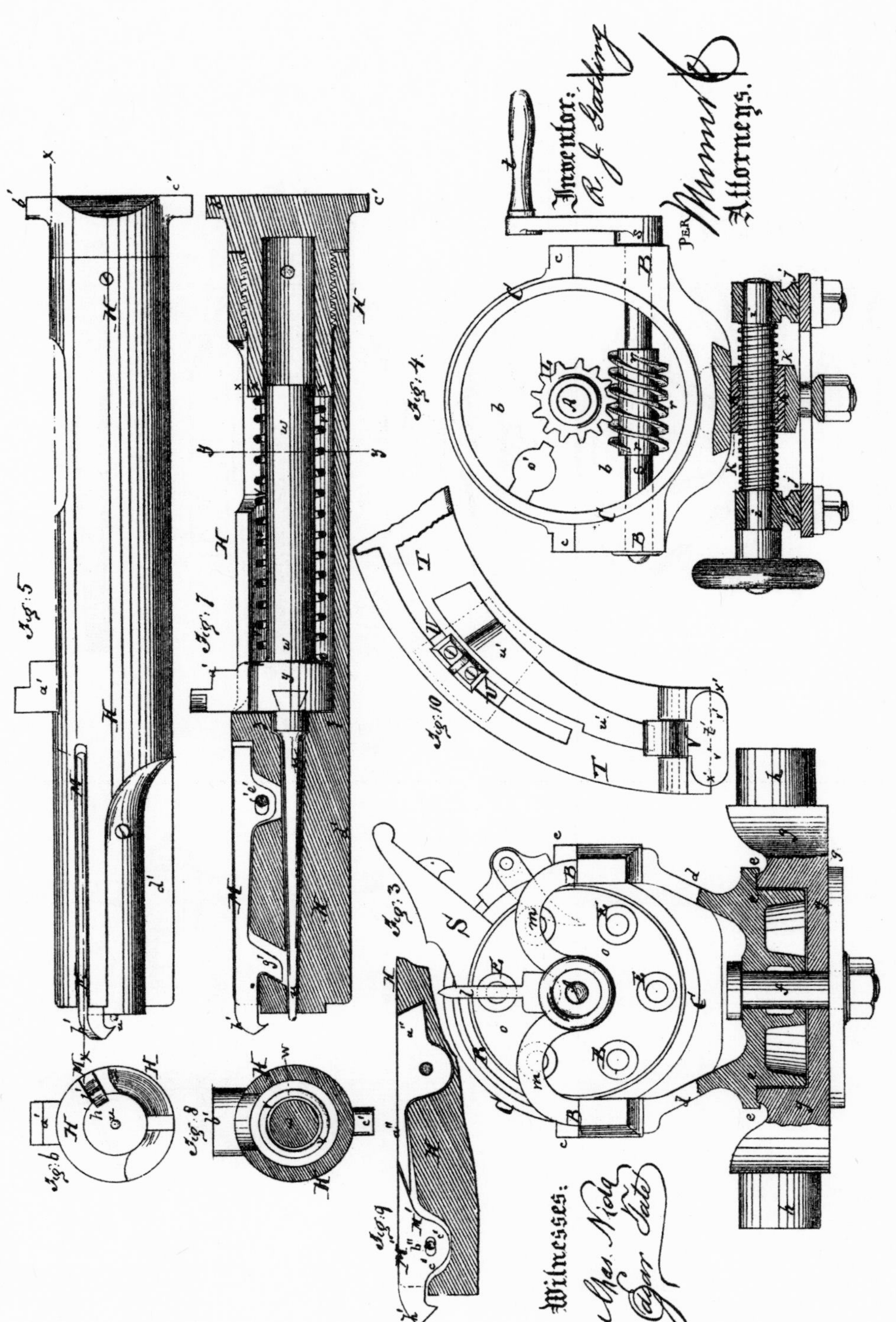

Detail drawing, Model 1871 Gatling. Note heavier breech bolt (Fig. 5, 6, 7, 8), also curved magazine (Fig. 10).

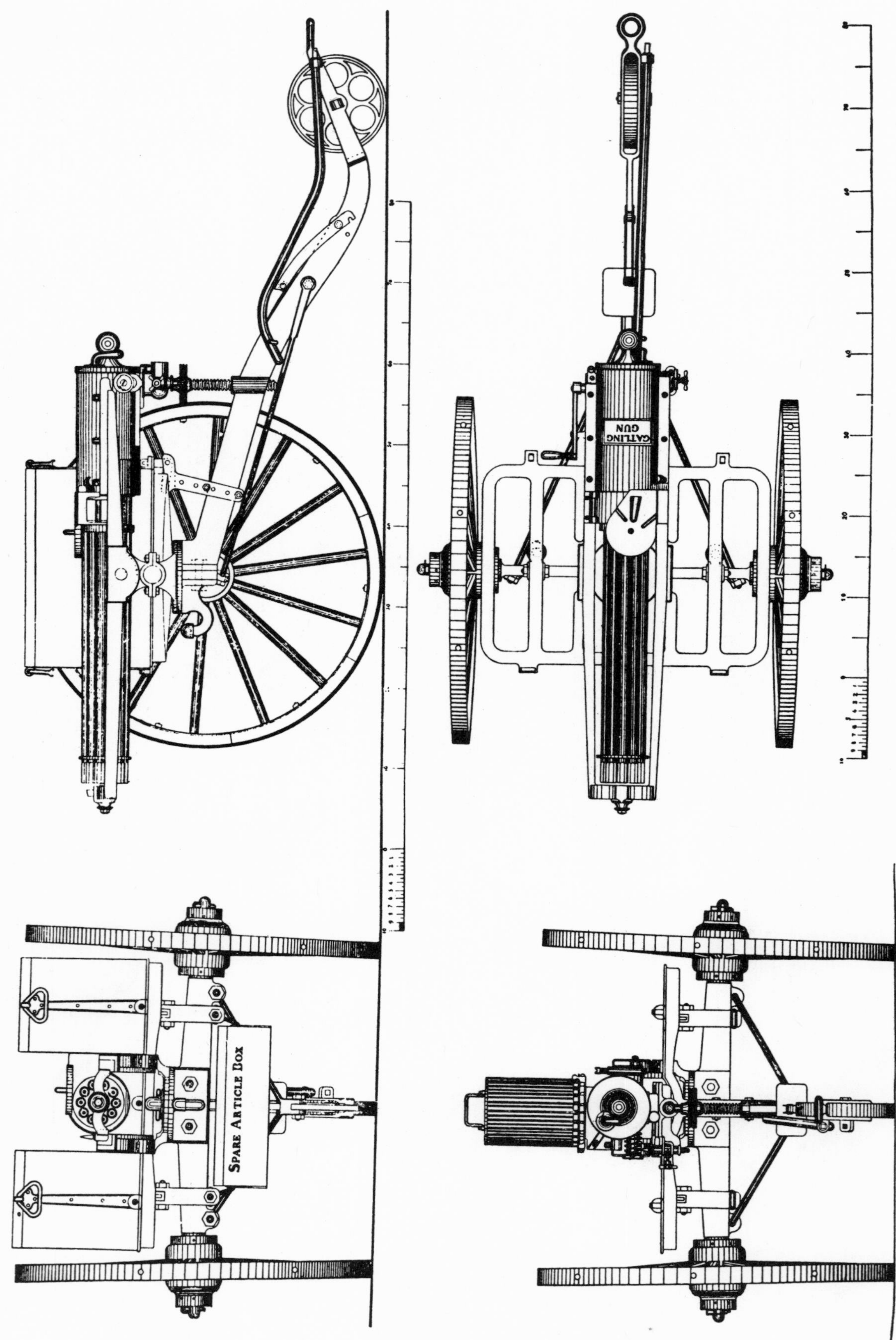

Model 1871 Long Gatling Gun, caliber .50, on U.S. Navy landing carriage. 400-round Broadwell drum feed. Automatic oscillating device. Ammunition chests, hinged to axle, could be tilted forward and out of the way during firing.

Aside from the aforementioned improvements, specifications of the 1871–1873 Gatlings were similar to those of the Model 1865 type. Standard Model 1871 guns had ten barrels, but could be ordered with five or six barrels, at the customer's option. The U.S. Army purchased nine of the Model 1871 Gatlings in caliber .50, serial numbers 100-108. A few were bought by the U.S. Navy, and quantities of this model, in various calibers and numbers of barrels, were ordered by Holland, Russia, and Tunis.

Only one Model 1871 gun in caliber 1-inch saw service: U.S. Army Gatling No. 121. This was the last of the Colt-manufactured 1-inch guns. Gatling's European licensees continued to make the big-bored model, but very few were sold.

TRIALS AT SHOEBURYNESS, ENGLAND

The British were first to test the new, improved Gatling. In August and September, 1870, prototype guns in calibers .42, .65, and 1-inch were tested at the Shoeburyness proving ground. For purposes of comparison with the Gatlings, breechloader twelve-pounder and muzzle-loading nine-pounder field guns, the Montigny Mitrailleuse, as well as several types of military rifles, were included in these trials, each weapon being subjected to a similar course of testing.

Firing was conducted at ranges of from 300 to 1,200 yards at a line of targets, each 9 feet square. A firing time limit of two minutes was imposed. At a distance of 300 yards, a Gatling Gun scored 369 hits out of 616 shots fired, while a Mitrailleuse fired 185 rounds, of which 171 scored on the target.

In a second experiment, the Gatling and Mitrailleuse were fired at the same targets at 400 yards. Each gun discharged 185 rounds; the Mitrailleuse scored 177 hits to the Gatling's 169.

The third Gatling vs. Mitrailleuse trial had each weapon fired at ranges from 1,200 to 1,400 yards. Guns were to be fired at maximum rate of fire for two minutes. At 1,400 yards, the Gatling fired 545 shots with 104 hits; the Mitrailleuse, 296 shots with 68 hits.

In the fourth trial, targets were 134 man-sized dummies placed in loose order on uneven ground to simulate an infantry force retiring. At 300 yards, the Gatling scored more than twice as many hits as did the Mitrailleuse; at 650 yards, results were similar. The Gatling Gun made 177 hits, compared with only nine by the Mitrailleuse, at 950 yards.

Competing against cannon, the Gatling scored 2,803 hits with an expenditure of 492 pounds of ammunition, while a twelve-pounder breechloading field gun required 1,232 pounds of ammunition to score 2,286 hits on the targets. As a control, picked companies of riflemen, armed with Martini-Henry and Snider rifles, fired volleys at the same targets and ranges; at 450 yards, less than half the rifle bullets found their marks.

Summing up its report, the committee for the Shoeburyness tests stated:

> The results of the recent inquiry have fully satisfied the committee of the expediency of introducing a certain proportion of these machine guns, to act as auxiliaries to the other arms of the service, and, of the several designs which have been submitted for their consideration, including those that have been under trial, they are persuaded that the Gatling Gun is the best adapted to meet all military requirements.

This recommendation of the Shoeburyness Trial Board paved the way for sales of Gatling Guns to England. The next quarter century saw the Gatling used extensively in British military operations.

ANNAPOLIS TRIALS BY THE U. S. NAVY

Trials of the .50 caliber Gatling Gun were conducted at Fort Madison, near Annapolis, Maryland, October 23–25, 1873, by Lt. Comdr. J. D. Marvin, U.S.N. Purposes of these tests were to determine the reliability under torturous conditions of both the Gatling Gun and the ammunition made for it by U.S. Cartridge Co., of Lowell, Massachusetts. Testing began on the morning of October 23.

In the first test, ten drums of 400 rounds each were fired as rapidly as possible, the 4,000 cartridges being discharged within 10 minutes and 48 seconds. During that day, an additional 28,000 rounds were fired from the Gatling.

Firing was resumed the following day—October 24—and that evening Gatling wrote, in a letter to Edgar T. Welles, Secretary, Gatling Gun Company:

> The trials of the gun today were a great success —Between sixty four & sixty five thousand cartridges were fired in the gun today without cleaning,—a thing that was never before done by any other gun. . . . All the officers are highly pleased with the results of the firing which they think most remarkable.

On the third and final day of the Annapolis trials, the remainder of the 100,000 cartridges, furnished for this testing, were fired from the same Gatling Gun.

Commander Marvin stated in his report: "The working of the gun throughout this severe trial was eminently satisfactory, no derangement of any im-

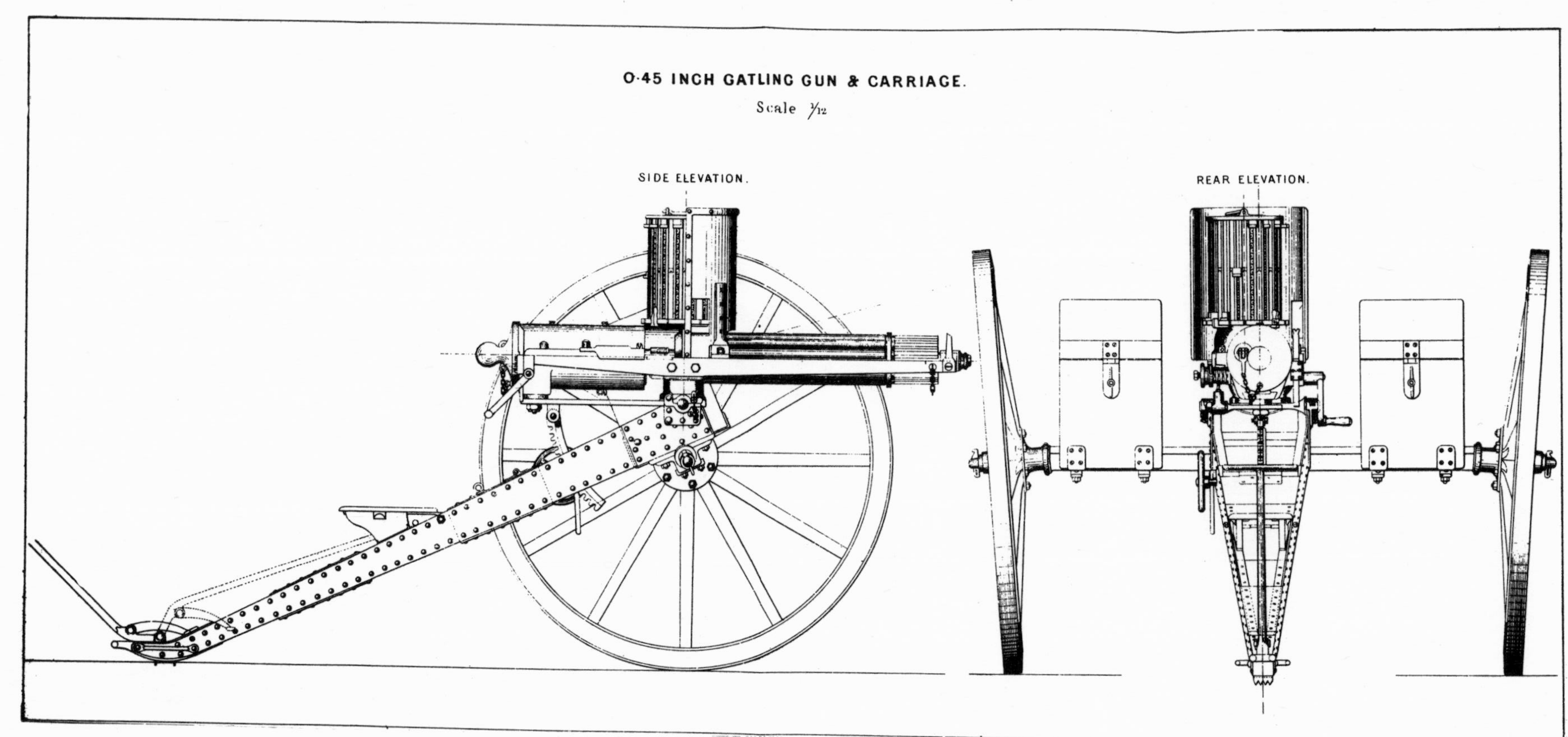

British Gatling Gun, 1871 type, manufactured by Sir William Armstrong & Co. Rack-and-pinion elevating system was more flexible and quicker adjusting than jack screw of contemporary Colt-made Gatlings. Steel shield protected Broadwell drum—a unique feature.

portance whatever occurring." The U.S. Cartridge Co. ammunition, too, seems to have come through the Navy's torture tests with flying colors.

As an indication of just how "severe" Commander Marvin's tests were: it was found that, after the rapid-firing of 4,000 rounds in ten minutes, barrel temperatures, as shown by color test, exceeded 500° F. Fearing that this heat might cause premature discharge of cartridges in the feed system of the weapon, the testing gun crew threw buckets of cold water on the glowing barrels to cool them. Even such treatment had no adverse effect on the performance of the Gatling Gun.

FORTRESS MONROE TRIALS

Because of the major changes made in the Gatling design during the early 1870's, a series of trials to evaluate these improvements was held by the U.S. Army Ordnance Department at Fortress Monroe, Virginia, October–December 1873. The favorable findings of this test board firmed the status of the Gatling Gun as an important component of the United States' armament.

Guns chosen for trial were 1-inch and .42 caliber. The latter, chambered for the .42 Berdan cartridge standard for Russian military rifles, actually was one of the Gatlings produced, under contract, for Russia and incorporated design improvements made by General Gorloff. When subsequently furnished to the U.S. Government, guns of this Model 1874 pattern were, of course, chambered for the U.S. caliber .45 cartridge.

The Gatling Guns were tried in competition with two issue artillery pieces: the 8-inch siege howitzer and the 12-pounder Napoleon. As an added control, forty picked marksmen fired Springfield rifles at the same type of targets as those presented the larger guns.

Targets used were varied. One test employed ten targets made of 1-inch thick yellow pine boards, each 6 feet high by 50 feet wide, representing columns of infantry, maneuvering by companies on the field. The nearest "wooden company" was 1,000 yards from the gun; the others were placed in file, 50 feet apart. To test dispersion of fire, canvas targets 9 feet high by 45 feet wide were used. Penetration was judged by the number of 1-inch thick yellow pine boards, spaced 1-inch apart, that different types of projectile pierced.

Firing at the 9 by 35 foot canvas target at 200 yards, the .42 caliber Gatling Gun scored 618 hits out of 637 shots fired. In marked contrast, the 1-inch Gatling, firing canister shot, fired 213 rounds containing a total of 3,834 balls, of which only 846 struck the target. The cannon made scores almost as poor as that of the 1-inch Gatling: of 1,452 canister balls discharged from the 12-pounder Napoleon, 379 found their mark; the 8-inch howitzer firing service canister scored 52 hits out of 192 balls. Springfield-armed riflemen did a little better: they fired a total of 601 rounds, of which 320 were hits. It seems safe to assume that, had these marksmen been firing in battle rather than on a target range, their effectiveness would have been considerably less.

In penetration tests, bullets fired from the .42 caliber Gatling went through six to seven of the one-inch thick yellow pine boards. Canister shot from the 1-inch Gatling penetrated only one board, while the Napoleon and howitzer produced an average penetration of two to three boards.

The .42 caliber Gatling Gun came through all thirty-four tests, to which the different weapons were subjected, with the top record. In the official report, published in 1874 as *Ordnance Memorandum No. 17,* it was stated:

> This record shows in a striking manner the vast superiority of the Gatling Gun against troops at ranges beyond effective reach of canister or say beyond two hundred and fifty yards, for the projectiles in competition with it, whether case-shot or shell, are subject to a variety of disadvantageous conditions, more or less beyond control, among which may be enumerated the inaccuracy common to smooth bore guns; the varying effects of wind due to changes in either force or direction, or to both; the eccentricity of the projectiles, and the imperfection of fuses, the latter having been, during the trials of the board, a conspicuous and fruitful cause of the very poor results obtained.
>
> At five hundred yards one Gatling, fired with oscillator, gave fifty-eight per cent more hits than two twelve pounder Napoleons and one eight inch howitzer firing together, each firing one minute and 30 seconds.
>
> At eight hundred yards the proportions of hits were largely increased in favor of the Gatling, there being an average of 320 hits for one Gatling as against an aggregate of only 38 hits for two Napoleons and one howitzer.

The board, headed by Maj. Stephen V. Benét, recommended adoption of the Gatling Gun, chambered for the .45 caliber cartridge, for the defense of fortifications, and as an auxiliary arm for all branches of the service. It was further suggested that a board of officers be appointed to determine the number of Gatlings required for military use, their report to be submitted by July 1, 1874.

More than any previous trials, the exhaustive tests conducted at Fortress Monroe during the fall of 1873 established the Gatling Gun, hitherto regarded as essentially a flank defense weapon, as a

Gatling-equipped camel corps.

truly versatile arm of greater effectiveness in general use than the conventional field guns and rifles with which it was compared. The subsequent, almost universal, adoption of the Gatling Gun by the world's armies and navies came largely as a result of the conclusive Fortress Monroe Trials.

GATLING MODELS OF 1874-1877

The musket-caliber Gatling Gun that performed so outstandingly in the 1873 trials was a forerunner of the Model 1874, first of the "Classic Gatlings." Smaller and lighter than any of its predecessors, with hopper and breech housing of bronze, this model was far handsomer too.

In 1873, Colt produced a few of these guns in .50/70 caliber. Early the following year, the weapon was standardized as Model 1874, chambered for the .45/70 Government cartridge.

Reduction of size and weight in the Model 1874 gun resulted chiefly from the adoption of a newly developed, smaller breech bolt, permitting the breech housing to be made shorter and more slender, as well as lighter in weight.

Among the features of the Model 1874 were an improved oscillator, headspace adjusting system, insulated barrel shaft, feed hopper, and magazine.

More compact and sturdier than the complicated oscillator of 1871, the new type (Gatling's patent No. 145,563) could be set for automatic traverse of the target area or, alternatively, the oscillating device could be used as a manually adjusted windage control.

Headspace—distance from bolt face to head of chambered round—always had been a problem in Gatling Guns: if set before firing, it soon became too tight as the barrel unit heated and expanded. The Model 1874 had an adjustable set screw, passing through the center of the frame and bearing on the front end of the axle on which the cluster of barrels revolved. By adjustment of this screw, the barrels could be brought closer to or farther away from the breech bolts, setting headspace to the proper tolerance. Often, it was necessary to make this adjustment during lulls in firing and, necessarily, the man performing this operation had to stand in front of the gun muzzles. After several casualties, guns were fitted with a crank lock to prevent accidental firing and later instruction manuals directed that this safety device be engaged before any member of the crew stepped in front of the business end of the Gatling.

The barrel shaft or axle, between the front and rear barrel-supporting disks, was covered by a leather tube, intended to insulate the axle against the heat radiated from the barrels and, thus, prevented excessive expansion of this critical component. Since nearly all of the major operating parts of the gun were suspended from this central shaft, any change in its dimensions would derange the normal working tolerances (quite close) of these parts and bind the gun.

An improved feed hopper was incorporated in the Model 1874 Gatling. It was designed to accept a new type of magazine. With the exception of the drum feed, all previous magazines were inserted into the gun at a 45° angle, the hopper being designed in such a way that view of the centrally located sights was not obscured by the magazine. In the Model 1874, sights were mounted on the right side of the arm, and the hopper mouth, located to the left of center on top of the piece, accepted vertical insertion of the magazine.

The magazine was a tin-plated box, trapezoidal in cross section, with a brass top and bottom; it was fitted with a heavy brass follower, the weight of which forced the cartridges downward into the hopper. Bottom end of the magazine, open to permit the rounds to feed into the gun, had a spring catch to keep cartridges from falling out; this catch automatically disengaged when the magazine was instered into the hopper mouth. This gravity-fed box magazine held 40 rounds of ammunition.

Model 1874 Gatling Guns were made in two types: the long, "musket length" model and the smaller, short-barreled "Camel Gun." To arms collectors, the latter is one of the more desirable specimens—not only because of its comparative rarity, but also because its relatively small size and light weight make the gun more convenient to handle and display.

Chambered for the .45/70 Government cartridge (commercial and export guns were available in other calibers to order), the long Model 1874 Gatling had ten 32-inch barrels, measured 49 inches overall, and weighed 200 pounds (without carriage and limber, which added 326 and 387 pounds respectively). Ammunition was gravity-fed from a box magazine; a few of these guns were equipped with Broadwell drum feed and also accepted the standard magazine. The bronze breech casing bore a legend plate of the same material with both Colt and Gatling markings. Located on the right side of the gun, the rear sight was adjustable for elevation, the front sight folded along the frame when not in use (a feature found only in this model). Mounted on a wheeled artillery carriage, the gun was traversed, automatically or manually at the gunner's option, by an improved oscillating device; elevation was obtained through a jackscrew in the trail. Model 1874 guns purchased by the U.S. Army bore serial numbers 57 through 63, and 105.

While small, short-barreled Gatling Guns were produced as early as 1871, it was the improvements incorporated in the Model 1874 that made possible the development of the true Camel Gun, most of which were manufactured in 1874, although a few were produced in 1875 and 1876. Essentially, the Camel Gun specifications were like those of the long Model 1874 gun, with these exceptions: barrel length, 18 inches; over-all length of gun, 35½ inches; weight of gun, 135 pounds; mounted on its cavalry cart, total weight of gun and implements, 925 pounds. In addition to the cavalry cart, mounts for the Model 1874 Camel Gun included tripod and camel saddle type. Camel Guns No. 1-56 were bought by the U.S. Army.

Gatling and his associates, ever cognizant of the value of publicity, adopted the exotic name, "Camel Gun," to designate the short model Gatling and the use of bizarre camel corps pictures for the attention these were sure to attract. The Camel Gun possessed great utility as a weapon and mounting on a camel probably was the least of its possibilities for military service. While some camel mounts were made—portions are extant—there is no evidence that there ever was a Gatling-equipped camel corps.

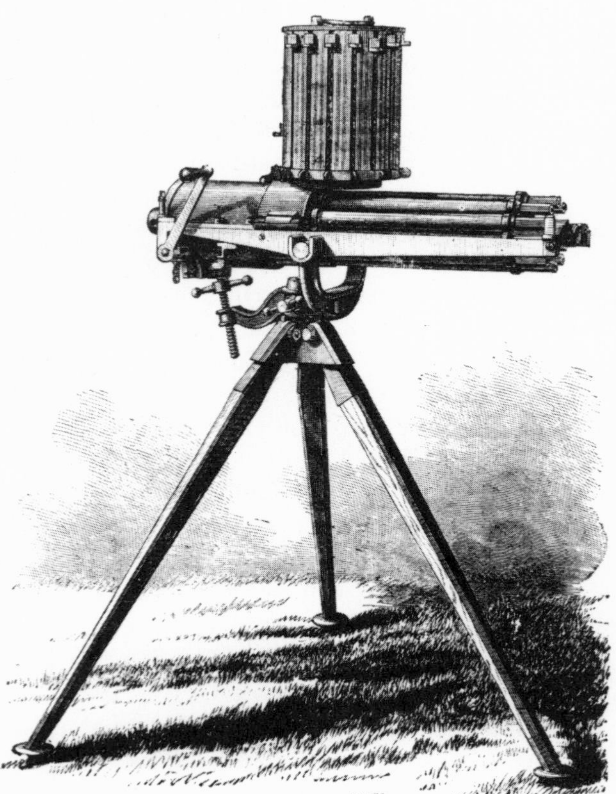

Model 1874 Gatling Camel Gun. Prototype circa 1872.

Frequently, it has been suggested that England's Col. Maxwell had much to do with the development of the Gatling Gun, particularly the Camel Gun type. *Army & Navy Journal,* March 9, 1872, commented on this:

> . . . the suggestion of this gun [Camel Gatling] may be due to arguments of Col. Maxwell, of the East Indian service, who has been an earnest advocate of the use of camels to bear small guns in war. Col. Maxwell, as superintendent of the Cossipore gun foundry in India, and more recently we believe, as member of one or more ordnance commissions in England, has gained a deservedly high reputation in the ordnance and engineering circles; yet we fancy he is entitled to no greater credit in the construction of this Camel Gatling than may belong to any shrewd applicator of the possibilities of the Gatling system. Two years since, at least, we remember talking to the inventor about the adaptability of his guns, with weight and proportions properly reduced, to similar service. . . . We have yet to find in our English files any intimation that Col. Maxwell is entitled to any credit for the Camel Gatling Gun, except the credit of being the first to appreciate its value.

Capt. E. Rogers suggested the possible source of the artist's inspiration for the picture of the Gatling-equipped camel corps in a paper, "The Gatling Gun; Its Place in Tactics," published in the *Journal of the Royal United Service Institution* (Vol. XIX, 1876, pp. 427–428):

> More than 150 years ago, an Afghan Chief crossed the deserts of Kerman with an army, for the most part mounted on camels, a number of the latter bearing, in addition to their riders, a swivel gun. Approaching Ispahan, they encountered a Persian Army nearly three times their number and provided in addition with 24 formidable pieces of ordnance. On the Persian Army's approach, the left wing of the Afghans gave away; the former immediately pursued with vigour, but soon their enemies' ranks opened and disclosed a line of 100 camels kneeling down, each with a gun on its back. The fire knocked over the leading ranks of the Persians, and a charge of cavalry completed their discomfiture. Colonel Maxwell, R.A., who recounted this story some years ago to an audience at Woolwich, became, no doubt, unknowingly responsible for the hint as magnified by an American Artist, who has depicted an army of camels with short-barrelled Gatlings duly mounted, deployed for action on a vast plain in double ranks, front rank kneeling. The terrible effects of such a volume of volleys is, in fact, the only thing left to the imagination in the picture! But it was, I believe, at the

Model 1874 Gatling on full field carriage.

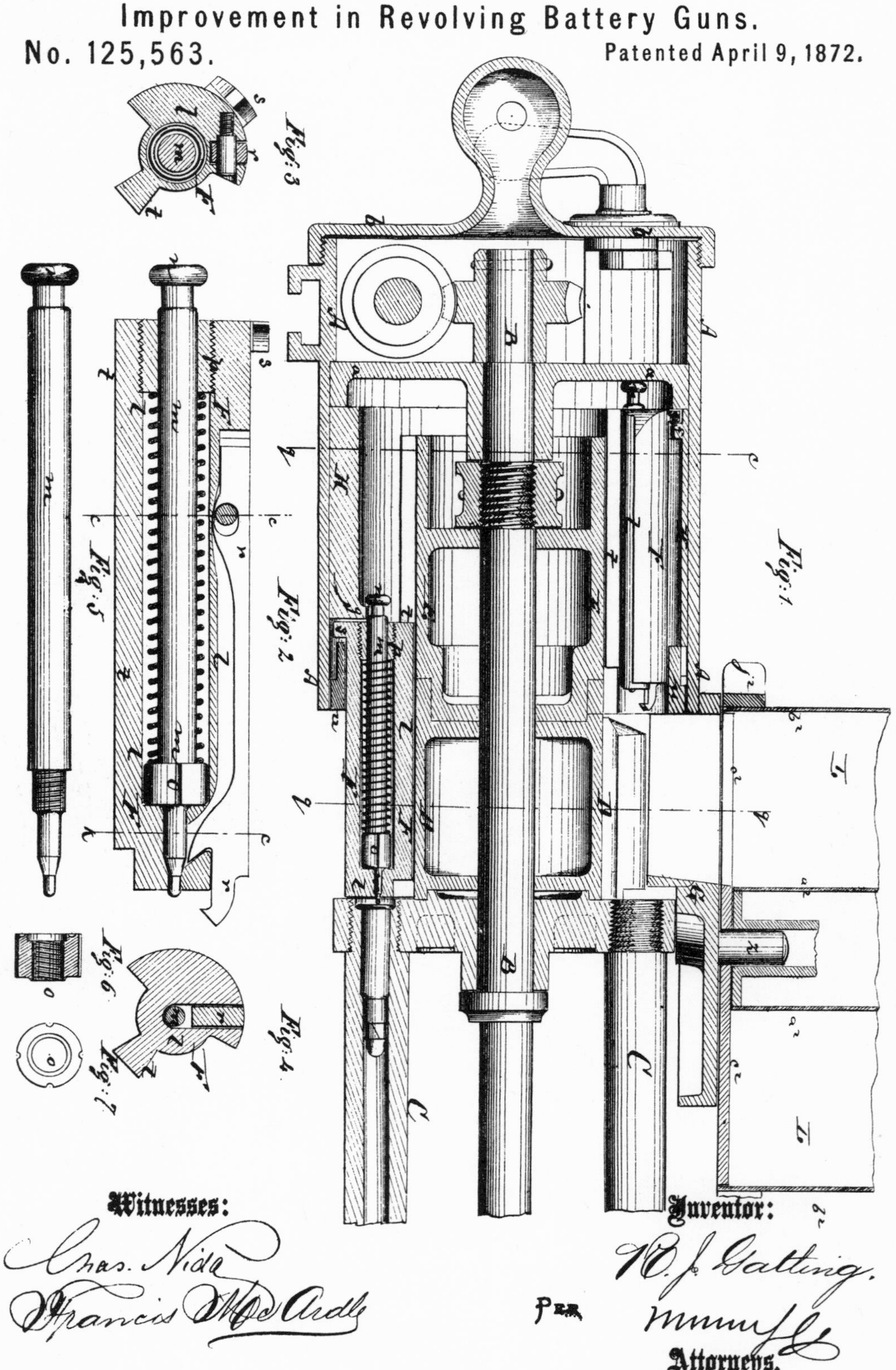

Cross section of Gatling Gun, illustrating improvements patented April 9, 1872. Note short breech bolts, used from 1874, and that gun shown is fitted with Broadwell drum.

serious suggestion of this same artillery officer, that Dr. Gatling planned the camel gun, weighing 135 pounds only, and capable of being worked from a fixed tripod, or from the back of a camel or elephant!

The camel-saddle mount attracted the attention of the press, but the more conventional tripod and cavalry cart were the mounts ordered by the military for general service use.

A Gatling tripod consisted of a steel turntable on which the tripod head, with gun-supporting yoke and containing the windage and elevation controls, revolved. On the bottom of the turntable were three iron fittings to receive the wooden legs. Some tripods had chains connecting the legs to prevent them from spreading too far apart. From the collector's standpoint, the tripod is the rarest and most desirable of all Gatling Gun mounts.

The cavalry cart was the lightest artillery mount ever used with a Gatling Gun. Yoke assembly was mounted on the floor of a two-wheeled cart; on each side of the gun, there was a wooden ammunition chest containing 24 forty-round magazines; a third chest, slung under the cart's axle, carried an additional 2,000 cartridges in their original packing boxes, as well as the gunner's implements. There was a pair of shafts for the off-horse and a singletree for the driver's horse (original instruction book advises the use of "one horse for good roads, two horses for bad"); the shafts doubled as a trail or rear brace.

With the inception of Model 1874, Colt began using a system of consecutive serial numbering starting with Camel Gun No. 1, which was maintained until the end of Gatling Gun production in 1911. All Gatlings, from 1874 on, bore two sets of numbers: the serial number stamped or engraved on the right side of the frame at the trunnion; every part of the weapon bore an assembly number, each year's production beginning with No. 1, indicating the number of the particular weapon within its series. Navy Gatlings had a U.S.N. Bureau of Ordnance number engraved on top of the barrel housing ahead of the hopper.

In 1875, the gun was improved in several ways. The rather vulnerable folding front sight was replaced with a fixed one. To provide better support for the sides of the magazine, the hopper was redesigned with higher walls on the port. Some jamming was experienced with Model 1874; to correct this, bolt faces were beveled on one edge for smoother feeding. The U.S. Army bought 44 long Model 1875 Gatlings (serial Nos. 107-146, 163-166) and four Camel Guns (Nos. 159-162). A number of 1874-1875 Gatlings of a special U.S. Navy

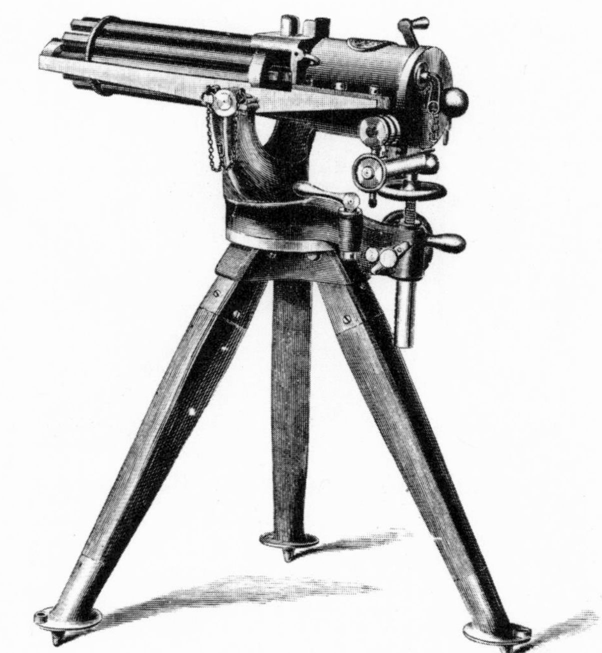

Model 1876 Gatling Camel Gun on improved tripod.

Cavalry cart for short model Gatlings.

Short Model 1875 Gatling on U.S. Navy steel carriage.

Model 1877 Gatling on full field carriage.

model also were produced. These differed in having barrel length midway between those of the standard long model and the Camel Gun, and in that the entire gun was encased in a bronze jacket. Navy Gatlings were furnished with a very light wheeled carriage, designed for deck and landing use.

The Model 1876 Gatling, while much like the previous year's model, incorporated several improvements. The mouth of the hopper was relocated from the left side to the center of the gun. Front and rear cartridge guides were introduced into the hopper to facilitate passage of cartridges into the barrel chambers. Additional screws were used in assembly of the interior parts of the breech casing to provide better support for the breech bolts. Bevel of the breech bolt edge was altered again for smoother feeding. The headspace adjusting screw washer was fitted with a new type of lock to minimize slippage in this critical setting. Eighteen Model 1876 musket-length Catlings were purchased by the U.S. Army (serial Nos. 170-188).

Further changes were made in the Model 1877 gun. The long type had an entirely new feed hopper, more open in design for easier ejection of fired cases and with a small, fluted drum that rotated to control passage of cartridges so that only one round could fall into position in front of each breech bolt. Gears were changed to a faster pitch for a higher rate of fire. This was the last model to use the cam-operated oscillator introduced in 1874. Eleven guns of the 1877 model were sold to the U.S. Army (serial Nos. 191-193, 196-201, 225, 226).

Disassembly procedure for Gatling Models of 1874–1877:

1. Turn the crank and, as each mark on the rear barrel plate comes opposite the arrow on the front of the hopper, remove the breech bolt—this is accomplished by turning the handle of the lock plug

Model 1877 with limber.

Short Model 1874 Gatling mounted on gunwale of a ship.

Close-up of muzzle end, Model 1874 Gatling. Folding front sight is found only on guns made in 1874. Cap at center covers headspace adjusting screw.

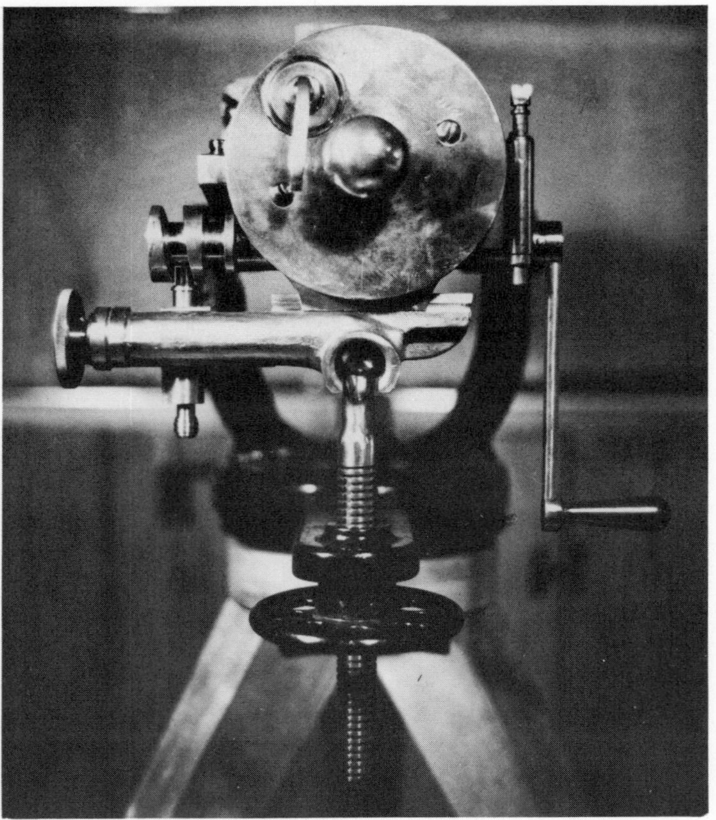

Rear view, Model 1874 Gatling, showing improved oscillator. With vertical pin (left) in camming groove, gun would swing from side to side. When pin rode in straight groove, oscillator functioned just as lateral adjustment, manually controlled by hand wheel.

and, with it, drawing the bolt out through the port in the cascabel plate.

2. Remove screws and take off the cascabel plate.

3. Remove the screw on the left end of the crank shaft and take off the oscillating drum.

4. Remove the worm gear lock pin; then, turn the crank in reverse to loosen the worm gear. Remove crank shaft, worm gear, and sleeve.

5. Using the gear puller supplied with the gun, remove the gear from the rear end of the barrel axle. On some models, it will be necessary first to remove the gear lock screw.

6. Remove rear sight assembly.

7. Remove the six large breech casing screws and slide off the breech casing to the rear. Be careful to support the barrel unit during this operation, so that it does not fall and damage the frame of the gun.

8. Remove the screws that secure the lock camming sleeve or cylinder to the inside of the breech casing. Remove the sleeve and take out the cocking cam piston and spring.

9. Remove the cover on the front of the frame to expose the headspace adjusting screw. Use special wrench furnished with gun.

The foregoing procedures are all that is necessary to disassemble the Gatling Gun for cleaning or overhaul. It is inadvisable to unscrew the barrels from the barrel unit, except for replacement.

GATLING GUNS FOR CUBA

In 1868, Cuban patriots, under the leadership of Manuel de Céspedes, began their fight for independence from Spain, the so-called "Ten Years War." The discontent of the native Cuban population stemmed from a multitude of grievances, chief among these: excessive taxation, restrictions on trade, and lack of representation in government. There were no major battles in this long war, just endless guerrilla fighting, mainly in the eastern provinces. The war ended in 1878 with the Treaty of Zanjón, which was supposed to grant the reforms and governmental representation for which the Cubans had fought for so many years. Since these promises were not kept by Spain, the Ten Years War really was without result, except that it foreshadowed the Spanish-American War of two decades later.

Recognizing the value of easily transported, tripod-mounted Camel Gatlings in jungle fighting against guerrilla bands, the Spanish Government ordered, in December, 1873, forty-six such guns chambered for the .43 Spanish cartridge, to be delivered to the Captain General of the Island of Cuba. Prices quoted by the Gatling Gun Company were as follows:

Thank you for visiting the
Allen County Public Library.

Item ID: 223389
Title: ILL - THE GATLING
GUN AND FLYING MACHINE
OF RICHA
Author: JOHNSON, F. ROY
Date due: 4/11/2017,23:59

Item ID: 223388
Title: ILL - THE GATLING
GUN
Author: WAHL, PAUL
Date due: 3/17/2017,23:59

Telephone Renewal: 421-
1240
Website Renewal: www.acpl.
info

Camel Gun, Caliber .43, with spare parts, implements, three feed drums, limber chest, and elevating screw	$920.
Tripod	80.
Traversing, oscillating part, fitted to the gun and tripod	40.
Packing, boxes, and freight from Hartford to vessel in New York	20.

Payment, it was specified in the agreement, to be made in gold.

Although the Spanish, in 1873, saw the advantages of the small, tripod-mounted Gatling for use in Cuba, twenty-five years later, the U.S. Army's Gatling Gun Detachment used long-barreled Gatlings on field carriages in the Battle of Santiago de Cuba, during the Spanish-American War.

THE KHIVAN CAMPAIGN

Once a great kingdom—in ancient and medieval times, Khiva latterly has fallen upon evil days, physiographically and politically. The land has become increasingly more desiccated because of the eastward shift of the Amu Darya river and the deterioration of irrigation facilities. Since 1924, Khiva has been divided between two Soviet Socialist Republics of Asiatic Russia, Uzbek and Turkmen.

The ancients knew Khiva as Chorasmia; it is mentioned in the *History* of Herodotus (fifth century B.C.), in whose day it was a satrapy of Persia, under Darius the Great, *et al.* Formerly, the Oxus (Amu Darya) flowed to the Caspian Sea, providing a waterway linking the oasis kingdom of Khiva with the western world. Over the centuries, the river has changed its course and now has its outlet in the Aral Sea. In early times, its position commanding the Oxus gave considerable strategic importance to Khiva. This river figured prominently in the campaigns of Alexander the Great and in Persian history generally. Khiva lies south of the Aral Sea and of the Amu Darya river in central Asia. Conquered by the Uzbeks in 1515, the khanate of Khiva remained an independent Moslem Uzbek state until its conquest by Russia in 1873. From that date until the Russian Revolution, the khanate was a Russian protectorate; from 1920 to 1924, it formed the Khorezm Soviet People's Republic until partitioned between Uzbek and Turkmen.

Russian attention was drawn to Khiva as early as the seventeenth century, during which Yaik Cossack bands made forays into Khivan territory. Peter the Great, learning that gold had been found in the sands of the Oxus, in 1717, sent an expedition to Khiva, ostensibly to open trade and secure the release of Russian subjects held captive there. While the Russian invasion initially was successful, decisively defeating the forces of the khan, the Khivans, through trickery, subsequently succeeded in annihilating the invaders. The Perovsky expedition of 1839 similarly met with disaster.

In 1873, a large-scale campaign against Khiva was organized by Russia, with an army of 10,000 men under Gen. Kaufmann. Converging on Khiva from three directions—previously established bases at Krasnovosk on the east shore of the Caspian, Chkalov on the right bank of the Ural river, and Tashkent in the oasis of that name—the Russians met little opposition in their occupation of the country. All of the Khivan territory on the right bank of the Amu Darya was annexed to Russia. A heavy war indemnity was imposed upon the khanate with disastrous economic and political effects on the nation.

While history indicates that there was not much action involved in the Khivan expedition of 1873, a report by Captain A. Litvinoff, in the *Russian Artillery Journal,* January, 1874, tells interestingly of an incident involving the use by the Russians of Gatling guns in this campaign.

Action of Battery Guns in Khivean Expedition

. . . We left Zmukshir on the 13–25th of June, and after a march of twelve verstes [about 8 miles], stopped near the village of Chandir, close to the gardens which stretch without interruption from Chandir to Illialee. About 3 P.M. parties of horsemen commenced to make their appearance from different sides; they approached us nearer and nearer, and behind them we could descry larger masses. They commenced to engage our picket lines with great determination and daring. One of these pickets, composed of one officer (Ensign Kamentzky) and five Cossacks, swords in hand, threw themselves forward against an approaching mass of Toorkomans, and were completely cut to pieces. Two companies of the third battalion of sharpshooters, two of the eighth battalion of the line, and two battery guns (Gatlings), were ordered forward to drive away these bands of Toorkomans. The road we had to follow was very difficult, even for infantry and cavalry, as at every step we had to cross wide ditches dug for irrigation, which had abrupt sides; for artillery the road would have been impassable. Our light battery guns went on this road with perfect ease, the ammunition pack-horses alone giving some trouble. When we stopped, a line of sharpshooters and battery guns was formed along one of these ditches.

First I had to find out the range; for this purpose I fired three cartridges, changing each time the height of the sight. The distance found was between the limits of 1,050 and 1,170 yards. Then I laid down both guns, aiming one at a large band of Toorkomans, and the other at another band formed not far from the first. Opening at the first band, I fired rapidly twenty-five rounds; the band immediately dispersed, part of the men joining the second band. Opening from the second gun I fired fifty rounds without interruption; the second band dispersed at once, the men betook themselves to the broken ground, and disappeared behind some hills and in the irrigation ditches. Several times the enemy, collecting in masses of some strength, moved against us, but was each time driven back by our fire; thus I had several opportunities of firing a succession of twenty-five or fifty rounds, the directions of guns and their elevations varying somewhat, according to the circumstances. In the whole, the battery guns fired that day 408 cartridges. The guns were permitted a very slight side motion. The ground was of clay, covered with scant vegetation, and the fall of the bullets on such ground and their ricochets were easily seen from the battery, even at a distance of 1,170 yards.

. . . June 15–27th a general order was given to move forward early next morning, leaving all trains and baggage behind. As to this train and baggage, they received the order to remain on the same spot (Illialee), and at the break of the next day to form a wagenburg (a large square made of wagons), under the guard of two companies of the fourth battalion of sharpshooters, two battery guns, and a few men of each command sent back to take care of their respective baggage wagons.

At nightfall it was ascertained that in the vicinity of our camp the enemy had congregated in large numbers. Soon after midnight there was an alarm, when all the troops took up arms, but it proved to be without consequence. Apprehending a night attack, and considering that the wagons were much scattered about, it was ordered to collect all the wagons at once, without waiting for the breaking of day. These being collected, the formation of the wagenburg began. The left side and part of the front side of the square were well lined with wagons put close to one another. A company of sharpshooters of the fourth battalion occupied that line, the men either getting on top of the wagons or sitting under them on the ground. The enemy being expected chiefly from the right, I put my two guns in the corner formed by the front and right sides of the square. The right side and rear having as yet no wagons in line, and being somewhat protected by shallow ditches, were guarded, first by miscellaneous men of different commands taking charge of their wagons, officers' servants, sutlers, etc., all armed with pistols, revolvers, sporting-guns, etc., second by a platoon of sharpshooters lying on the ground. At 3 o'clock the attack of Toorkomans commenced.

[Here follows the description of the fight of the other troops.]

At the first howls of the attacking enemy I hastened to form a cover for my guns. I put on the right wing ten privates of Soonja and Daguestan, who were with the train guarding their wagons; on the left, fifteen sharpshooters and twelve men of my battery guns command, with whom I could dispense for the present; these men were also armed with rifles. Leaving thus with the battery guns only the most indispensable men to assist in firing, I took myself the crankhandle of the first gun, invited Capt. Cachourin (Cossack) to take the handle of the other gun, and enjoined on all my group not to commence the fire before the word of command was given.

The guns formed an obtuse angle one with another, as it was necessary to direct them to the precise spot where the shoutings of the enemy were heard, and whence they were approaching us. We had not long to wait. The cries of the Toorkomans who had succeeded in breaking through the lines of our detachment and turning their flanks, suddenly rose from all sides and became deafening. Though it was dark, we perceived in front of us the galloping masses of the enemy with uplifted glittering swords. When they approached us to within about twenty paces, I shouted the command "Fire." This was followed by a salvo of all the men forming the cover, and a continuous simultaneous rattle of the two battery guns. In this roar, the cries of the enemy at once became weak, and then ceased altogether, vanishing as rapidly as they rose. The firing at once stopped, and as no enemy was visible before us, I ventured to get a look at the surrounding grounds, availing myself of the first lights of dawn. About 200 paces to the right of our square stood the eighth battalion of the line. Between it and us no enemy was to be seen, but at every step lay prostrated the dead bodies of the Yonoods, their hats being pushed up to their eyes. I saw no wounded—they were probably all carried away according to the usual Toorkoman warfare.

This account is of particular interest since it describes the effectiveness of machine guns, skillfully emplaced, against attacking forces virtually invisible in the dark of night.

Nameplate found on breech casing of 1874-78 Gatlings.

THE ASHANTI WAR

Prior to its annexation by the British in 1902, Ashanti was a powerful native kingdom of western Africa. It was, until 1957, when the independent state of Ghana was formed, a principal district of the British colony of the Gold Coast on the Gulf of Guinea. Modern Ashanti, with approximately the same boundaries as the former kingdom, has an area of 24,379 square miles. The country is bisected, northwest to southeast, by the Kwahu scarp; south of the slope is a plateau covered by a dense forest, to the north lies a vast, undulating savanna. Seat of the kingdom was Kumasi, located about in the center of the forest.

While the coastal peoples were friendly and traded peacefully with the whites, the warlike Ashantis resented the British dominance of the Gold Coast area, not only because it interfered with their plans for expansion of the Ashanti union, but also since Britain's abolition of the slave trade had ruined the market for their principal export. Faced with a superabundance of slaves, the Ashantis increased their practice of human sacrifice to take care of the surplus. By 1863, there was open hostility between the British and Ashantis; however, there was no serious conflict until 1873, when the *Asantehene* (king of the Ashantis) Kofi Karikari launched a full-scale attack on the coastal tribes; the Denkera and Fanti, who were under the protection of Great Britain, were soon defeated. As the Ashanti warriors ravaged the surrounding area, the neighboring tribes lived in terror, having intimate knowledge of the Ashantis' extreme cruelty to enslaved captives, as well as their especially fearsome witchcraft.

During the summer of 1873, Britain recognized the fact that it was faced with the choice of abandoning its interests on the Gold Coast or taking punitive action against "King Koffee", as they called Kofi Karikari. An expedition, officially designated "Special Service on the West Coast of Africa," was organized under the command of Maj.-Gen. Sir Garnet Wolseley.

On October 6, 1873, *The London Times* published the following commentary by its military correspondent:

Preparations for the Ashantee War

History teaches us that warfare with a semi-savage nation is marked by certain peculiar characteristics, which require to be fully recognized and provided for. The savage does not fight by the rules of modern tactics. He knows nothing of those intricate manoeuvres which characterize civilized warfare, and in general his idea of victory is connected with the number of foes he has slain, or the number of scalps he has taken. His weapons are comparatively rude, and have little effect except in hand-to-hand fighting. Thus a battle between two opposing savage forces partakes of the nature of an indiscriminate melee. In scientific warfare the absolute number of slain is a matter of secondary consideration. Modern battles are won more by moral than by physical effects. We employ engines that terrify as well as kill, and we find it more advantageous to kill a few, provided the rest run away, than to slaughter a number while the remainder stand fast. Thus, a flight of rockets—a comparatively harmless warlike engine—might cause a regular "skedaddle" among a set of savages without the loss of a single life.

The country of Ashantee, according to all accounts, mainly consists of thick jungle, with narrow paths for roads. Horse or bullock draught is unknown, and locomotion depends upon manual labour. The question, therefore, of Sir Garnet Wolseley's artillery was decided by the peculiar nature of the country in which he is going to operate. It would have been manifestly absurd to send out 9-pounder or 16-pounder field guns, which could not move up country without some species of four-footed traction, but it was desirable that the expeditionary force should be supplied with some description of artillery. In mountainous countries or in those inaccessible to ordinary artillery carriages it has always been found necessary to employ very light guns and equipment, which are usually transported either on the backs of mules or on specially constructed carriages designed for man draught. The artillery which Sir Garnet Wolseley will take into the field is of this nature. He will first have one or two batteries of 7-pounder rifled guns, four guns per battery. He will also have a battery of little smooth-bore howitzers, a few Gatling guns, and some 9 lb. Hale rockets. This will comprise his artillery. . . . The Gatling guns which accompany the Expedition are those known as the 0.45 inch. They will be mounted on carriages somewhat similar to the guns, and, we presume, are mainly intended for the defence of stockaded positions. For fighting in the bush a Gatling would be of as much use as a fire engine, but if by any lucky chance Sir Garnet Wolseley manages to catch a good mob of savages in the open, and at a moderate distance, he cannot do better than treat them to a little Gatling music. When well served, the machine gun is terribly effective at distances from 400 to 600 yards. . . . a perfect rain of bullets may issue from the ten muzzles. The gun is also fitted with an arrangement by which a traversing motion may be given to the barrels while the firing continues. It is obvious that it would be absurd constantly to fire a Gatling gun in one direction. A few men immediately in front would be perforated, while those on the flanks would escape. But the traversing arrangement enables us to "waterpot" the enemy with a leaden rain. Altogether, we cannot wish the Ashantees worse luck than to get in the way of a Gatling well served, but we would impress upon those who use this formidable weapon the utter uselessness of it under certain circum-

Artillery park in camp at Prahsu, scene of Captain Rait's impressive de monstration. Gatling Gun is behind and to right of row of small cannon.

> stances. If the enemy takes to the bush he must be shelled out of his cover, and for this purpose resort must be had to guns and not to Gatlings. . . .

On July 30, 1873, two Gatling Guns, with 10,000 rounds of ammunition for each, were shipped to West Africa by mail packet. Capt. Rait and the headquarters of Rait's Artillery marched from Cape Coast on the Gulf of Guinea, November 28, 1873, taking with them the two Gatlings, as well as a 7-pounder and a 4-2/5 howitzer. Mounted as they were on wheeled carriages of the type used for artillery, it soon became apparent that these Gatling Guns were unsuited for movement over the narrow trails of the West African bush country. To facilitate transport, one of the Gatlings was fitted with an extemporized carriage of narrower track; this, of course, made the piece top-heavy and it tipped over many times enroute. They did, however, manage to get the Gatling to the base at Prahsu, where it figured in a much-publicized incident of the war.

A group of Ashanti envoys, bearing peace proposals from Kofi Karikari, arrived at Prahsu, where Sir Garnet Wolseley had established his headquarters. This was on January 2, 1874.

> . . . On the following day [January 3, 1874] a little practice with the Gatling was held for the benefit of the Ashanti envoys, Captain Rait firing a drum of ammunition up the stream where the accuracy and force with which the bullets struck the water, at a range of some 500 yards, was shown by the fountain of spray that was thrown up. The well-bred native envoys looked cooly on and seemed but little surprised. But the view of the Gatling was destined yet to bear fruit.
>
> At 1 o'clock on the morning of the 5th, we were awakened by a shot fired in the hut where the Ashantis were under guard, and on visiting the hut it was found that one of the scouts had put the muzzle of his gun to his throat and, pulling the trigger with his toe, had blown his brains out. It was a strange and ghastly sight, the dead man lying on the guard bed with his brains scattered on the side wall, shown by the lantern light. At first the other messengers expressed ignorance as to the cause of the act, but a court of inquiry was held on the 5th and witnesses were examined. One of the Ashantis said that the dead man, Quamina Owoosoo by name, had expressed his opinion that all the scouts were going to be killed, and only the messenger allowed to return, and had consequently blown out his brains. Sein Quaku, the messenger, spoke to the same effect, and it appeared that they had all been more or less surprised and astonished at the firing of the Gatling; and that this man, being of rather a cowardly nature, had determined to destroy himself. . . .
>
> —Brackenbury, Capt. Henry, R.A. *The Ashanti War*. Edinburgh and London. Wilkes Blackwood and Sons. 1874.

This incident made quite an impression not only on the Ashanti envoys but also on the gentlemen of the press.

> Envoys from King Koffee to General Wolseley had arrived with overtures of peace, and had been shown over the extemporized encampment of the British brigade. The tables were about to be turned, and the invasion of Ashantee was succeeding to the Ashantee invasion. The Prah had been crossed—the Adansie Hills occupied and the surrounding country successfully reconnoitered—the Envoys gazed amazedly on the awful preparations, the steadily increasing resources of the British into their territory. They witnessed the performance of Gatlingeers with their hydra-barrelled field-piece, and according to the evidence of a Court of Inquiry, one of the frightened Envoys made away with himself in sheer horror of the situation—his king's best general forced to quit the Protectorate, the army disbanded and utterly demoralized, and the white faces sternly advancing to the attack armed with such man-slaying guns!
>
> —*United Service Magazine*

> We are not surprised that the Ashantees were awe-struck before the power of the Gatling gun. It is easy to understand that it is a weapon which is specially adapted to terrify a barbarous or semi-civilized foe. The Ashantee correspondent of the *New York Herald* says that the reputation of the Gatling is now spread throughout Ashantee. "It is a terrible gun which shoots all day. Nothing could stand before it; the water of the Prah ran back affrighted." "The effect of this," remarks the writer, "combined with many other things, has been to induce the King and his Council to deliberate and reflect on the possibility of peace."
>
> —*Army and Navy Journal*

The Ashanti War ended after British troops invaded Ashanti, captured and destroyed the capital, Kumasi, on February 4, 1874. Subsequently, the Treaty of Fomena was signed; under the terms of this agreement, the Ashantis relinquished all claims to Denkera, Akim, Assin, Adansi, and the coastal forest, and promised to give up their practices of slavery and human sacrifice, and to pay indemnities. His people were rankled by this humiliation and, later in 1874, Kofi Karikari was destooled—i.e., deposed as ruler.

From all accounts of the Ashanti War consulted, it appears that, while two Gatling Guns were sent out from England, only one saw use, and this piece was taken no further than the banks of the frontier river Prah, where—aside from the effective demonstration for the benefit of the Ashanti envoys—it was employed to guard a bridge against possible attack, which never came. Even though the Gatling fired no shots in battle during the Ashanti War, it seems to have served well, in camp, as a weapon of psychological warfare.

Presence of Gatling Guns among the artillery of the Ashanti Expedition of 1873-1874 is noteworthy since, at the time, the gun had not as yet been adopted officially by the British Army. The Gatlings sent to West Africa in 1873 had been purchased during the winter of 1870-1871 for trial. Their non-use in this campaign pointed up the need for more portable machine guns, suitable for colonial warfare where, frequently, the only means by which artillery could be transported was manpower (on the Gold Coast, native women were used as "beasts of burden"). In 1875, Artilleryman Rait, who had served with distinction in the Ashanti War and was then a major, suggested the development of a "Pistol Gatling", as he called it, presumably to be of smaller caliber and weigh about 100 pounds. Undoubtedly, Maj. Rait's trying experience in struggling over West African bush country trails to bring a Gatling to Prahsu in 1873 suggested a lighter, more easily transported gun. Actually, he was anticipated by Gatling, who introduced his famous "Camel Gun" early in 1872. Weighing only 135 pounds, and available with tripod mount, the Camel Gun would have been ideally suited to the needs of the Ashanti campaign.

Standard magazine used with most .45-70 Gatlings. Trapezoidal in cross section; it was made of sheet iron, tin-plated, with bronze fittings. Heavy bronze follower weight aided in forcing cartridges into gun. Spring catch at lower end kept cartridges from falling out; upon insertion of magazine into hopper, this catch disengaged automatically.

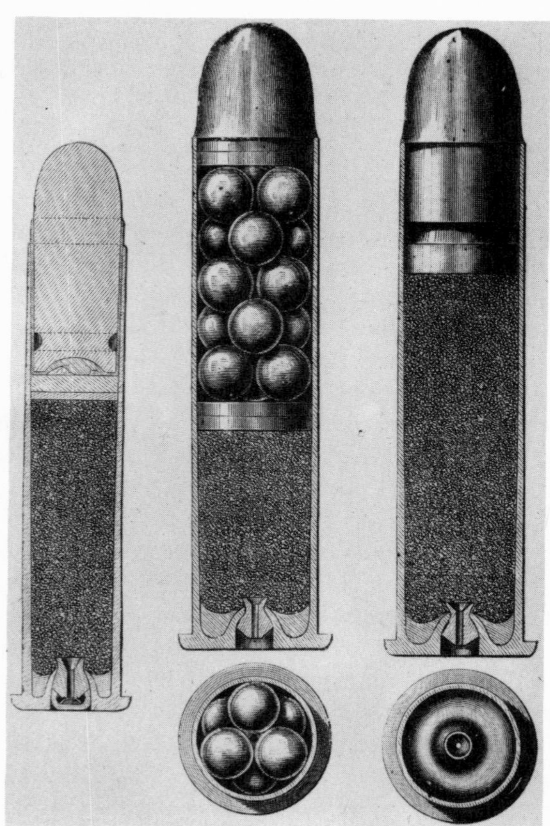

Early types of Gatling cartridges.

"KEEP UP THE PRICES OF THE GUNS"

Writing to Edgar T. Welles, Secretary of the Gatling Gun Company, on October 30, 1874, Gatling advised: "Tell Broadwell our best policy will be to keep up the prices of the guns & give liberal commissions." In another letter, dated October 8, 1875, he informs Welles: "McClure & Jones apparently major stockholders in the Gatling Gun Company think we ought to give 10 per cent commission on the guns—Such a commission will make agents & gun men, consuls, &c whom we can enlist in our interest work energeticly in getting orders." As will be seen, the Gatling Gun Company easily could afford to pay such commissions on the sales of their guns.

The Gatling Gun, in its heyday, was a very profitable item for both the Gatling Gun Company and the manufacturer, Colt's Patent Fire Arms Mfg. Co. Just how profitable is shown by the following tabulation, based upon a study of the records of the two firms for the 1874-1876 period. Actually, the prices paid and received by Gatling varied somewhat; however, these figures are close to average (Colt's costs are taken from an estimate prepared March 27, 1875).

MODEL	GATLING GUN COMPANY Selling Price	Cost	Profit	COLT'S PAT. F. A. MFG. CO. Cost	Profit
1-inch caliber, 10 barrels	$1,800.00	$1,100.00	$700.00	$627.60	$472.40
Musket caliber, 10 long barrels	1,000.00	490.00	510.00	230.56	260.44
Musket caliber, 10 short barrels	850.00	445.00	405.00	206.38	238.62

Proposed methods of transporting Gatling Gun, tripod, and Broadwell drums.

Gatling Camel Gun and Broadwell drums carried in special pack saddle.

Hotchkiss Machine Gun.

THE GATLING'S RIVALS

In 1871, Benjamin Hotchkiss invented the revolver-type machine gun bearing his name. This weapon looked like an oversized Gatling and, as indicated in some of his letters, Gatling bitterly considered Hotchkiss a copyist. However, much as these guns resembled each other externally, they differed considerably internally. The Hotchkiss had a single, fixed breechlock, at which position each barrel was fired. As the barrels revolved past other stations in their circular path, separate mechanisms accomplished loading and ejecting. Actually, the Hotchkiss was a *machine cannon*, since its ammunition was 37mm. caliber and contained a fuse and bursting charge. Furthermore, the considerable size and weight of the gun put it in the classification of at least a medium field-piece. Many Hotchkiss guns saw naval service; for such use, cage or cone mounts were employed. While originally promoted as a naval weapon for defense against torpedo boats, the Hotchkiss frequently was mounted on a field carriage, and was adapted to almost every kind of mount capable of handling its great weight. In their heyday, Hotchkiss guns were adopted by many, if not most, of the world's navies.

Another weapon competitive to the Gatling, the Gardner gun, was invented in 1874 by William Gardner, of Toledo, Ohio. Subsequently, it was

Gardner Machine Gun.

manufactured by Pratt & Whitney, of Hartford, Connecticut. Gardner guns were produced in models with two to five barrels, behind each of which was a reciprocating breechlock activated by a crank-powered cam. The feed system employed tracked chutes, not unlike the Bruce feed of the Gatling. A typical Gardner five-barrel model, caliber .45, with portable tripod, weighed 369 pounds; it was capable of firing a maximum of 1,200 shots per minute. The Gardner gun often was a contender against the Gatling in European military trials. Principal purchaser of this weapon was England, although in 1898, according to Parker *(Tactical Organization and Uses of Machine Guns in the Field),* the U.S. Army had approximately 75 Gardners of the two-barreled type on hand. A lightweight (70-lb.), single-barreled version of the Gardner was adopted and purchased in small quantity by the U.S. Navy.

An interesting weapon, closely resembling the Gatling in appearance, the Lowell Machine Gun was invented in 1875 by DeWitt Clinton Farrington. Although it presented several innovations in machine-gun design, the Lowell gun could not meet the competition of the well-established Gatling. Only a few Lowells were made before the company failed. This arm had four barrels, although they were not fired successively as in the Gatling. When the barrel used in firing became overheated, a handle permitted the gunner to rotate the barrel group to bring a fresh, cool barrel into firing position. The standard breechblock had a conventional firing pin and spring; however, an available accessory breechblock had a semi-fixed firing pin. This was the first use of the "inertia firing" principle employed in many modern machine guns, in which breechblock and firing pin slam forward as a unit, chambering and firing the round at almost the same instant. The feed system of the Lowell involved a single-tracked hopper much like those of the Bruce and Gardner feeds.

Helge Palmcrantz, a Swede, invented the Nordenfeldt Machine Gun, named for its backer, Thorsten Nordenfeldt, a financier and countryman of Palmcrantz. This weapon was, for some years, one of the Gatling's chief competitors. It was adopted by England in 1878. Lever-operated, most Nordenfeldts used reciprocating breechblocks with rotating bolt heads, a revolutionary feature in their day. Models with from one to twelve barrels were available. In all Nordenfeldt guns, ammunition was gravity-fed from hoppers. Produced in a variety of calibers from relatively small-bore to over one-inch, the Nordenfeldt was provided, optionally, even in the smaller calibers, with armor-piercing ammuni-

Lowell Battery Gun.

Nordenfeldt Gun: (left) on galloping carriage, (right) on tripod.

tion, bullets having hard steel cores—a Nordenfeldt "first". A typical Nordenfeldt, the Anti-Torpedo-Boat Machine Gun chambered for the 1-inch Nordenfeldt cartridge, capable of penetrating an inch of iron at 300 yards, had a hopper holding 40 rounds, could fire up to 200 shots per minute. It weighed about 700 pounds. Owing chiefly to expert promotion, the Nordenfeldt Machine Gun, despite its rather clumsy design, was a highly successful weapon, having been adopted by a number of European nations. During the Spanish-American War, it was found that many Spanish warships were armed with Nordenfeldts.

CENTENNIAL EXPOSITION

On the morning of May 10, 1876, President Ulysses S. Grant officially opened the first world's fair held by the United States, the great International Centennial Exposition, at Philadelphia, celebrating the 100th anniversary of the Declaration of Independence. The exhibition site in Fairmount Park was dominated by the Main Building, an imposing structure with an area of 936,000 square feet, more than 21 acres, claimed to be the largest building in the world; the central nave was 120 feet wide and one-third of a mile in length; 7,000,000 feet of lumber and 8,000,000 pounds of iron were used in its construction, which required 18 months and the services of 3,000 men to complete. Almost ten million people visited the fair during its 159 days. Among those present on opening day was R. J. Gatling, who signed the visitors' register at the Connecticut Cottage on May 10. His signature appears again under date of July 6, together with those of his wife and daughter, Ida. Gatling Guns were exhibited both in the Main and the United States buildings.

J. G. Accles, one of Gatling's chief lieutenants, was in constant attendance at the Gatling Gun Company exhibit, explaining the guns to thousands of visitors daily. Souvenir cards and descriptive pamphlets were available to those interested. Gatling spent about ten days in Philadelphia, after the opening of the exposition. His primary interest seems to have been the judging of the award for machine guns, which he naturally coveted for his Gatling Gun. Winning over the Gardner, Hotchkiss, and other battery guns, needless to say, could be used to great advantage in the Gatling Gun Company's sales promotional efforts. On May 12, Gatling wrote to the company's secretary, Edgar T. Welles:

> . . . I desire that you try and arrange your business so as to be here on the 24th inst which is the day the Judges of awards meet.—Lyford is one of the Judges on firearms, so is Capt. Noble of Woolwich . . .

Evidently, Gatling and Welles were personally acquainted with at least two of the judges: S. C. Lyford (mentioned in Gatling's letter of June 1, 1875*) and Capt. R. A. Noble, Royal Artillery. It is interesting, also, to note that among the original promoters of the Centennial Exhibition was Brig. Gen. Charles B. Norton, whose friendship for Richard Jordan Gatling and championship of the Gatling Gun is apparent to the reader of his book, *American Breech-loading Small Arms.* Maj. Gen. W. B. Franklin, of Colt's, was chairman of the Committee of Judges at the Exhibition.

Having returned to Hartford, on May 24, 1876, Gatling again wrote to Edgar T. Welles, then representing him at the Exposition:

> . . . Do not forget to suggest to Lyford & the other Judges, that the Hotchkiss gun in most of its main features is copied after the Gatling gun:—for instance, the frame, mainshaft & the discs or flanges in which the barrels are held are copied from my gun. He also uses a spiral cam for loading the cartridges & uses breech çasing with a diaphragm or partition in it which parts are claimed in my patents.—The Judges should not give an imitator, or a copyist, an award over the original invention:—The Gatling however is a better gun than the Hotchkiss & fires with five times—yes, ten times the rapidity. The larger Hotchkiss gun weighs in my judgement over 1200 lbs. & is entirely too heavy for field service. I speak of these things so you may be able to post Lyford & others in regard to the facts in the case.

With characteristic thoroughness, Gatling provided Accles with a breech casing, cam, lock, etc., to permit explanation of the mechanism to the judges, without having to disassemble the gun on display. Whether the Gatling Gun won over its rivals solely on the basis of its superiority as a weapon or with an assist from the persuasiveness of Mr. Welles armed with Gatling's arguments, we do not know, but on September 27, when the awards were presented in Judges' Hall, the recipients included Richard Jordan Gatling, who was presented with the only medal given for a machine gun at the Centennial Exhibition. These medals were of bronze, 4 inches in diameter—the largest ever struck at the Philadelphia Mint.

* Reproduced on pages 76-77.

Gatling Gun Company stand, Centennial Exhibition.

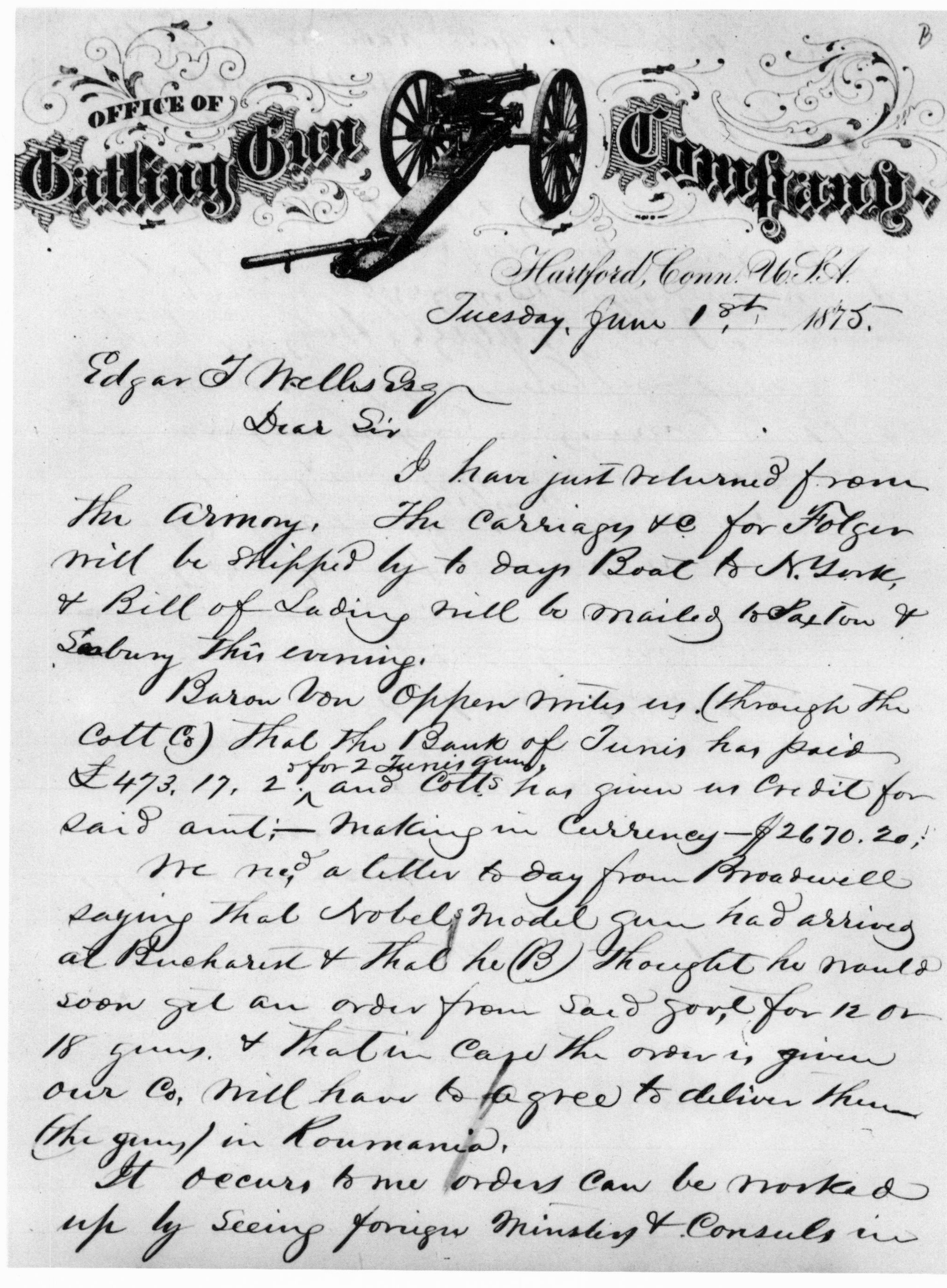

Tuesday, June 1st, 1875.

Edgar T. Welles Esq
Dear Sir

I have just returned from the armory. The Carriages &c. for Folger will be shipped by to days Boat to N. York, & Bill of Lading will be mailed to Paxton & Seabury this evening.

Baron Von Oppen writes us (through the Colt Co) that the Bank of Tunis has paid £473. 17. 2d for 2 Tunis guns and Colts has given us Credit for said amt;— Making in Currency—$2670.20;

We recd a letter to day from Broadwell saying that Nobels Model gun had arrived at Bucharest & that he (B) thought he would soon get an order from said Govt. for 12 or 18 guns. & that in case the order is given our Co. will have to agree to deliver them (the guns) in Roumania.

It occurs to me orders can be worked up by seeing foreign Ministers & Consuls in

Washington.— If you have no time to see such officials, please request Syford & Genl. B. to speak a good word for the Gatling when they meet such parties.— a word from them fitly & timely spoken, might lay the foundation of future orders.
Nothing new here since you left.
Yours truly
R J Gatling

Letter referred to in text on page 75.

GATLING GUN.

The Gatling Gun.

As a practical military machine gun, the GATLING has no equal. It fires from 800 to 1,000 shots per minute, has great accuracy, and the larger calibres have an effective range of over two miles. The following calibres are made: .42, .43, .45, .50, .55, .65, .75, and one inch. It has been adopted by nearly all the principal governments of the world.

Gatling Gun Company,
HARTFORD, CONN., U. S. A.

Advertising card distributed by Gatling Gun Company at Centennial Exhibition.

BULLDOG GATLING MODEL 1877

Nearly all earlier Gatlings had exposed barrels—notable exceptions were some bronze-encased Model 1874 and 1875 guns made for the U.S. Navy. The 1877 Bulldog was the first regular production model to have its barrels and breech section fully enclosed in a cylindrical housing of bronze, giving the gun the appearance of a small cannon. Front end was covered by a bronze plate, through which the muzzles protruded slightly.

The main shaft or axle, about which the barrels revolved, extended the length of the gun from muzzle plate back through the cascabel plate at the other end. Operating crank was rear-mounted in the Bulldog, rather than being located at the side, as in other Gatlings, and was attached directly to the end of the main shaft. Thus, instead of operating through the usual system of gears, which slowed the rate of fire, the Bulldog's drive was direct and each turn of the crank produced a complete revolution of the barrel unit. Rate of fire was as high as *1,000* rounds per minute—about twice that of the typical machine gun of World War II.

A nut, screwed on the rear end of the main shaft, served not only to hold the crank on, but also as the headspace adjustment. Breech bolts were always in the same place, locked at the moment of discharge, but the barrel unit actually "floated" inside the bronze outer jacket. Headspace was ad-

Model 1877 Bulldog Gatling, ten-barrel, on lightweight carriage.

justed by tightening or loosening the nut, which either brought the barrel unit to the rear or allowed it to go forward, altering the distance from the face of the breech bolt to the head of a chambered round. Improper headspace was readily detected: if the barrel unit revolved with difficulty and the heads of fired cartridge cases bore scratches from the bolts, headspace was too tight; bulged cases, caused by insufficient support of the cartridge at firing, indicated excessive headspace.

Headspace adjustment procedure was as follows: (1) remove all bolts but one and place an empty case in the corresponding chamber; (2) press crank spring and adjust the nut until friction against the case head just barely can be felt as the crank is turned; (3) fire a round in this barrel and note the effect on the cartridge case; if normal, replace all of the other breech bolts.

The trunnions and front sight of the Bulldog were integral with the bronze barrel housing. This was the first Gatling Gun to have a front sight adjustable for windage. The rear sight moved up and down in a groove in the cascabel plate.

Feed hopper, designed to accept the standard trapezoidal magazine, was hinged directly to the barrel housing. Although the Bruce feed, introduced a few years later, could be fitted to this type of hopper by means of an adapter, many 1877 Bulldogs subsequently were converted to take the Bruce feed only by replacement of the feed hopper.

The mechanical oscillator, last such device to be used on a Gatling Gun, differed from those incorporated in earlier models. On the underside of the breech casing were two heavy lugs, between which were supported the traversing screw and oscillating mechanism. At each end of the traversing screw was a hand wheel—the left controlled windage adjustment, the right adjusted the tension of two opposing springs located on either side of the oscillator. Centered between these springs, the oscillating unit was not rigidly attached to the gun, but had about an inch of lateral movement. As the rear-mounted crank was turned, the piece was caused to whip slightly from side to side. This motion was governed by the tension of the opposing springs, allowing various fields of fire. As spring tension was reduced, the whipping motion increased, widening the field of fire. This oscillator, while it performed its function satisfactorily, was complex in construction and its repair required the services of an expert technician. It was not used on any model other than the Bulldog.

Chambered for the .45/70 Government cartridge, the Model 1877 Bulldog had five 18-inch barrels, rifled one turn in 22 inches (a number of guns, most of which were bought by China, had ten barrels). It weighed only 90 pounds and usually was mounted on a tripod of the type of the Model 1876 Gatling; a few of these guns were fitted to small, almost miniature, artillery carriages, while some of the ten-barreled variety were furnished on cavalry carts. Ammunition was gravity-fed from a box magazine; some guns later were adapted to Bruce feed. A round, bronze legend plate on the breech casing bore both Colt and Gatling markings; serial number appeared on the casing just above the right trunnion. Lateral aiming adjustment was obtained through the oscillating device. Elevation adjustment was controlled by a jackscrew in the base of the yoke or through the trail of the field carriage.

Model 1877 Bulldog Gatling, five-barrel, on tripod.

Close-up of carrier block, Model 1877, showing troughs into which cartridges fed from magazine; bolts pushed cartridges forward in troughs and into chambers.

During the summer of 1876, prototypes of the Model 1877 Bulldog were submitted to the U.S. Government for testing: a short, five-barrel model and a similar gun with ten barrels of musket length. Trials were held August 16–23 at Sandy Hook, New Jersey, by a board of army officers headed by Col. Silas Crispin. An inventor in his own right—the Crispin metallic cartridges (now much sought by collectors) and such firearms as the Crispin revolver, patented 1865, manufactured by Smith Arms Company, New York City—Crispin was a career ordnanceman of considerable ability and experience. The Gatling Gun had to be good to pass his expert scrutiny.

On August 18, the small gun was tested for rapidity of fire; 1,000 rounds were discharged in one minute nineteen seconds, an unheard-of performance in those days. The same gun, when tested for accuracy, scored 996 hits out of 1,000 shots fired at a range of 500 yards. Tested with several different brands of ammunition, it functioned satisfactorily with all.

One defect was noted: it was found that a number of fired cases had the heads torn off by the extractors. At the gun's high rate of fire, the initial rearward movement of the breech bolt was so powerful that it occasionally would rip the head from a cartridge case. The trial board recommended a wider extractor that would grasp a greater area of the cartridge rim and minimize this hazard.

The following extract from the report of the board on the Sandy Hook Trials of 1876 is quoted from *American Breech-loading Small Arms* by Charles B. Norton (1882 edition):

> Two guns were submitted by the company for tests, one being a short five-barreled gun, designed for cavalry service, the other a long ten-barreled gun for flank defense.
>
> The improvements in the gun intended for service with cavalry, consist in a change of the position and attachment of the crank from the side to the rear, greatly facilitating and increasing the speed of revolution of the gun and rapidity of its fire; the feed-cases are entered more readily to the receiver, and stand vertically, thus insuring a direct fall and feed of the metallic cases; the exterior form of the receivers admits of reversing the motion of the crank without danger of jamming the cases. All the working parts as well as the barrels are encased in bronze, affording better protection from dust and dirt to the gun. It is lighter and of less expensive construction, and more compact in appearance. An automatic device attached to the breech of this gun gives a traversing motion through a small angle, which can be set to suit range and circumstances of fire, and is worked by the crank operating the gun. The increased rapidity of fire is seen, from the examination of the record, to be more than double that of the old model ten-barreled gun, and its accuracy is by no means impaired.
>
> The board is of opinion that the application of the crank to the rear, vertical feed, automatic traversing motion, lightness, cheapness, etc., are all important improvements.
>
> All the changes and improvements in the Gatling gun for cavalry service are equally applicable to the long-barreled gun for flank defense.

The U.S. Army subsequently bought seventeen of the Model 1877 Bulldogs (serial Nos. 190, 203-218) and several also were purchased by the U.S. Navy.

Probably the best of the Gatling Guns, the Bulldog enjoyed a considerable sale in the U.S. and abroad.

Disassembly procedure for Bulldog Gatling Model 1877:

1. Turn the handle of the lock plug to horizontal and remove. Remove breech bolts.
2. Depress the crank spring and unscrew the headspace adjusting nut.
3. Remove crank.
4. Remove the cascabel plate screws. Turn the plate until its engraved arrow is opposite the arrow on the breech casing. Draw plate off to the rear.
5. Open the hopper and push the barrel unit several inches out of the muzzle end of the casing. Drive out pin that fastens the muzzle plate to the barrel unit. Remove muzzle plate.
6. Pull the barrel unit out through the rear end of the casing.
7. Drive out the hopper hinge pin and remove hopper.

THE AMERICAN INDIAN WARS

As railroads cut across the Great Plains and settlers in ever-increasing numbers moved into the Trans-Mississippi West, the Indian found himself driven from his historic hunting grounds and herded onto often inhospitable reservations, and saw the wanton destruction of the bison upon which he depended for his existence. Repeatedly, the white man had broken treaties that the Indian had made with him in good faith and kept. Embittered by constant encroachment and a multitude of just grievances, the Plains Indian painted his face, sang his death song, and went on his last warpath. For the quarter of a century that followed the War Between the States, most of the United States' Regular Army was kept busy fighting Indians on the Western Frontier.

Nearly all garrisons in Indian country had Gatlings in their armament, often used in the defenses of forts. Gatling Guns usually accompanied sizable expeditions.

Commanded by Lieut. James W. Pope, a Gatling Gun detachment with Maj. Gen. Nelson A. Miles' Indian Territory Expedition of 1874-1875, played a decisive part in the fight, August 30, 1874, near El Llano Estacado ("The Staked Plains") in West Texas. At 4 A.M., as the advance party of scouts entered a place where the trail led between bluffs, the Indians—some 250 strong—struck from ambush, charging down from both sides. At the sound of firing, Lieutenant Pope quickly brought up his Gatlings and went into action, scattering the attacking warriors with a withering fire. Pursued by cavalry, the Indians fled across the plains, their retreat becoming a rout.

Among the troops ordered out to suppress the 1874 uprising of Arapaho, Cheyenne, Comanche, and Kiowa in the Southwest was a battalion of the 8th Cavalry under Maj. William Redwood Price. One of five converging columns in a containing movement planned by General Sheridan, they rode east from Fort Union, New Mexico, as Miles marched south from Camp Supply, Indian Territory. Major Price's battalion fought several skirmishes with hostile bands during the summer and fall of 1874; one incident of their campaign is mentioned by Capt. E. Rogers in his paper (written 1875), "The Gatling Gun; Its Place in Tactics," published 1876 in the British *Journal of the Royal United Service Institution:*

> In the autumn of last year two Gatlings were reported to have done "splendid service" in frequent encounters with the Redskins on the Western Frontier. On one of these occasions, Major Price, of the 8th United States' Cavalry, was attacked by 600 or 700 Indians, and he used his Gatlings with such excellent effect as to quite demoralize and drive off his savage assailants.

Since it was quite common to overestimate the number of Indians engaged, "600 or 700" probably was an exaggeration.

In the Sioux War of 1876, famous for "Custer's Last Stand," Gatling Guns accompanied the columns led by Maj. Gen. Alfred H. Terry and Brig. Gen. John Gibbon. With Terry was a platoon of three Gatlings, handled by two officers and thirty-two men of the 20th Infantry; Gibbon had two .50 caliber Gatlings.

Some chroniclers of the Custer Fight have made much of the fact that, on June 22, 1876, when Maj. Gen. George Armstrong Custer and the 7th Cavalry rode out of the Powder River camp, headed for the Little Big Horn and disaster, they left three Gatling Guns behind. It has been suggested that the outcome of the Battle of the Little Big Horn might have been different if Custer had taken the Gatlings.

General Custer was offered the three Gatling Guns of the 20th Infantry and he refused them. Mounted like cannon on wheeled carriages, the heavy Gatlings were drawn by teams of four condemned cavalry horses, totally unfit for accompanying a fast-moving column of cavalry. Custer felt that these guns would not be able to keep up with his troops over the rough terrain to be traveled—just as they had lagged behind Col. Marcus A. Reno's scouting party a few days before.

Later as the Gatling Gun detachment accompanied General Terry, Custer's judgment was vindicated. The Gatling Gun crews experienced great difficulty in moving their unwieldy pieces over the rugged country and constantly fell behind, slowing down Terry's advance. During the night march, the Gatling Gun detachment got lost in the dark, having fallen far behind, and strayed more than a mile away from the column. It had to be called by repeated trumpet signals before it was found and rejoined the rest of the party.

Study of detailed accounts reconstructing the Battle of the Little Big Horn leads to the conviction that, even if the three Gatlings could have been brought to the scene of the fight and put into action —which seems unlikely—the presence of these guns would not have saved Custer and his 200 men from annihilation. The odds against the cavalrymen were overwhelming. When the Indians moved out after the battle, their column was said to have been three miles long and a half mile wide. Whatever mistakes in judgment may be charged against General Custer, leaving the Gatlings behind is not among them.

The Nez Percé campaign of 1877 was, in the words of General Sherman, "one of the most extraordinary Indian Wars of which there is any record." At their greatest strength, the Nez Percé bands under Chief Joseph numbered about 600 persons, less than 200 of whom were warriors. During the eleven weeks of the war, they traveled 1,600 miles and, in thirteen battles, defeated or fought to a stand-off ten separate U.S. Army commands sent against them.

On July 11, 1877, Brig. Gen. Oliver Otis Howard, with a force of 400 regulars—infantry, cavalry, and artillery—together with some 180 volunteers, surprised the Indian camp on the Clearwater River. Unable to overrun the camp, Howard had to entrench in a defensive position. In the two-day fight that ensued, Chief Joseph and his band fought well, but were forced back across the river. Howard lost thirteen men killed and twenty-seven wounded; the Indians, twenty-three killed, forty-six wounded. According to the *New York Times* of July 17, 1877, "This last affair derives additional interest from the successful employment in it of Gatling Guns and howitzers, to which, in fact, the dislodgement of Joseph was largely due." General Howard used two Gatlings and a 4-inch howitzer in this fight.

In his last battle, September 30-October 4, 1877, in the Bear Paw Mountains, Chief Joseph's warriors again faced a Gatling. He was besieged by Maj. Gen. Nelson A. Miles with a force of 600 men, a Gatling Gun and a twelve-pound Napoleon. After four days, the Nez Percé could hold out no longer and Chief Joseph surrendered to General Miles, saying "From where the sun now stands, I fight no more against the white man"—and he kept his word.

The Bannock-Shoshone War of 1878 began with the slip of the pen by a government clerk, copying the treaty terms under which the Bannocks were to be put on a reservation, to include the Camas Prairie, a region of great importance to these Indians as the source of a staple food, the camass root. The clerk wrote "Kansas" for "Camas" and, since there was no such place as "Kansas Prairie,"

General Miles charging the Nez Perce camp.

it was left out of the final draft of the treaty and the Bannocks were excluded from the Camas Prairie. When white settlers began to pasture their hogs and cattle on the Camas Prairie and the camass roots became hog feed, the Bannocks had taken all they could bear. After shooting two cattlemen on the prairie, the Bannocks led by Chief Buffalo Horn, who was to be killed early in the campaign, jumped the reservation and went on the warpath.

Troopers of the 1st Cavalry spent the next two months chasing the Bannocks and their Piute, Shoshone, and Umatilla allies all over Idaho, Oregon, Montana, and Wyoming, until the Bannocks finally wound up back on their reservation *sans* warpaint, the fight out of their systems, and ready for a handout. Actually, nothing had been accomplished. It wasn't much of a "war"—except to the eighty Indians, thirty-one white settlers, and nine soldiers killed in it—but it cost the U.S. taxpayers about a half-million dollars.

An incident of this campaign, related by Lieut. John H. Parker in *Tactical Organization and Uses of Machine Guns in the Field,* is the only detailed report found on the use of Gatling Guns in the Indian Wars:

> This campaign afforded one instance of the effective use of the .45 caliber Gatling gun against savages. A band of Bannocks and Shoshones were making a break for the Umatilla Agency, with a view to inducing the Indians at that place to go on the war path. The 1st United States Cavalry, under Captain (subsequently Colonel) Bernard, went after them to prevent this. The regiment was accompanied by three of these Gatlings. They overhauled the hostiles near the Umatilla Agency, and the latter took refuge on a high bluff, which was commanded by ground equally high to the right. Three troops were dismounted as skirmishers and pushed forward to attack the bluff on which the Indians were lurking. On reaching the foot of the bluff, over an open space of about 600 yards, the skirmishers found themselves in front of a nearly vertical wall, at the top of which the Indians were lying and from which they began to pour in a most galling fire. The three troops were certain to suffer heavily if they retreated across the open ground, and were unable to climb the bluff in the face of the fire. Just as they were beginning to suffer heavily, the Gatlings opened from the high ground to the right, to which place they had been moved on a run, and the fire from the Indians on the bluff at once ceased. The fight was terminated by the defeat of the Indians, who were struck on flank by another force as they left the bluff. There can be no doubt that these three troops would have suffered very heavily if they had not received the aid of machine guns. This account of the skirmish is furnished by a participant. It will be observed that this is a typical use of the guns with cavalry, in either Indian or civilized warfare. To gain a flank and pour in a sharp and unexpected fire upon the enemy is usually a decisive maneuver, and one particularly adapted to these guns.

RUSSO-TURKISH WAR

Relations between the Bulgarians and the Turks had been fairly peaceful for many generations, but in 1875 and 1876 there were uprisings of Bulgarian nationalists. These outbreaks may have been incited by Russian agents provocateur. Russia long had cast a covetous eye on the Balkan territories and sought an excuse for war with Turkey as an opportunity to extend Russian domination into this area. To restore order in Bulgaria, the Turkish government sent detachments of Circassian troops—the dread Bashi-Bazouks—who accomplished their assignment in a simple and direct manner; they butchered every Bulgarian—man, woman, and child—within reach. More than sixty villages were put to the sword and torch, over 15,000 inhabitants slain.

Obviously, Czar Alexander II, a fellow Slav and coreligionist, could not stand by as a detached observer while thousands in the Balkans suffered at the hands of Turkish troops. Aware that their nation really was not prepared for such a campaign, General Totleben, famed "Defender of Sevastopol" in the Crimean War, and other Russian military experts opposed intervention in the Balkan trouble; however, the leaders of the Pan-Slav movement, then strong in Russia, influenced the Czar's decision to declare war. On April 24, 1877, Alexander II announced that a state of war existed between Imperial Russia and the Ottoman Empire.

Apparently believing their own propaganda that Turkey was "The Sick Man of Europe," the Russians underestimated their foe and entered the war with insufficient forces, a condition which frequently took them to the very brink of disaster. While the Czar's armies possessed more modern weapons, including the latest, improved Gatlings, the men were ill-trained and unused to their handling. Turkey, too, had Gatling Guns, but in lesser number and of an early type—many of these were inferior pieces produced in Vienna by Paget.

Commenting on the Gatling Guns in Russian service, Capt. E. Rogers wrote in "The Gatling Gun; Its Place in Tactics," *Journal of the Royal United Service Institution,* 1876:

> . . . Russia, in particular, possesses a formidable array. 400 Gatlings formed into batteries of 8 guns each, attached to the artillery branch of the service, are according to the information of our intelligence Department, distributed as follows:—328 are stationed in European Russia, 48 protect the Caucasian territories (one of the batteres being assigned to the Cavalry) and 24 are placed in Eastern Siberia and Turkestan.

The principal campaign of the war was the bloody siege of Plevna, a town in northern Bulgaria, protected by a well-planned system of redoubts and trenches manned by its Turkish defenders. For 143 days, after the Russians invested the town, Osman Pasha and his Turks held out against opposing forces of 95,000, well equipped with artillery, which kept up a steady bombardment. His supplies perilously low, Osman Pasha decided to make a last desperate attempt to break through the siege. After several hours of fierce combat, Osman was convinced that his position was hopeless and, on December 10, 1877, he surrendered. The fall of Plevna caused the Turks to ask for an armistice early in 1878. This was the first war in which the Gatling Guns were used by both sides.

The promotional booklet, *The Gatling Guns, For Service Ashore and Afloat,* states:

> The Russians used Gatling Guns in the siege of Plevna. A special correspondent of the London *Times* writing under date of November 26, 1877, from the headquarters of the Army of Bulgaria, at Bogot, says:—
>
> "The Gatling Guns were in constant action until midnight, splitting the air with their harsh, rattling reports." Another account (November 26th) says: "The Russians are using their mitrailleurs Gatlings great deal more at night, probably with the intention of keeping the Turks occupied, so as to relax the tension on the infantry in the trenches."
>
> Of the engagement at Shpka Pass in August, 1877, the cable correspondent of the *Cincinnati Commercial,* says:—
>
> "The Gatling Guns of the Turks that day proved their superiority over any other cannon, as the Russians suffered the loss of several hundred men, while the Turks remained quite out of reach."

On September 8, 1877, the *Army & Navy Journal* reported:

> *The Hartford Daily Courant* says: "The Turks have a few of the old style Gatling guns—not nearly as efficient as the improved weapon, and yet at the fight at Shipka Pass, August 22nd, they did exactly what has been claimed for them—they effectively defended the pass aganst the advance of the Russians."

Ruszki Invalid, in 1887, published an essay on mitrailleuses—a term then used to describe all machine guns—by General Tchebichef, a professor at the Russian Artillery School. Two occasions in the Russo-Turkish War of 1877-1878 in which Gatling Guns played important roles, are cited by Tchebichef, who concludes by saying that an army should always be equipped with such guns. The first incident was at the siege of Nicopolis, where the Russian Gatlings opened fire on the Turks at 900 meters;

Effect of Russian Gatlings at Shipka Pass. Turkish loss: 800 men in 10 minutes.

the second was at Plevna, where the range was 1,000 meters. In both instances, Tchebichef says, the Gatling Guns had great and quick effect on the enemy.

Longstaff and Atteridge, in *The Book of the Machine Gun* (1917), stated:

> As we have seen, the first European army which added machine guns to its armament, after 1870, was that of Russia. The guns had done good service in expeditions against the Turcomans in Central Asia, and when the war with Turkey began in 1877 a number of batteries of improved Gatling guns were sent to the front. At the siege of Plevna they were used for defending the Russian entrenchments, and on several occasions they proved effective in stopping sorties of the Turkish garrison. For this purpose the gun was placed in position at twilight, and marks were set up to show in what direction it should be trained, in order to sweep with its fire bridges or other narrow lines of approach.

THE ZULU WAR

In 1800, the Zulu were a relatively unimportant Bantu tribe of some 2,000; less than a quarter of a century later, through the aggressive leadership of Dingiswayo and Shaka, Zulu rule had been extended to more than 50,000 people and, militarily, they had become the dominant nation of southeastern Africa, systematically conquering the territory surrounding Zululand.

Under Shaka, sometimes called the "Attila of Africa," the military system developed by Dingiswayo from the *ama Buto* (circumcision guilds) progressed in organization and tactics. By the 1820's, there were about 15 Zulu *impis*, regiments of well-trained, rigidly disciplined, young warriors, upon whom strict celibacy was imposed by their leaders. A highly mobile force, the Zulu impi was capable of covering as much as 40 miles in a single day. Principal weapon of the Zulu warrior was the *assegai,* a short stabbing spear, said to have been invented by Shaka himself; their defense was a shield of improved design. Thus lightly armed, the Zulu were able to move rapidly on the battle field; their customary tactic was a fearsome mass charge.

Mpande, who succeeded his warlike brother as Zulu king, was a comparatively peaceful man, who accepted Boer rule of Natal in 1840 and in 1843 signed a treaty with their British successors. His son, Cetywayo, who became king upon the death of Mpande in 1872, was of sterner stuff than his parent and resolved not to submit to foreign domination. To that end, he revived the military establishment of Shaka. Sir Bartle Frere, British High Commissioner for South Africa, was convinced that Cetywayo's formidable army constituted a serious threat to Britain's dominion in Natal and the Transvaal. On December 11, 1878, he delivered an ultimatum to Cetywayo, ordering him to disband his troops and to submit to the supervision of a British resident. Given thirty days to comply with these demands, the Zulu king ignored them.

Zululand was invaded, January, 1879, by General Lord Chelmsford with a force of 5,000 Europeans and 8,200 native auxiliaries. For six years, Cetywayo had been building up his army and, when hostilities began in 1879, Zulu forces numbered at least 40,000 men.

Chelmsford's expedition entered Zululand unopposed and advanced in three columns, which were to converge on the royal *kraal,* Ulundi. Soon, however, all three forces were engaged by the Zulus. Surprised in their camp at Isandhlwana by 10,000 warriors, the center column was virtually annihilated. Meanwhile, British troops under Col. C. K. Pearson were bottled up at Ekowe, and Col. Evelyn Wood, narrowly avoiding encirclement at Hlobane Mountain, fell back to a fortified position at Kambula, which he held against the best Cetywayo could field against him. After defeating the Zulus at Kambula in March, Lord Chelmsford was again victorious in a close battle at Ginginhlove in April, and later that month successfully relieved Ekowe.

Upon the arrival of reinforcements, rushed from England, Chelmsford again advanced on Ulundi. On July 4, 1879, he crossed the White Mfolosi with a force of 4,200 whites and 100 natives; he attacked Ulundi, winning a brilliant victory against the Zulu. Capture of the royal kraal broke the Zulus' resistance. Cetywayo fled, but was taken prisoner a month later. On September 1, the Zulu chiefs made peace with England.

The Zulu War was the first important land operation in which Gatling Guns were employed by the British Army. Although in regular service with the Royal Navy, the Army had not as yet officially adopted the Gatling.

Press reports of the effectiveness of Gatling Guns in the Zulu War were glowing:

> The Gatling Guns, landed with the naval contingent from the Active and Tenedos, have astonished the Zulus, who have been trying an engagement with our blue jackets. They found the fire much too hot, and the naval force has had the satisfaction of carrying more than one contested position. It is a pity that Gatlings are not more plentiful with Lord Chelmsford's army. The naval brigade have got some, but the artillery have none. If there had been a couple of Gatlings with the force annihilated the other day, the result of the fight might

The Zulu mass charge.

have been different, for Gatlings are the best of all engines of war to deal with the rush of a dense crowd.

—*Army and Navy Gazette,* London, February 22, 1879.

A special telegram from Pietermaritzburg, Africa, says, "The Gatling Gun did great execution among the enemy, etc."

—*London Daily News,* February 20, 1879.

In consequence of the statement in the latest news from the seat of war that the Gatling Guns did useful work, it is determined to send out more of those remarkable weapons.

—*London Daily Telegraph,* February 22, 1879.

It was no use offering mercy to the Zulus. The wounded, as our men came up, fought on to the last, firing their rifles, stabbing with their assegais, and even seizing the natives as they passed over them with their teeth, biting like dogs, so, in spite of the efforts of our officers, they were all cut down.

When all was over, and we counted the dead, there lay, within a radius of 500 yards, 473 Zulus. They lay in groups in some places, of fourteen to thirty dead, mowed down by the fire of the Gatling, which tells upon them more than the fire of the rifles.

—*London Standard,* May 7, 1879.

Less glowing, however, were the comments of General Lord Chelmsford, the commander-in-chief of this campaign, who was not as favorably impressed as were the newsmen:

On the advance to the relief of Ekowe, two Gatling guns accompanied the column, and at the battle of Ginginhlove did considerable execution amongst the Zulus *at the opening of their attack,* which commenced on the north side of our position. The Zulus very soon, however, worked around to the west and south of our laager, and the Gatlings were not in action therefore for any length of time.

At Ulundi we also had two Gatlings in the centre of the front face of our square. They jammed several times in the action, but when in work proved a very valuable addition to the strength of our defence on that flank. Machine guns are, I consider, most valuable weapons for expeditions such as that

Gatling gun crew at Fort Pearson, Zululand.

Men of HMS "Shah" at Ginghilove, Zululand.

which we had to undertake in Zululand, where the odds against us must necessarily be great, and where it is necessary to leave small detachments in charge of posts along the line of communications. The Gatlings, however, required too much care in firing, and could not be entrusted to any but skilled manipulators. If a machine gun can be invented that may safely be entrusted to infantry soldiers to work, and could be fired very much as one grinds an organ, I am satisfied of its great value. They should, however, be considered as essentially an infantry weapon, and should be worked by infantry soldiers. So utilized, they might, I feel sure, be used most effectively not only in defence, but *in covering* the last stage of an infantry attack upon a position, where the ttroops have at last to cease firing and endeavor to get home with the bayonet.

—*Journal of the Royal United Service Institution,* 1885.

The jamming of the Gatling Guns, mentioned by Lord Chelmsford, undoubtedly was due to the use of ordinary service rifle cartridges of the Boxer type. It was found that the Boxer cartridge was liable to have its base torn from the body of the case by the Gatling's extractor, leaving the metal case stuck in the chamber, resulting in a jam. With the solid-drawn cartridge cases, recommended for Gatling Gun use, no such difficulty was encountered.

It should be noted that Lord Chelmsford was far ahead of the military thought of his day in recognizing that the machine gun is properly an infantry, not an artillery, arm.

A STRANGE ENCOUNTER — THE NAVAL FIGHT OFF YLO, PERU

On May 29, 1877, the Peruvian ironclad ram, *Huáscar,* then in rebel hands, was attacked by two warships of the British Pacific squadron, the *Shah* and the *Amethyst,* off the seaport town of Ylo on the Peruvian coast. A Gatling Gun mounted in the foretop of H.M.S. *Shah,* it will be seen, played an important role in this engagement. An eyewitness account of the battle appeared in the July 21, 1877, issue of *The Illustrated London News:*

NAVAL CONFLICT AT YLO

The extraordinary conflict between two British ships of the Royal Navy and a Peruvian ironclad turret-ship, which had been seized by a lawless revolutionary party, and had committed some acts of piracy, was mentioned last week. An Illustration has been furnished by the sketch we have engraved, which we have received from an eye-witness of this curious action. The circumstances must here be relater. There was an attempted political revolution of late in the Republic of Peru. The leader of the defeated party, Nicholas de Pierola, was banished to Chile. His partisans at Callao, on May 6, seized the iron-clad ram and turret-ship Huascar, aided by the two brothers Carrasco, Lieutenants in the Peruvian Navy. They took her away to embark Perola at some Bolivan port, and then approached the southern ports of the Peruvian coast, near Iquique. The small town of Pisagua was bombarded for refusing to comply with their exactions. The Peruvian Government squadron, consisting of the Independencia, broadside inronclad, the corvette Union, and the gun-boat Pilcomayo, came up with the Huascar, and fought her an hour and a half, but were unable to capture or destroy her. The commander-in-chief of the British squadron on the Pacific station, Rear Admiral de Horsey, was sent for meanwhile by the British Chargé-d'Affaires at Lima on account of the Huascar's alleged depredations. He was informed that she had stopped two of the mail steam-ships, and had forcibly taken persons out of them, as well as coals and other stores. In his flag ship, H.M.S. Shah, unarmoured wooden corvette, joined by H.M.S. Amethyst, Admiral de Horsey pursued the Huascar. He overtook her off the seaport town of Ylo, on May 29, and demanded her surrender. This was refused by the rebel leader, Pierola, who was on board the Peruvian ship. The following is an account of the action which followed:—

"Admiral DeHorsey gave Pierola five minutes to consider and haul down his flag. At the expiration of this time a blank charge was fired; then a shotted gun across her bows. The flag remaining up, we commenced the action at six minutes past three o'clock in the afternoon. The Huscar replied with shell from her turret guns, and immediately steered full course toward Ylo. Her continued manoeuvring backwards and forwards in front of the town frequently causing us to cease firing, to avoid destroying property. The Huascar moved in evidently with the intention of drawing us after her, her draught of water being only 14 ft., and that of the Shah 27 ft.; while the navigation was rendered highly dangerous owing to rocks and shoals at the entrance of the bay. Our range was principally from 1500 to 2500 yards; but at this distance our two 9-in. guns were able to penetrate her turret and our broadside 7-in. guns her hull at the extremities; our 64-lb. shell guns and those of the Amethyst were only available for clearing the upper deck, destroying boats and upper works, which they did most effectually. Owing to the size and weight of the Shah, and the confined space to manoeuvre in, we were unable to benefit by steaming up to an effective range of 1000 or 1200 yards, and stopping to deliver a steady fire—the greater rapidity of the enemy's movements rendering such action dangerous, and the risk of being rammed before we could "gather way" again too great. About five o'clock the Huascar being clear of the shoals, we seized the opportunity to close. The enemy likewise closed, with evident signs of ramming, firing shell from her 40-pounder. Our Gatling gun then commenced firing from the foretop, causing the men on her upper-deck quarters to desert their guns. Our port guns immediately commenced "independent firing". A Whitehead torpedo was fired at the moment of passing, but as the Huascar at that instant altered

Battle of HMSS "Shah" and "Amethyst" against the Peruvian ironclad ram, "Huáscar."

course, turning stern on, the torpedo failed to reach her. The Huascar was going certainly eleven knots, and the torpedo, having only a speed of nine knots, could not overtake the vessel—the torpedo's track was observed going direct about half the distance towards her. The Huascar then steamed full speed close in under the town, and, darkness coming on, we ceased firing at a quarter to six, and steamed out of range.

"Neither the Shah nor the Amethyst was hulled during the action, though the shooting from the Huascar was good and well directed. Almost all her shot came striking the water close alongside us and ricochetted over our ship, doing little damage. The great disadvantage we laboured under was that, owing to the Huascar having the inshore position, we were but seldom able to ascertain her proper distance.

"At nine p.m. the steam pinnace, with an outrigger torpedo, and the whale-boat, with the Whitehead torpedo, in charge of Lieutenant Lindsay, were sent into Ylo bay, to attempt the destruction of the ironclad. On arriving off the town they discovered that the Huascar had slipped away under cover of the high land, the night being extremely dark, with a mist over the land. Our boats returned early in the morning. Being under the impression that the Huascar would stand toward Quilca to land Pierola, we steamed north, sending the Amethyst to Islay for intelligence. In the evening the Amethyst was seen standing out towards us, and we were informed that the Huascar had gone south to Iquique. We immediately steamed full speed to the southward, and we arrived off Iquique, intending, under cover of the night, again to attempt the destruction of the ironclad by means of torpedoes. The steam-pinnace was hoisted out, and the cutter and whaler prepared to accompany her, but a passing steamer informed us that the Huascar had surrendered that morning to the Peruvian squadron. We remained off Iquique till daylight, when we anchored under salutes from the Peruvian squadron. We found the Huascar at anchor surrounded by the squadron. Pierola and his officers were prisoners, and the revolution was at an end. This is the third time Pierola has attempted to overthrow the Government and failed; his last venture being also at Ylo, in the Talisman, an English vessel, the seizure of which gave rise to a difference between England and Peru.

"The gunnery Lieutenant and a Lieutenant of the Royal Marine Artillery were sent on board the Huascar, by permission of the Peruvian commodore, to make notes on the damage done during the late engagement. The Huascar is an ironclad turret-vessel, built by Laird, of Birkenhead; the plating on the hull is 4½-inch iron, tapering to 2½-inch at bow and stern, with 14-inch teak backing and inner skin of ⅝-inch iron; the turret 5½-nch plating, with 14-inch backing and ⅝ inner skin. The turret mounts two 300-pounder Armstrong M.L.R. guns, throwing segment and common shell and chilled shot, and a steel battering shot—the two former being fitted with percussion fusees, were used during the action;

"Huáscar" after the fight off Ylo. (1) Starboard side of the vessel with shot holes in hull, damaged gun turret, and remains of captain's turret. (2) Gun turret with two 300-pounders.

Gatling gun firing from man-of-war's top.

40-pounder on each side of quarter deck, one 12-pounder aft under the poop—all Armstrong M.L.R. As near as could be judged, from seventy to eighty projectiles must have struck the vessel, principally about the upper deck, funnel casing, bridge, masts, and boats, with numbers of pieces of shell sticking into the wood-work; one 9-inch common shell struck the hull, the starboard side, about two feet from the water line and 50 feet from the stern, in the foremost ward-room cabin, bursting in the backing—the head, splintered in all directions, wounded one man; the base continued its course, killing the sentry and going through the casing in an opposite cabin, brought up against the inner skin; the plating at this spot was 3½ inches, same backing and skin. One bulwark each side was blown away, two 64-pounder shell had penetrated the bulwarks and left indentations in the plating; one heavy shot, evidently a ricochet, hit upper edge of plating, starboard side, scoring it to a depth of three inches, after going through the bulwark; another hit the plating two feet from water-line at an angle, making a dent of 2 in. in depth and 18 in. in length. On the port side there was a similar shot to the richochet. The hull itself showed that several 64-pounder shell had struck it, only leaving a mark; one shot struck the poop on port quarter and went out on starboard side, splintering on an iron beam. The funnel-casing and funnel had been struck about twelve times and pierced by the Gatling gun. The turret had only been struck once by a 7-in. projectile, hitting direct and penetrating 3 in. The port fore rigging was shot away, and every boat destroyed. The Huascar was admirably fought and manoeuvred.

"With regard to casualties, only one killed and one wounded have as yet been authenticated, though rumours are rife of a larger number. The former was buried at Iquique, covered with the Peruvian ensign, and a placard placed on the coffin bearing the following inscription:—'This man died while fighting for his country against the British.'

"This is the first instance of an English man-of-war engaging an ironclad of any description, and the first also of wooden ships attacking a turret-vessel; and it cannot fail to be of interest."

Our correspondent's sketch represents the moment when the Huascar attempted to ram the Shah, and had run on within four hundred yards of her. The Huascar could not stand the fire of the Shah's guns, and therefore suddenly turned about, and ran in to the shore. It seems, however, that the propriety of Admiral de Horsey's conduct, in attacking the Huascar, is likely to be questioned. Some persons deny that the Huascar had really committed acts of piracy or done injury to British property, and the Peruvian Government itself is disposed to complain, though its ship was in the hands of rebels.

As far as is known, this was the earliest recorded use of a Gatling gun in an engagement at sea. In his account of the fight, Peruvian Navy Captain Aurelio García y García wrote:

> The firing became even more severe from the English frigates, and as the distance between the antagonists had been reduced to two cable-lengths, more or less, the admiral brought to bear all his attacking forces, which on board the *Shah* were very formidable in character. From the tops a Gatling gun threw a hail of bullets at the decks of the *Huascar,* together with steady volleys of musketry and rifles.

Another Peruvian report says:

> A small Gatling gun stationed in her tops very seriously incommoded the combatants on the ram, and her smoke-stack is riddled with bullets.

Despite the considerable damage inflicted on the *Huáscar* in this engagement with British warships, the ram "lived to fight another day"—in the War of the Pacific, two years later. When next heard of, the ship had been refitted and, the Peruvian Navy having learned a lesson at Ylo, the armament of the *Huáscar* included Gatling Guns.

WAR OF THE PACIFIC

Fought to a great extent at sea, the War of the Pacific of 1879–1884 actually began in the deserts of the then Bolivian province of Atacama. The Chilean Nitrate Company had been granted the concession to work the Atacama nitrate fields for 25 years, without additional taxation, under the terms of an agreement signed between Bolivia and Chile in 1874. When Hilarión Daza became president of Bolivia in 1878, after a *coup d'état,* an additional tax was levied on nitrate exports from the Bolivian littoral. The Chileans objected and Daza rescinded the nitrate mining contract and ordered seizure of the Chilean Nitrate Company's assets in Bolivia. To protect Chilean interests, Colonel Sotomayor, with 500 soldiers, was sent to occupy the port city of Antofogasta, Bolivia, founded by the Chileans in 1870 to facilitate export of nitrates mined in Atacama. On February 14, 1879, Bolivia proclaimed a state of war. Peru, under a secret treaty of alliance with Bolivia, refused to guarantee neutrality, and Chile declared war against Bolivia and Peru.

The Chilean forces were completely victorious in their campaign against Bolivia and Peru. By the end of the year of 1879, they occupied the entire Bolivian seaboard, as well as Tarapaca in Peru, and had eliminated the enemy navy. During 1880, Chile consolidated its conquest and, on January 17, 1881, took Peru's capital city, Lima. Bolivia and Peru had been defeated and, save for a few scattered minor engagements, the War of the Pacific was over, although the peace treaty between Chile and Peru was not signed until 1883. The truce between Bolivia and Chile was agreed upon the next year.

As a result of the war, Chile acquired the nitrate-rich province of Atacama, by which Bolivia lost its only coastal area, and Peru had to cede Tarapaca to Chile, as well as control for ten years of the provinces of Tacna and Arica. These consequences of her alliance with Bolivia against Chile brought Peru to the verge of national collapse and recovery took many years.

Both sides in the War of the Pacific had equipped their armed forces with Gatlings and these guns figured in many land, as well as sea, actions. Accounts of two such actions, recorded in detail, are given here.

In the first naval action of the war, off Iquique, on May 21, 1879, the Peruvian ironclad ram *Huáscar* engaged and sank the Chilean corvette *Esmeralda* in a hard-fought four-hour contest. A report of this engagement was published in *The New York Times*, Sunday, July 20, 1879:

THE FIGHT OFF IQUIQUE
OFFICIAL CHILIAN ACCOUNT OF THE ENGAGEMENT – SINKING OF THE ESMERALDA BY THE HUASCAR.

The following is the official report of the Chilian commander to his Government of the engagement off Iquique between the Peruvian iron-clad ram Huascar and the Chilian corvette Esmeralda, in which the latter was sunk. It is specially translated for *The Times* from the original document:

Iquique, May 29, 1879.

To the Commander General of the Navy:

Sir: I have the honor to inform you that on the 21st inst. we have a hardly fought contest, which lasted four hours, with the Peruvian iron-clad Huascar and the Chilian corvette Esmeralda was sunk after being rammed the third time. The honor of our flag has been sustained but we must mourn the loss of three of her most gallant defenders—Commander Prat, Lieut. Serrano, and Midshipman Riquelme.

At 7 A.M. of the said day we observed two vessels toward the north, and we prepared immediately for action. We soon ascertained that the vessels were the Peruvian ram Huascar and the frigate Independencia. Commander Prat ordered the Chilian gun-boat Covadonga to take her position between the town of Iquique and our enemy. But while changing our position, one of the boilers of the Esmeralda got out of order, and the speed of the ship was reduced to two knots an hour. At 8:30 A.M. the battle became general, and while the Esmeralda was holding the engagement about 200 metres from shore, the Covadonga ran southward fighting the Peruvian frigate Independencia. From that position we fought the enemy. Our shots for a time were uncertain, but after awhile they improved, and many of the shells burst in the turret and on the deck of the Huascar, but without doing her any damage. The shots of the Huascar were fired too high, and most of them lodged in the town of Iquique.

Our position was not unfavorable until the batteries on shore opened their fire against us; consequently, Commander Prat was obliged to change position with the loss of three men killed and several wounded. At this moment, 10 A.M., a shell fired by the Huascar entered our port side and exploded near the water line, causing a fire, which was at once suffocated by the energy of the crew. In the meantime the Huascar had approached within the distance of 600 metres, and the engagement continued at that distance for nearly an hour without receiving any other damage. We then observed the Huascar preparing to ram, but our lack of speed would not permit us to avoid the collision. The ram entered our port side forward the mizzenmast and fired her two heavy guns, causing a terrible slaughter of our crew. Commander Prat, who had been standing on the bridge since the beginning of the engagement, jumped at once to the bow of the enemy's vessel, crying "board her," but unfortunately his voice was drowned by the heavy firing, and failed to be heard by the crew. The Huascar recoiled instantly, making it impossible to execute the commander's order. As I was standing on the bridge I observed, with grief, our gallant commander, Prat, instantly killed by the turret of the Huascar. I then assumed at once the command of the Esmeralda, and continued the engagement almost at the mouth of our cannon, but our projectiles failed to take effect on the heavy armor of the Huascar. On the contrary, the fire of our enemy caused terrible ravages and our upper and lower decks were literally covered with killed and wounded.

The Huascar attacked us again directing her bow to the middle of our ship. I steered to prevent the shock, but our want of speed made it impossible and the iron-clad struck our vessel midships. In that moment Lieut. Serrano, followed by a dozen sailors, jumped on the deck of the Huascar and they were all killed by the shots of musketry and Gatling guns fired from the turret and behind the parapets of the stern. The boarding of the enemy's vessel proved also to be impossible because she recoiled so quickly after striking our sides. At the same time our crew was considerably reduced, having more than 100 men killed, the magazine full of water, and the engine nearly destroyed. The few cartridges that we had on deck were used to fire our last shots on receiving the third blow of the enemy's ram. The Midshipman, Don Ernesto Riquelme, whose gallant behavior had been noted during the whole engagement, shot the last gun. He was seen no more, and it is supposed that he was killed by the shells of the Huascar. The Esmeralda, with her living crew and the national flag in the top of her masts, sunk at the third ram of the enemy, and thus were obeyed the orders of our courageous commander, who, at the commencement of the engagement, had delivered the following address:

"My boys, we must fight an unequal match. Chili has never struck her colors before the enemy, and I trust this will not be the first time. While I live, that glorious flag will be in her place, and if I die I am sure that my officers will do their duty."

When our ship was no more seen, the boats of the Huascar took the few living and on the evening of that same day we were landed prisoners in Iquique. I inclose the list of the officers and sailors of our crew who are at present prisoners in this port. Your obedient servant, *Luis Uribe*.

Abandoning their blockade of the Peruvian coast, the Chilean Navy set forth to find and sink the *Huáscar*. After more than four months, their mission was accomplished. Engaged off Angamos by two more heavily gunned and armor vessels, the Chilean frigates *Almirante Cocrane* and *Blanco Encolada*, the *Huáscar*, after six hours of desperate battle, shattered and shot-riddled, her steering-gear disabled, and nearly sinking, was towed into the port of Antofagasta by the victorious Chileans. Of the *Huáscar's* complement of 210 officers and men, only 83 survived the battle. Its commander, Vice-Admiral Don Miguel Grau, although severely wounded early in the fight, continued to direct operations from his command turret until it received the direct hit which literally blew him to pieces.

As was typical of first-class ships of the day, the *Huáscar*, as well as the *Almirante Cochrane* and *Blanco Encolada*, carried Gatling Guns as secondary batteries. Undoubtedly, these guns accounted for their share of the heavy personnel losses suffered in this engagement.

On November 2, 1879, an expeditionary force of some 8,000 Chilean troops landed and, after a fierce battle, took the key town of Pisagua, situated on the Peruvian coast between Iquique and Arica; this put them in a position to prevent the juncture of the allied armies of Bolivia and Peru. After falling back from Pisagua, the allies regrouped and, numbering 10,000 men, attacked the Chilean position at San Francisco heights, near Dolores, on November 19. On December 17, 1879, the *New York Herald* reported on this battle:

> A letter from Lima, describing the defeat of the Peruvian army at San Francisco heights, says: "The earthworks were defended by a strong Chilean force, plentifully supplied with Krupp field pieces and Gatling guns. Here Buendia committed the error which has cost the allies the best division in their army. Instead of making a detour, which he could easily have done, and thus compelling the enemy to descend to attack him in the pampa at the rear of the hill, or submit to having his communications with Pisagua cut off, Buendia gave the order to charge up the rugged hill and carry the works by storm. The attempt was gallantly made. Three times the shattered regiments, which had undertaken a feat which it was impossible to perform, were compelled to fall back and re-form, leaving the hillside thickly covered with their dead and dying, who had fallen in masses before the Krupps and Gatlings long ere they could make their rifles tell.

GATLINGS IN NAVAL SERVICE

Although, during the late nineteenth century, nearly every vessel of the U.S. Navy included Gatling Guns in its secondary battery, this branch of the service seems to have neglected the proper training of ships' Gatling Gun crews.

Lt.-Comdr. William M. Folger, U.S.N., who was, for some years, an employee of the Gatling Gun Company, wrote in a report to the Bureau of Ordnance, Navy Department, dated December 5, 1879:

> . . . a more efficient instruction is urged for the gun servants than has usually been apparent on board most of our vessels. The exercise has generally been neglected, a variety of reasons sufficient and otherwise, contributing to this fact. The crews have frequently been selected from the carpenters for example—with the assumption, perhaps, that their usual duties at quarters would admit of an expansion, or it may be of a supposed familiarity with mechanical contrivances.
>
> Both of these assumptions usually proving entirely groundless, the gun has generally been kept stored below, or perhaps retained on deck as a showpiece for the lady friends of the "young gentlemen."

Two months prior to the date of Commander Folger's report, however, Gatling Guns figured prominently in the Grand Naval Review and Maneuvers of Naval Apprentices at Hampton Roads, Virginia, October 14 and 15, 1879. Since apprentice seamen apparently received Gatling Gun instruction, it probably was negligence on the part of ships' officers that led to the conditions mentioned by Commander Folger.

GATLING MODELS OF 1879-1882

Prior to the introduction of the Model 1879, all Gatling Guns were equipped with elevating and traversing systems much like those found on cannon of the period. This, of course, reflected the then prevalent military view of machine guns, which regarded these weapons as artillery or auxiliary to conventional cannon and limiting their use to long-range flank defense. Changing the point of aim of

Grand naval review and maneuvers of naval apprentices, Hampton Roads, Virginia, October 14-15, 1879. Sailors of USS "Powhatan" are landing Gatling gun from a raft.

a Gatling Gun involved much turning of cranks and wheels and, while the piece could be sighted precisely to direct fire at distant targets, it was virtually useless in closer combat. Plainly, there was a need for improved mounting to permit the Gatling to be elevated and swung freely and rapidly. The answer came in the Model 1879, the first Gatling Gun adapted to use as a machine gun in the modern tactical sense.

The new mount retained the swivel type yoke of the 1874 series, but permitted traverse through approximately 80°, affording an arc of fire much wider than was possible with any of the earlier models. Instead of employing an oscillator, the yoke turned freely on a cast iron turntable and could be locked at any point by application of a friction brake.

Elevation adjustment was provided in a pointing bar, hinged to the yoke, and extending to the rear where it passed through a binder box on the underside of the breech casing. As the handle of the pointing bar was depressed, the muzzles of the gun were elevated; the binder box, sliding along the pointing bar, could be locked at any point to maintain that degree of elevation.

With the adoption of this new type of mounting, a number of changes were made in the gun proper which, although it would fit the yokes designed for previous models, could not be fired from such mounts because of the radically different elevating system of the Model 1879. Trunnions were located back farther, moving the balance of the gun forward to facilitate operation of the pointing bar. Instead of being slotted for the oscillator, the breech casing had two lugs near the rear of its underside; the binder box was attached between these lugs with a large pin and a locking wedge.

Adjusting headspace, as frequently required during the course of firing, was a hazardous procedure with earlier Gatlings—it had to be performed at the muzzle end. In the Model 1879, headspace was adjusted at the rear of the weapon and without tools. The main shaft, protruding through the cascabel

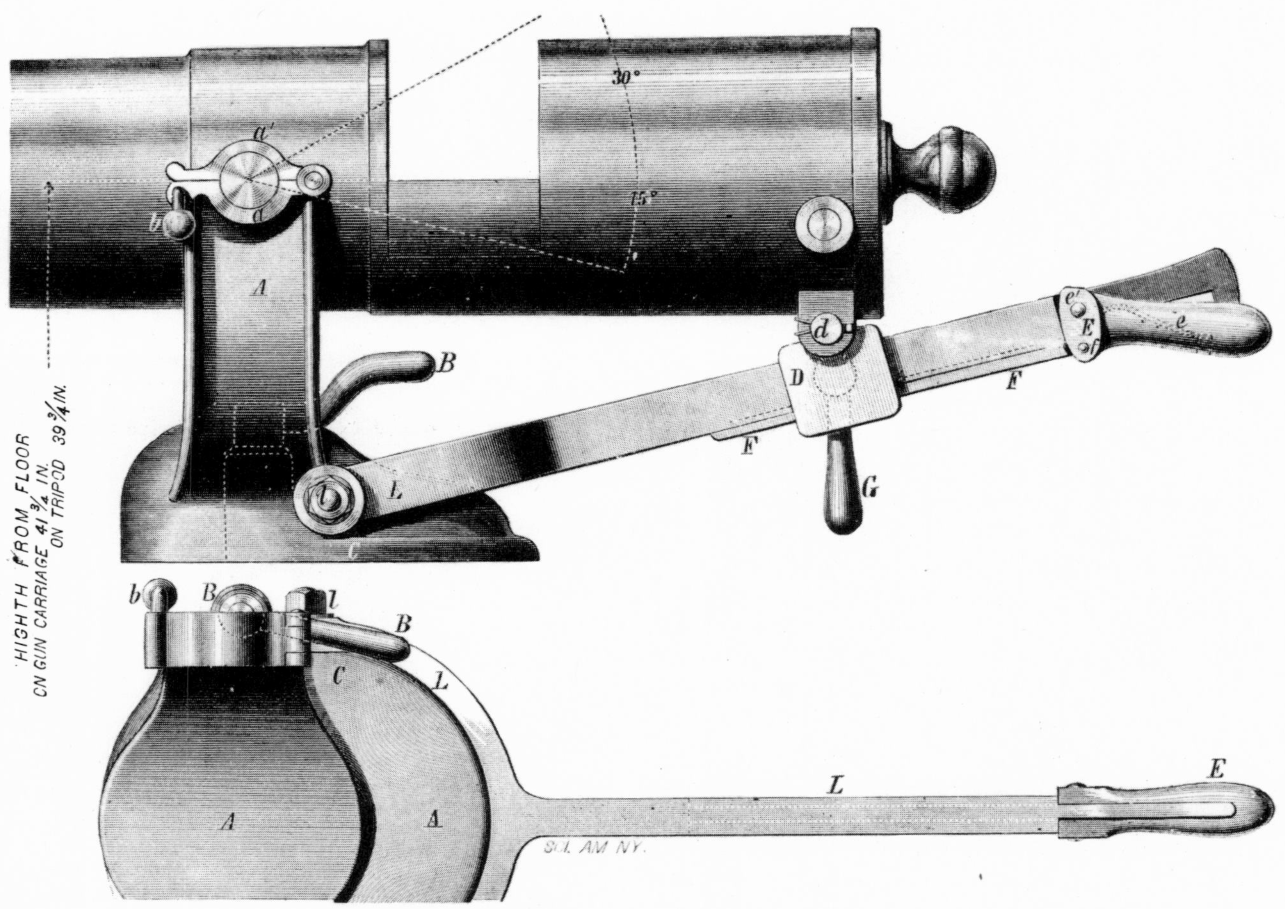

Details of 1879 type pointing bar and yoke assembly. Binder box (D) allowed gun to be locked at any desired elevation; brake handle (B) locked yoke at any position of traverse.

Cascabel plate, Model 1881 Gatling, with breech-bolt access port open. Note headspace adjustment notches around base of cascabel knob. Knob was turned so that proper notch engaged spring catch above knob.

plate, was fitted with a knob on its threaded end. As this bronze cascabel knob was turned clockwise, the shaft was drawn rearward, bringing the barrels closer to the breech bolts, thus reducing headspace; counter-clockwise turning, of course, produced the opposite effect. A spring lock held the cascabel knob at the required headspace setting.

Although the proper designation of this model is "1879," some guns of this type actually were produced during the preceding year. Usually mounted on a wheeled artillery carriage (a few of these guns were equipped with tripods), the Model 1879 Gatling Gun was 49 inches long and weighed 200 pounds—without mount. Its ten barrels were 32 inches in length and chambered for the official .45/70 U.S. cartridge. The standard, trapezoidal, tin-plated box magazine, holding forty rounds, was used. Sights were located on the right side of the piece. Markings and model data were engraved on top of the bronze breech casing.

In 1879, the U.S. Army purchased eighteen guns of this model (serial No. 225 and 226—each of which numbers appears on two guns due to a factory error, 228, 229, 231-242) and, the following year, fourteen more were bought (serial No. 245-258).

The Model 1881 Gatling Gun was similar to the Model 1879 except that the mouth of the feed hopper was modified to accept the recently developed Bruce feed. Twenty-five of these guns (serial No. 295-319) were purchased by the U.S. Army in 1881 and an additional two (serial No. 321, 323) the next year. These were the last Gatlings with exposed barrels sold to the U.S. Government until 1889.

Earlier model Gatlings were designed to load from tin feed cases or the 400-round Broadwell drum; because of the weight and bulk of such magazines, ammunition usually was transported in a large limber. The Bruce feed, which became the most popular Gatling loading system, permitted the gun to be loaded directly from cardboard boxes of twenty rounds. Thus, an adequate supply of cartridges in the ammunition factory's packages could be carried in relatively small chests mounted on the gun carriage.

The Bruce feed, named for its inventor, L. F. Bruce, consisted of a bronze frame on which was mounted a steel bar with two T-shaped slots milled in its face to accept the head of a .45/70 cartridge. This bar was designed to swing from side to side, so that the two grooves alternately aligned with a central channel leading to the feed hopper of the gun. In use, a paper box of 20 rounds was placed against the upper extension of the bronze plate and brought downward so that the heads of the two rows of cartridges entered the channels; the box was then pulled forward, away from the cartridges which remained in the channels. The rounds were gravity-fed, sliding downward into the hopper. When one channel was emptied, the weight of the cartridges in the other caused that to move over the track leading into the hopper and, thus, con-

1879 type flexible yoke adapted to tripod mount.

Special, bronze-encased, Model 1879 Gatling made for U.S. Navy. Improved carriage with flexible mount afforded wider arc of fire than possible with cannon-type adjustments of earlier field carriages.

tinue feeding ammunition into the gun. By continually inserting boxes of cartridges into the Bruce feed, an uninterrupted fire could be maintained. Usually, two Bruce feeds came with the gun as standard equipment: one for actual use and the other to be held in reserve as a spare.

The first Bruce feeds had adapter bases, permitting them to be clamped in place over feed hoppers designed to accept the standard tin feed cases. Later, Gatlings were produced with hoppers for Bruce feed only. This is particularly true of guns chambered for .30-40 Krag and .30-06 Springfield cartridges.

During the 1890's when the U.S. Government engaged in a Gatling Gun modernization program, many Bruce feeds were manufactured at its arsenals by special arrangement with the Gatling Gun Company. Unlike those produced by Colt's, these Bruce feeds are unmarked; the former type bear the patent notice stamped on the back of the bronze plate.

The Bruce feed was so well-received in military circles that variations soon appeared on competitive battery guns. Gardner and Lowell guns, for example, had "Bruce type" feeds.

(No Model.) 4 Sheets—Sheet 1.
L. F. BRUCE.
CARTRIDGE FEEDER FOR MACHINE GUNS.
No. 247,158. Patented Sept. 20, 1881.

Bruce feed with base to fit hoppers designed for standard magazines.

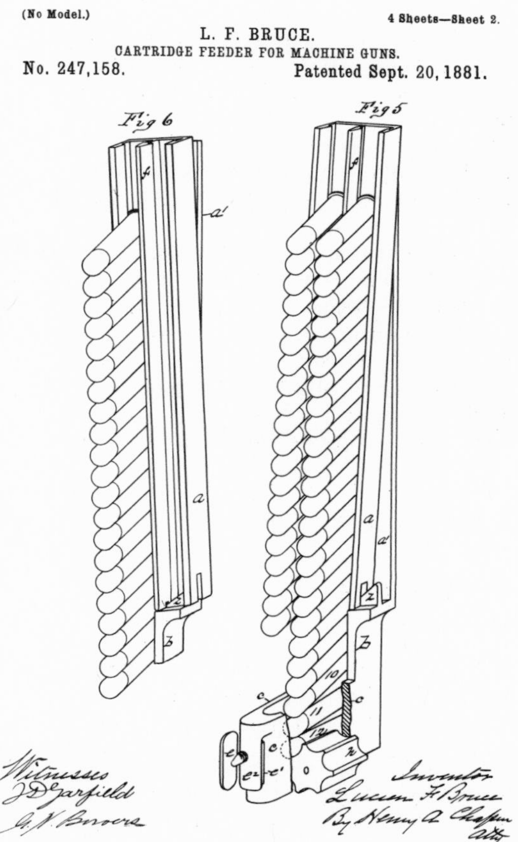

Bruce feed with cartridges loaded. Shown with and without adapter base for standard feed hoppers.

FIVE: 1880-1911

THE LATTER YEARS

FACED with growing competition, especially from the Gardner, Hotchkiss, and Nordenfeldt machine guns, Richard Jordan Gatling published in the August 27, 1881, issue of *Army & Navy Journal* a challenge to his competitors:

A NOTICE

The Gatling Gun

Many articles have recently appeared in the press, claiming the superior advantages of the Gardner and other machine guns over the Gatling gun.

In order to decide which is the best gun, the undersigned offers to fire his gun (the Gatling) against any other gun, on the following wagers, viz.:

First, $500 that the Gatling can fire more shots in a given time, say one minute.

Second, $500 that the Gatling can give more hits on a target, firing, say one minute—at a range of 800 or 1000 yards.

The winner to contribute the money won to some charitable object.

The time and place for the trials to be mutually agreed upon.

R. J. Gatling
of Hartford, Conn.

On October 15, 1881, the *Broad Arrow* (London) commented: "We have heard no response as yet to the challenge Dr. Gatling recently published in the *Army & Navy Journal*. Cannot the price of $500 be obtained by some of the owners of our machine guns for transfer to the sufferers by the Michigan fire, before the cold weather is upon them?" As far as is known, none took up the gauntlet thrown down by Gatling.

A MILITARY APPRAISAL

In the 1882 edition of his book, *American Breech-loading Small Arms,* General Norton wrote:

Truly the world moves! for a hundred men armed with Gatlings could easily prove more than a match for the mighty host of Xerxes.*

Unquestionably the most interesting problem in the next great war will be the changes rendered necessary by the use of Gatlings.

Directly applicable to this thought are remarks in the standard book in America on manoeuvres, "Strategos, the American Game of War," by Lieut. Totten, U. S. Army. We quote:

"The Gatling will probably keep apace, if not ahead, of any improvement incident to small-arm ammunition and its efficient employment. The dispersion commences at the muzzle of each gun, and is a slightly curved, fan-shaped surface of some 12° maximum spread. This, at 20 yards' interval between the guns, causes the front at 100 yards' range (to wit, 121 yards) to be just covered by the six guns of a battery. Up to this range there are dead spaces between the guns; but beyond it a cross-fire obtains, which searches the front with an effect that increases up to 600 yards almost as rapidly as the effect from thence (100 yards) diminishes on account of the constant angle of dispersion. There results from these circumstances an effect sufficient, when at its best, to carry away the whole line exposed within the limits of the dispersion, and up to 600 yards' range. This state of affairs can be readily seen by the student himself with the aid of a single diagram, constructed to a scale and indicating the cross-fire in front of such a battery. From the peculiar sheet sort of dispersion attained by means of the Gatling oscillator, uninfluenced as it is at the last moment by any additional and disturbing cone,

* According to the *History of Herodotus,* Book VII, when Xerxes numbered his soldiers at Doriscus, the whole land army was found to amount to *one million seven hundred thousand men.* In view of this, General Norton's statement seems overly sanguine in its estimate of the Gatling's effectiveness!

due to the bursting of individual projectiles, the fire of this gun loses less effect (one-half) through the intervals than canister, shrapnel, or shell fire. From 1,000 to 2,000 yards this loss gradually increases to two-thirds, remaining constant thereafter. The targets show how evenly the Gatling projectiles fly, how little the target is spattered, and how effectively it is swept. This control that can thus be exercised over each pellet, as it were, that flies from the Gatling battery, is not the least argument in its behalf. Owing to what may not inaptly be termed the sûrplus effect of this gun, the following proposition may not be unworthy of discussion and experiment: to wit, to fire less rapidly at short range, increasing, say, from 200 rounds per minute at 100 yards up to 400, the maximum, at 1,000 yards, and thence maintaining this latter rate at least up to the limits of distinct vision. Several important objects will be thus realized. If the gun is well handled (and at short range there will be less excitement incident to rapidity, and therefore more time for accurate aiming), the same 'effect' will be realized at the shorter ranges, and this with far less 'lost effect' while at long ranges the already deadly effect may be practically doubled! And if, now, we compare such an effect with that attainable by infantry 'in line, and firing at the same long ranges with average (six per minute) rapidity and their best per cent, it will be evident that the preponderance of effect is vastly in favor of the Gatling gun'. The startling proposition therefore suggests itself *to do most, if not all, of our long-range firing with Gatling batteries.* In future wars this fire must be systematically resorted to, and we submit that the proposition here made offers the simplest and most effective method of realizing it. It means, of course, to increase our number of Gatling guns until we have a Gatling corps as numerous as artillery itself. The first expense is of small moment comparable with *promises* and *results* of warlike preparations; and this method promises not only double the effect with about one-half the transportation and expenditure of ammunition, but will enable us to keep our infantry well in hand, and more or less out of the battle until within short range and decisive distances.

"As we go to print, we notice that the possible rapidity of fire of this gun has been most wonderfully increased. Unfortunately, it is too late to alter our tables. The new Gatling gun, now on trial before the English Ordnance Board, is reported to fire 1,000 rounds per minute! (At the works, in Hartford, Conn., the rapidity of fire has even been reported as high as 1,200 per minute.) With such a deadly rain of lead, it has become *possible* to carry away an entire line of battle, even up to very nearly the limits of distinct vision!

"It is almost impossible to keep pace with the improvement now in progress in this branch of our subject; but it is therefore more than ever necessary that the soldier be *indefatigable in professional study and reading.* In our age it is his bounden duty, he cannot afford to fall behind-hand in this important matter.

"This increased efficiency of the Gatling gun simply intensifies the argument we have just advanced in reference to its employment."

GATLING'S TORPEDO GUN

From 1879 to 1881, Gatling devoted much time to the development of a Torpedo Gun. Although the name might mislead, this type of weapon had nothing to do with the discharge of torpedoes; rather, it was a large-bore gun, intended for defense against torpedo boats. Gatling's Torpedo Gun was described in the *Army & Navy Journal* of January 23, 1881:

The last development of the Gatling system is the new Torpedo gun, which has just been completed at Colt's Armory. Though the first and best known of machine gun inventors, Dr. Gatling had, to the surprise of ordnance people, seemed to have lost sight of the uses as a defensive medium for ships, against the aggressive little steam launches of present naval warfare. Both Hotchkiss and Nordenfeldt have scored successes with their effective ship-defenders, while the brain which originally evolved the practicability of their type of rapid-firing engines was apparently listless. For nearly two years, however, Dr. Gatling had been studying the details of a new machine gun, and the result is at last reached in an invention which combines the theory of the old breech action with the new mechanical devices demanded by the conditions of range and calibre.

The Gatling Torpedo gun has a calibre of 1.45 inches, with a barrel of the extraordinary length of 50 inches, thus assuring the entire consumption of the maximum powder charge. The barrel is of fine steel, enclosed in a casing of gun metal, giving it the appearance of a cannon of small calibre but great length. The projectiles may be either steel pointed solid bolts or cast iron shell. The breech mechanism, beautifully designed and finished, is capable of taking care of from seventy to eighty cartridges per minute, these being fed by hand. As, however, all guns of this type must be aimed after each discharge, the object being in constant motion, the volume of fire will be somewhat less than this theoretical possibility. The mount of the gun, as seen by us at the armory, is the ordinary army carriage. The piece is hung and properly balanced on trunnions, resting in the bearing of a swivel, so that it may be used either on the carriage, or secured by the clamps of the vertical socket in which the swivel plays, to the gunwale—the latter position admitting a horizontal sweep of the entire horizon, with an elevation or depression of 45 degrees. If secured to the gunwale, an appliance of wood on the left side of the breech received the pressure of the gunner's shoulder, enabling him with his left hand to range the piece, which moves in its socket with the greatest ease, while with his right hand he actuates the firing crank. An important feature of

British naval brigade clearing streets of Alexandria with Gatling gun.

the action is the new mechanism which absolutely prevents cocking until the cartridge is fully home in the chamber and the breech entirely closed, the firing-pin being thus positively retired from the cartridge head except at the moment of firing, so that a premature explosion is impossible.

The facility with which the arm is aimed is one of its most striking features. The angle of depression, 45 degrees, enables the marksman managing the arm to continue firing until the torpedo-boat is within a few yards of the ship. The gun is to be tested at Sandy Hook under the direction of the board of ordnance officers. The mechanical work has been done by Captain Charles Saunders, one of the most skillful machinists in the country, while Mr. Evarts, the expert draughtsman at Colt's, has attended to the drawings and plans. It should be stated that the gun can be used for field service with the most effective results. The sighting apparatus is so nicely adjustable that aim can be secured and the gun fired at least a dozen times before an ordinary artillery gun can be sighted.

Contrary to the statement, made in the foregoing articles, premature explosion was possible, as Captain Saunders unhappily learned. In a letter to Colt's, dated December 13, 1881, Gatling wrote:

I have just learned that in firing my torpedo gun rapidly a cartridge exploded prematurely injuring Mr. Saunders who was operating the crank. I am at a loss to determine how the accident should have occurred—perhaps it was caused by a "hang fire" in attempting to fire the gun too fast; be that as it may, I desire that you have the matter fully investigated and please have the gun repaired if the injury to it is slight, & you think it best to do so.

What effect this accident had on the future of the Gatling Torpedo Gun is not known; however, no further reports on this gun have been found and no picture of it seems to be extant.

It is interesting to note that, in this design, Gatling departed considerably from the principles of his well-proved Gatling Gun, while Hotchkiss and Nordenfeldt Torpedo Guns were essentially larger versions of their standard guns.

EGYPT AND SUDAN CAMPAIGNS

The crisis of 1882 in Egypt was the direct result of the failure of the British and French Governments, in 1881, to support their protégé, Tewfik Pasha, Khedive of Egypt, in his efforts to resist the seizure of power by the nationalistic military party, headed by Ahmed Arabi. Tewfik was forced to appoint a cabinet of ministers formed by the military party, giving control of the government to this antiforeign element. In May, 1882, France and Great Britain, who jointly controlled Egypt's finances since 1876 when Ismail Pasha's extravagances had brought the country to near bankruptcy, succeeded in forcing the resignation of the nationalist cabinet; however, subsequent pressure from the military party secured the reinstatement of Arabi as minister of war.

By late May, despite the fact that French and British warships were anchored off Alexandria, the situation of foreign residents of the city became desperate as they faced the menace of growing hostility on the part of the native troops. Early in June, antiforeign riots broke out, with massacres occurring on the 11th; mobs of incendiaries and looters ran wild in Alexandria. A month later, on July 11, after France had refused to join them in intervention, the British Navy began the bombardment of Alexandria. The effect of this bombardment was slight; the fire of the warships did little significant damage to the defenses of the port. Gatling Guns, mounted in the ships' tops, proved of little value because of the conditions under which they were used:

At the bombardment of Alexandria in the summer of 1882 machine guns were mounted in the tops of ships, in order to bring a plunging fire upon Egyptian batteries, but the results were disappointing, probably on account of smoke obscuring the view; the ranging was bad, and an examination of the batteries after the bombardment showed very few marks of machine-gun bullets. During the attack the gunners in the tops of the ships were wrapped in a fog of powder-smoke from the big guns lower down, and the machine guns themselves produced another dense cloud round the tops. One may say that smokeless powder is almost a necessity for the thoroughly efficient working of any kind of quick-firing gun, whether cannon or machine gun.—Longstaff and Atteridge, *The Book of the Machine Gun.*

At 3 P.M. on July 13, 1882, a party of bluejackets and marines was landed at Alexandria. The story of their effective use of Gatling Guns is told by Lord Charles Beresford, of the Royal Navy:

. . . When the Gatling Guns were landed at Alexandria, after the bombardment, the effect of their fire upon the wild mob of fanatic incendiaries and looters was quite extraordinary. These guns were not fired at the people, but a little over their heads, as a massacre would have been the result, had the guns been steadily trained on the mob. The rain of bullets, which they heard screaming over their heads, produced a moral effect not easily described. I asked an Egyptian officer, some weeks afterwards, how on earth it was that Arabi and his 9,000 regular troops, who were within five miles, did not march down upon the town in the first four days after the bombardment, when Arabi knew that Captain Fisher's Naval Brigade, which held the lines,

Naval brigade, with Gatling guns, occupying Alexandria.

numbered less than 400 men. The Egyptian officer replied, "That he knew no army which could face machines which 'pumped lead,' and that all the gates were defended by such machines, as well as having torpedoes under the bridges, such defences could not be faced." This certainly was the case. I believe the Egyptian officer spoke the truth, and that the moral effect produced by the Gatlings on the people in the first landing prevented the army from attacking the diminutive force which held the lines afterwards.

. . . .

Replying for "The Navy", at a dinner of the Cutler's Company, Lord Charles Beresford said: "The great value of machine guns has been shown. With the Gatlings, the landing parties had cleared the streets of Alexandria and prevented Arabi from returning, and, if they had been allowed to land immediately after the bombardment, they might have dispersed the crowds laden with loot, have captured Arabi, Toalba Pasha, and other leaders, and saved the town; but the Government had promised that no man should land, and they were bound by the promise."

. . . .

In my opinion, machine guns, if properly worked, would decide the fate of a campaign, and would be equally useful ashore or afloat.—*Army and Navy Gazette,* London, November 4, 1882.

Captain Fisher, who commanded the Naval Brigade in the first British landing at Alexandria, displayed his ingenuity in devising an armored train, which was used on the railway near Alexandria during the Egyptian campaign. This unusual conveyance was described in *Illustrated London News,* August 12, 1882:

Naval Armoured Railway Train

This locomotive fortress consists of six trucks protected by iron shields, the engine being in the centre. A Nordenfeldt gun looks over the bows of the leading truck, and three Gatlings over the stern of the hindmost. The men in the trucks are protected from musketry by a row of sandbags. Two field guns are carried in one of the other trucks or waggons, built for heavy weights; but it is intended to place a seven-ton gun in this waggon. Captain Fisher of HMS Inflexible, assisted by Lieutenant Poore, contrived the whole affair, and superintended its construction and equipment, afterwards directing its movements with two hundred picked men to form the proper crew. The train is provided with mines, electric gear, and all appliances for laying down or destroying rails. It is also furnished with a powerful steam-crane for shifting guns and other heavy articles. An empty waggon goes before the train, and can be shunted forward, the train stopping, from time to time, to try whether the line is clear, and to explode any mines that may have been laid beneath the rails.

Following their success in the occupation of riot-

Armored train, rear, with Gatling gun.

Armored train on railway near Alexandria.

torn Alexandria, the British forces proceeded to seize the Suez Canal, and occupy Ismailia as their base for an advance on Cairo. As indicated by press reports, the Gatling Guns played an important part in these land operations.

The *London News,* on August 22, 1882, published the following dispatch from its Special Correspondent in Egypt:

> I have returned from Chalouf, fourteen miles up the Canal, where I witnessed the conclusion of a fight in which 250 men, including the 72nd Highlanders, with the blue jackets and marines from the gunboats Seagull and Mosquito, brilliantly defeated a force twice their number. The fighting lasted from eleven until nearly five. The Gatling Guns, in the tops of the gunboats, worked with admirable precision, doing much execution among the enemy, who had advanced to within 100 yards of the Canal bank.

A report in the *New York Herald,* August 26, 1882, states:

> In a telegram dispatched at 2 o'clock this morning, General Wolseley adds: "I omitted to say that I had with me, yesterday, two Gatling Guns, worked by seamen, which did their duty admirably."

An incident of the Battle of Tel-el-Mahouta, involving Gatling Guns, is recounted in the London *Army & Navy Gazette,* June 16, 1883:

> A correspondent serving in the Mediterranean brings to our notice an episode in the Egyptian campaign which has escaped notice, though well deserving a place in the records of that war. According to our correspondent, Lieutenant Cecil Burney, R.N., of the "Carysfort," was landed at Ismailia, in charge of two Gatling Guns. Here he appears to have been forgotten or lost sight of, for he advanced with the division of the Army under General Willis, and found himself, on August 24 [1882], on the extreme right of that officer's command when the battle of Tel-el-Mahouta commenced. During the day the Egyptian troops pressed hard on the British right, and General Willis and staff watched the advance of the enemy in this direction, not entirely without aprehension. No one knew the Gatlings were there, hence Lieutenant Burney was left to act on his own judgment and responsibility. Like a true seaman, this young officer preferred close quarters to long bowling, and waited for Arabi's troops to get well within point-blank range before opening fire. Then the Gatlings were allowed to rattle out their deadly fire, and much to the relief of General Willis, the enemy was seen to halt, waver, break, and fly, utterly routed.

From *Broad Arrow* (London), September 2, 1882:

> On all sides it is acknowledged that the Gatling has proved itself an effective arm of service to the present campaign. At Chalouf, and at Mahuta, the Naval Gatling was admirably served by our blue jackets, and afforded "invaluable assistance." Indeed, it may be broadly affirmed that, in the encounter with the enemy at the former place, the results attained were chiefly ascribable to the action of the Gatlings from the tops of the gunboats Seagull and Mosquito. One hundred and sixty-eight Egyptian soldiers, out of 600, which composed the outpost, were placed *hors de combat*. Under these circumstances, it is not unlikely that Sir Garnet Wolseley will employ Gatling batteries extensively in future operations.

On September 12, 1882, British troops attacked the Egyptian stronghold at Tel-el-Kebir, defended by a force of 38,000 and 60 pieces of artillery. The fight began at 11 P.M. with the advance of the attackers, 15,000 strong; it continued through the night and, by 6 A.M. the following morning, Egyptian resistance had ceased. The English lost only 58 killed, 379 wounded, and 22 missing, while the Egyptian losses were almost 2,000 killed and more than 500 wounded.

The story of Gatlings in action at Tel-el-Kebir is reported in the *Army and Navy Gazette* (London), October 14, 1882, in the florid prose of that era:

> The naval machine gun battery, consisting of six Gatlings, manned by thirty seamen, reached the position assigned to it in the English lines on September 10th and, on Tuesday, September 12th, received orders to advance. They came within easy range of the Tel-el-Kebir earthworks, and observed guns in front, guns to the right, guns to the left, and a living line of fire above them. Nothing daunted, the order, "action-front," was given, and was taken up joyously by every gun's crew. Round whisked the Gatlings, r-r-r-r-rum! r-r-r-r-rum! r-r-r-r-r-rum! that hellish noise the soldier so much detests in action, not for what it has done, so much as what it could do, rattled out. The report of the machine guns, as they rattle away, rings out clearly on the morning air. The parapets are swept. The embrasures are literally plugged with bullets. The flashes cease to come from them. With a cheer the blue jackets double over the dam, and dash over the parapet, only just in time to find their enemy in full retreat. That machine gun was too much for them. Skulking under the parapet were found a few poor devils, too frightened to retire, yet willing enough to stab a Christian, if helpless and wounded. The trenches were full of dead. But few wounded were found. Captain Fitz Roy led his men most gallantly, and followed up the retreating foe until the main camp was reached. Here the halt was sounded. Admiral Sir Beauchamp Seymour and staff now came up and addressed the battery, complimenting the officers and men on their gallantry.

Fort Royal. Earthwork at Port Said manned by seamen with Gatling gun.

Battle of El Teb. Naval brigade with Gatling and Gardner guns.

Both sides in Sudan campaign used Gatlings. This view, inside the rebel battery at El Teb, shows a Gatling (second from left), as well as Krupp guns. The Mahdists were well-equipped.

The British promptly followed up their victory at Tel-el-Kebir with an assault on Cairo, 65 miles away. On September 14, 1882, the Egyptian troops defending Cairo surrendered. Shortly thereafter, all Egyptian resistance ended and the British were in full control of the country.

In 1881, the Mahdists, followers of the self-proclaimed Mahdi (divine guide) of Islam, Mohammed Ahmed, revolted in the Sudan. The Mahdists scored impressive victories over the English and Egyptians at El Obeid in 1883 and at Khartoum in 1885. The famed English general, Charles George ("Chinese") Gordon, who had been governor-general of Sudan from 1877 to 1879, returned in 1884 to lead the fight against the Mahdist rebels. Besieged at Khartoum for ten months, General Gordon was killed on January 26, 1885, when the city was taken by the Mahdists. Just two days later, the relief expedition arrived from England. The fall of the Gladstone government in 1885 was largely due to public indignation at the Khartoum affair and the death of the popular hero, "Chinese" Gordon. Britain's campaigns in the Sudan lasted until 1898, when the power of the Mahdists finally was broken by the Anglo-Egyptian army commanded by Lord Kitchener.

As they did in nearly every war of the era, Gatlings played an important role in the Sudan campaigns. At the Battle of El Teb, February 29, 1884, these guns were used by both sides.

GATLING'S STEAM GUN

In 1883, Gatling invented a new type of gun to be operated by either steam or compressed air. This was patented February 10, 1885, as *Breech Loading Ordnance,* U. S. Patent No. 311,973. Designed for use with metallic cartridges and operated by steam or compressed-air power, this gun was expected to deliver a fairly high rate of fire for a single-shot piece.

After the cartridge was inserted in the chamber, the operator pulled the firing handle to the rear; causing steam or compressed air to enter the right port of the cylinder, moving the piston to the left and with it the breech block, closing the breech and firing the round. The firing handle was then pushed forward, sending steam or compressed air to the left cylinder port, opening the breech, ejecting the fired shell; the gun was then ready for the next round.

To facilitate loading this gun, Gatling subsequently invented a *Loading Device,* also patented February 10, 1885, U. S. Patent No. 311,974. Essentially, this device was a trough, serving as a cartridge guide, having a sliding follower with a lever-handle to seat the round in the chamber of the gun. Although intended primarily for use with fixed ammunition in connection with Gatling's breech-loading gun, described in the preceding paragraphs, this device also could be used in loading balls separate from the charge of powder.

THE GATLING GUN IN RIOTS

Time and again, during its long history, the Gatling Gun proved itself as a "super riot gun"—a little of its characteristic "music" or just the sight of its menacing, multiple muzzles, coupled with the gun's deadly reputation, usually was enough to discourage a mob. The first recorded instance of the employment of Gatling Guns was during the New York Draft Riots of 1863.

In July, 1877, during the Erie Railroad Strike, the Gatling Gun Detachment of the 23rd Regiment, from Brooklyn, played an important role in subduing a mob of some 2,000 strikers at Hornellsville, New York.

As related in the following newspaper accounts, British forces used Gatlings in the Port Said Riot of April 29, 1883.

> Disturbances broke out at Port Said yesterday, between the Greek and Arab populations, on account of the religious ceremonies on the occasion of the Greek Easter. In the rioting which ensued, several Greeks and Arabs were killed and wounded, as well as some members of the Egyptian police who had intervened to restore order. British troops and sailors from H.M. gunboat Falcon, with Gatling Guns, surrounded the Greek church to protect it from injury. The Greek Consul took refuge on board the Falcon. The disturbances have been quelled, but the excitement has not yet subsided.—*London Daily News*, April 30, 1883.
>
> We see by the cable dispatches, that on the 29th of April, at Port Said, on the Suez Canal, a serious riot occurred between the Greeks and Arabs on account of some religious ceremonies. Several were killed and many wounded. The riot was quelled by the landing of the British troops and sailors with Gatling Guns. It is said this alone saved the European residents from general massacre. This gun is a wonderful "peacemaker" in such cases. It will be recollected that the great "Kearney riots," that threatened to be so serious in San Francisco, were quelled by the presence of the police with a Gatling.—*Daily Intelligencer*, Belleville (Canada), May 8, 1883.

GATLING MODELS OF 1883-1887

The success of the bronze-encased Model 1877 Bulldog Gatling naturally led to the incorporation of a number of its features in subsequent models. Like the Bulldog, the Model 1883 did not have the exposed barrels and steel frame typical of most earlier Gatlings, but was enclosed from muzzles to cascabel plate in a tubular jacket of bronze, giving the appearance of a cannon.

In the Model 1883, the main shaft or barrel axle extended rearward through both cascabel plate and knob. Ordinarily, a side-mounted crank was used in firing the gun; operating through gears with a reduced ratio, this drive produced a rate of fire of approximately 800 rounds per minute. For very rapid firing, the crank could be detached from its side shaft and fitted directly to the protruding rear end of the main shaft, as in the Bulldog Model. With the rear-mounted crank, the Model 1883 was capable of a cyclic rate as high as *1,500* rounds per minute. Each complete turn of the crank fired a sequence of ten shots.

To stand up under the punishment of extreme rapid fire, the internal components of the Gatling Gun were beefed up considerably in the Model 1883. Because of the bulky Accles feed mechanism employed in this model, the breech bolts were nearly double the length of those found in earlier guns of the same caliber; firing pins rebounded after firing. Strong spring extractors grabbed more of the cartridge rim than did previous types, giving more positive extraction.

The cam cylinder or internal cocking cam ring, which caused the breech bolts to move back and forth as the barrel unit revolved, was modified to

Model 1883 Gatling with Accles feed, mounted on light, folding, steel tripod.

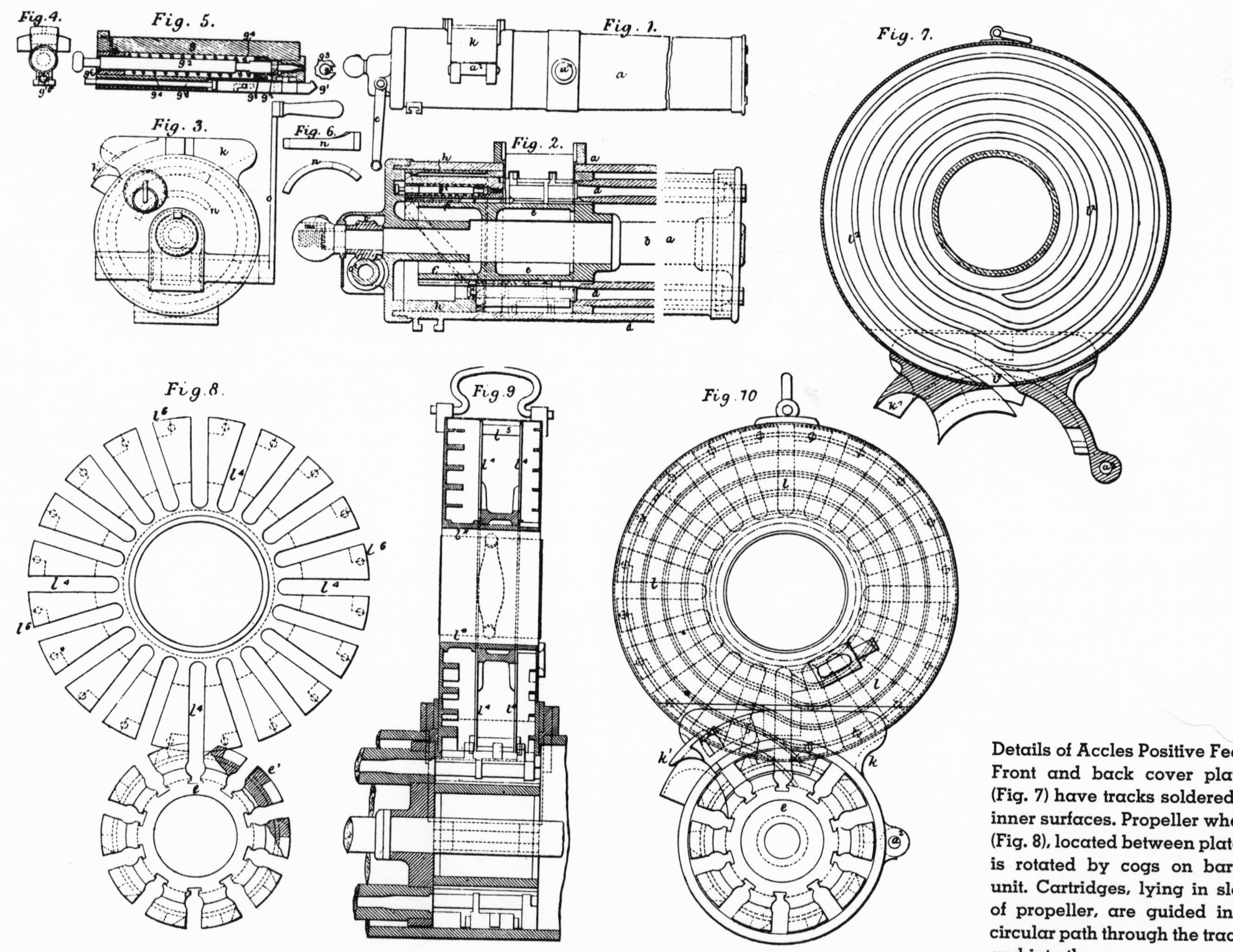

Details of Accles Positive Feed. Front and back cover plates (Fig. 7) have tracks soldered to inner surfaces. Propeller wheel (Fig. 8), located between plates, is rotated by cogs on barrel unit. Cartridges, lying in slots of propeller, are guided in a circular path through the tracks and into the gun.

include a cocking switch for disengaging the cocking mechanism. This allowed the barrel to be revolved without snapping the firing pins. It saved parts from unnecessary wear and possible breakage during "dry run" training exercises and functioned as a "safety" when the gun was being cleared of live rounds. Cocking switch control knob was located on the lower right side of the breech casing, midway between crank and trunnion. When the arrow on this knob pointed forward, the piece was ready to fire; when it pointed to the rear, the firing pins were inoperative.

By 1883, the official .45/70 Government cartridge was being loaded with both 405 and 500 grain bullets, with different ballistics. So that either load could be used without sight correction, the Model 1883 had two sets of sights: for 405-grain on the left side, for 500-grain on the right. Two spirit levels, respectively lengthwise and crosswise on the breech casing, enabled the gunner to set up his gun with its carriage leveled.

The Model 1883 Gatling had a unique yoke and pointing bar system that afforded it great flexibility. The bronze yoke, in which the gun was suspended, provided traverse of 50°, while an arc, attached to the underside of the gun and passing through the yoke, allowed the piece to be elevated through 74° or depressed through 78°. There was no oscillator on this model. The gunner directed the fire with a long pointing bar fastened to the bottom of the breech casing. Locking stops on the yoke and arc allowed elevation and traverse to be set in fixed positions. In operation, the gunner held the pointing bar under his left arm and thus could swing the gun up, down, right, left, at will.

Obviously, a gun with such an extreme range of elevation adjustment could not satisfactorily employ a gravity-fed cartridge loading system. Accordingly, the Model 1883 was equipped with a mechanical drum feed invented by James Accles.* Looking like a flat-sided doughnut, the Accles Positive Feed held 104 rounds. The drum was hollow and its front-to-back dimension was only slightly more than the length of a .45/70 round. Soldered to the inside of the front and back plates were spiral guide ribs and, rotating within the drum, was a cartridge propeller with a number of radial slots in which the cartridges lay. A series of lugs or fingers on the revolving carrier block of the gun engaged the rim of the propeller, providing the force needed to operate the feed. As the propeller rotated, cartridges followed the guide ribs and were fed into the gun.

Loading the Accles feed was a tedious job, made difficult because the drum's only opening was a small port through which the cartridges had to be inserted one at a time. In 1886, James Accles patented a much-needed loading device to facilitate

Model 1883 Gatling, with Accles feed, showing extreme depression at which gun could be fired.

Model 1883 Gatling mounted on lightweight metal field carriage.

* "The Accles 'positive feed,' not depending on gravity, could be worked from the side of a Gatling gun as well as from the top. Gatlings with the feed working from the side were made for the caponnières of the new Danish forts at Copenhagen. The guns had to be mounted in a confined space under a low roof, and there would not have been room for a top feed."—Longstaff and Atteridge, *The Book of the Machine Gun* (London: Hugh Rees, Ltd., 1917), p. 115.

Model 1883 Gatling on U.S. Army pattern metal carriage.

refilling the drums. The top of the loader worked like a Bruce feed: the cartridges were stripped into it from the 20-round cardboard boxes in which they were packaged, and a rotating feeder inserted the cartridges into the drum.

Although it was uniquely adapted to extreme high and low angle firing, the Accles Positive Feed proved unsuited to the rigors of military use. Its rather complex mechanism was easily deranged and difficult to repair. Unless kept absolutely clean —a virtual impossibility in the field—the cartridge propeller would not revolve freely, resulting in jamming. Even a slight dent in the fairly thin metal of the drum could render the feed—and perhaps the gun—*hors de combat* at a critical moment. Because of complaints on the Accles Positive Feed, L. F. Bruce in 1886 devised an adapter which, when inserted into the hopper of a Model 1883 Gatling, permitted use of the "more positive" Bruce feed. In 1898, the U.S. Government fitted all of its Model 1883 guns with Bruce feed adapters and retired the Accles feed from active service.

While all Model 1883 Gatlings had the same type of yoke, these guns were furnished with a variety of mounts.

The standard mount of the Model 1883 was an army carriage of heavy steel construction with fittings of solid bronze. Wheels were of the Archibald pattern with bronze hubs and replaceable spokes. Attached to the top of the trail was a folding seat for the gunner. Fastened to the axle, on either side of the gun, were two wood-lined metal chests, which together held four Accles drums, as well as parts and tools. Since the feeds were easily damaged, each pair was separated in the chest by a heavy wooden partition. Recesses were provided in the partitions to contain various tools and components of the gun. The left chest held a cam sleeve extractor, riveting hammer, oil can, wrench, and the left side sight; the right chest contained a crank handle, pin drift, breech bolt dismantling tool, wrench, and the right side sight.

Model 1883 Gatling on tricycle carriage. Small wheel folded to permit extreme high-angle firing.

Gatling Gun in China. Wheelbarrow mount for transporting Gatling over China's poor roads and rugged mountain trails. A similar mount was offered for the Accles machine gun of a decade later.

Each such carriage had a limber, also made of steel. The inside of the limber chest was divided into three compartments; the center one held four Accles feeds and 38 boxes of cartridges, while each of the side compartments contained 132 twenty-round boxes of ammunition. Thus, between the chests on the carriage and that of the limber, a total of 6,872 cartridges could be carried with the gun: 832 rounds in the drums ready to fire and the rest in boxes.

In addition to the metal carriages, Watervliet Arsenal manufactured a number of heavy, wooden carriages for the Model 1883 Gatling. This type also had two chests on the carriage axle; the right-hand chest was hinged so that it could swing forward out of the way of the crank. One chest held boxed ammunition, the other Accles feeds.

Model 1883 Gatlings in the U.S. Navy use generally were mounted on cones, usually on the ship's bridge. Others were placed on the rail of the fighting top and used to rake the enemy's decks from above. A few were provided with light, wheeled carriages for use in landings.

Bronze-encased from muzzles to cascabel plate, the Model 1883 Gatling Gun had ten barrels, 32 inches long and chambered for the .45/70 Government cartridge. The gun, without mount, weighed about 260 pounds, measured 52 inches overall; steel carriage weighed 594 pounds, the limber 754 pounds. Gatling Gun Company markings were elaborately engraved on the bronze jacket, near the breech, while those of Colt's appeared on the casing at the trunnions.

Models of 1885, 1886, and 1887 were modifications of the Model 1883, differing chiefly in improvements in the ejector and shell guide (a device to keep fired cases from getting stuck inside the breech casing).

Quite a number of the 1883-1887 series of Gatling Guns were bought by the U.S. Government. The U.S. Navy found that the protective bronze jacket of this model made it especially well adapted to sea duty. The following guns were purchased by the U.S. Army: Model 1883—serial No. 342-381; Model 1885—No. 405-425; Model 1886—No. 431-450; Model 1887—No. 457-476.

Disassembly procedure for Gatling Models of 1883-1887:

1. Remove hinge pin and take off hopper.

2. Remove lock plug and take out breech bolts.

3. Remove the cascabel knob by pressing in on the catch and turning the knob to the left.

4. Remove the lower gear cover. Pull out the crank shaft split pin and remove washer from end of shaft. Hold one hand under the gear housing and draw out crank shaft to right; worm gear will fall into hand.

5. Take off the cascabel plate. To do this, first set the cocking switch in firing position (arrow pointing forward). Remove cascabel plate screws. Remove cascabel plate by turning it to the left until arrows on plate and breech casing are aligned, and pull the plate off to the rear.

6. Pull the cocking switch outward, turning it to the right until it snaps in notch, arrow pointing downward. Take out lock cam or camming sleeve.

7. Remove three-fingered shell guide.

8. Slide the barrel unit forward until it projects about 3 inches out of the front of the bronze barrel housing. With a drift, drive out the pin holding the muzzle plate to the main barrel shaft. Remove the muzzle plate.

9. Pull the barrel unit rearward out of the barrel casing.

TRIALS IN ITALY AND AUSTRIA

The introduction of the Model 1883 Gatling produced great interest abroad, as well as in the United States. On October 10, 1883, the Italian Government held a trial of this gun at Turin. The Gatling was tried in competition with a number of other machine guns of the period, notably the Hotchkiss, Nordenfeldt, Gardner, Pratt & Whitney, and the Montigny Mitrailleuse. Targets were fired at ranges varying from 500 to 1,800 meters. As an indication of the general results of the trial, these scores should be noted: at 1,800 meters, 100 shots were fired by each of the guns—the Gardner made one hit, the Pratt & Whitney none, the Nordenfeldt none, while the Gatling scored 20 hits. During the portion of the trials which tested the rates of fire of the various guns involved, the Gatling fired a remarkable 100 shots in a mere 3¼ seconds. This was done with the gun elevated to 70°, an angle at which many of the other entrants would not even function.

The Austro-Hungarian Government was among those nations which purchased an 1883 Gatling for test purposes. Late in 1883, Gatling's Vienna representative submitted a gun to the Austrians. Trials were held to determine the accuracy, rate of fire, and general mechanical dependability of the gun. As an added test, the Gatling Gun Company demonstrators operated the gun for only part of the testing; Austrian artillerymen served the gun during the remainder of the trial. While the Gatling Gun made an excellent showing in these Austrian trials, it was never adopted by that government.

THE RIEL REBELLION

In 1869, when the Hudson's Bay Company territory was transferred to Canada, many of the Métis * and Indians of the Red River settlement felt that their land and other rights had been violated. They found a leader for their revolt in Louis Riel, himself the son of French and half-breed parents. Riel led the insurgents in forming a provisional government, which he headed. With the arrival at rebel-held Fort Garry, in 1870, of a substantial force of British and Canadian troops under the command of Col. Garnet Wolseley, the Red River Rebellion collapsed and Louis Riel fled the country.

Fourteen years later, the fanatic Riel—who had, in the interim, acquired something of a messiah complex and had spent several years in insane asylums—was summoned back by his Métis to lead them and a group of disgruntled Indians in an effort to secure titles to their lands. The ensuing Second Riel Rebellion was brought to an end with the defeat of the Métis and Indians at Batoche in May 1885. Louis Riel was captured, tried, and convicted of treason; he was hanged November 16, 1885.

As will be seen from the following reports, a Gatling Gun played an important role in the victory at Batoche.

RIEL REBELLION—A Hartford dispatch of April 2 reports that four Gatling guns and 5,000 rounds of ammunition were that day shipped to Winnipeg to be used against the insurgents. Lieut. A. L. Howard, of New Haven, commanding the Gatling gun platoon, 2nd Connecticut National Guard, has been commissioned by the Canadian Government to man the guns. *Army & Naval Journal,* April 4, 1885.

THE STORMING OF BATOCHE, Winnipeg, May 13. . . . The rebels had been pushed back by the continued and systematic use of four 9-pounder muzzle loading rifled Woolwich field guns supported by one Gatling gun under Capt. Howard who, it is said, is an American officer. This gentleman brought two of these guns to Canada by order of the Canadian government and took one to General Middleton's brigade to show how it should be used. His bravery and conduct through the continued rifle fire day by day has been highly praised and it appears a wonder how he escaped.—*Army & Navy Journal,* May 23, 1885.

THE REIL REBELLION IN CANADA—In the Riel Rebellion in the North West Provinces, it is well known that the opportune use of the Gatling Gun in the battle of Batouche, turned defeat into victory and ended the campaign, thereby saving millions of dollars for the Dominion Government.—*The Gatling Guns, For Service Ashore and Afloat.*

The following excerpts from newspaper articles are quoted from the same booklet.

New York Herald, May 11th, 1885. The Grenadiers advanced, skirmishing through the bush, on the right of the trail, the Gatling Gun being pushed forward down a declivity, toward Batouche, now plainly visible in the valley below. Here "A" Battery unlimbered on top of a ridge, sending shells into the enemy, and while doing so were surprised by a number of rebels, who crept up through the bush, not being discovered until twenty yards distant. They made a dash for our guns, firing and yelling as they ran. Captain Howard, who operated the Gatling, saw the danger, and, with cool daring, ran his gun a couple of yards in front of the battery, and, opening fire, literally mowed the rebels down. In dismay, those who were not killed, turned and fled like deer, making for the bush.

Correspondence of the Toronto Mail, May 1885. "The rebels suddenly rose from the ravine right in front of us and opened fire. The guns were ordered to the rear, and the Gatling which Howard had been working so well, rained down a fusilade; but our position was too high, and the bullets flew over the ravine, and did no harm. This was ticklish moment, and our men were thrown into some disorder. Howard, however, worked like a Trojan in the thick of it and kept the rebels from charging us. We should have lost many lives, and probably our guns, but for the Gatling. * * * * Some rebels with rifles on the other side of the river also took a hand in, but the Gatling silenced them * * * * Captain Howard was loudly cheered. His Gatling save us from disaster."

Among the records of the Gatling Gun Company was found a manuscript entitled "The War Record of the Gatling Gun," which appears to be in the handwriting of Frederick W. Prince, Secretary of the company circa 1900 when, it is believed, this article was written for use in a promotional brochure. Regarding the 1885 insurrection in Western Canada and its hero, Arthur L. Howard, it states: "In the Riel Rebellion, N. W. Canada, the Gatling Guns with Maj. Gen. Middleton's force, in charge of Capt. Howard (formerly of 2d. Conn. Machine Gun Platoon), did fine service. . . . Capt. Howard was killed in South Africa while serving with the Canadian contingent." [probably in the Boer War, 1899-1900]

GATLING MODELS OF 1889-1892

The bronze-encased Model 1883 Gatling Gun was costly to produce and its complex Accles Positive

* Also called Boisbrûlés (French, "burnt wood") for their dark complexions, these people were the part-Indian descendants of the early French fur traders of N.W. Canada.

Feed had proved troublesome in field service. In 1889, Gatling returned to the well-proved classic design with exposed barrels and steel frame. Essentially, the Model 1889 was an improved version of the Model 1881 gun. Improvements included a device called the "Murphy stop" (a cocking switch) and a new type of carriage. Its hopper accepted, interchangeably, a special Bruce feed or the old-style gravity-feed magazine.

Like the Model 1883 cocking switch, the Murphy stop allowed the gunner to disengage the cocking mechanism while unloading the gun and during training exercises without ammunition. The control knob was located, more conveniently, on the cascabel plate, and operation was more positive, since the knob had to be pulled out as well as turned.

This gun was mounted in a yoke similar to that of the Model 1881, but, instead of having the turntable used with wooden carriages, the yoke base had a stem that fitted a socket in the axle of the carriage. It was equipped with a pointing bar and a binder box for rapid changes in adjustment.

The carriage was made entirely of metal, except for the wooden spokes and rims of its iron-tired, bronze-hubbed, Archibald pattern wheels. There was no axle in the usual sense, but a hollow box beam of iron with a spindle at each to which wheels were fitted. The trail, too, was an iron box beam, reinforced by angle irons. Compartments in the axle beam and trail provided storage space for ammunition, etc. Cover of the lower of the two trail compartments could be raised and locked in position to form a seat for the gunner. Hinged to the end of the trail was a folding handspike of steel, used in maneuvering the carriage into position. In most earlier models (exceptions were a few 1883 carriages), the handspike was wooden and detachable—easily broken or lost.

Previously, no protection was provided for the gunner who, in his exposed position at the crank, was vulnerable to enemy small arms fire. The Model 1889 carriage remedied this situation, being fitted with a set of shields of heavy steel to give the much-needed cover. An upper shield, mounted on top of the axle beam, had a port for the gun; this opening was of size and shape to permit traverse and elevation within the limits of the yoke. To guard against enemy fire being directed at the gunner through the the port, the main shield was fitted with two disc shields, pivoted at the centers and moving with the gun; while this arrangement served the purpose for which it was intended, it also tended to interfere with proper sighting. An apron-like, lower shield, hinged to the bottom of the axle beam, protected the gunner's legs; while the gun was in transit, the lower shield could be folded back and hooked up, out of the way, on the underside of the trail.

A limber, with a steel frame and wooden ammunition chest, was issued with the Model 1889 carriage.

The Model 1889 Gatling, caliber .45/70 Government, had ten exposed barrels, 32 inches long. Overall length of the gun was 49 inches and it weighed 200 pounds, without carriage. The bronze breech housing was engraved with both Colt and Gatling markings. There was one set of sights, mounted on the right side of the gun. Rate of fire was 525 rounds per minute. Models of 1891 and 1892 were essentially identical to the 1889 Gatling.

The U.S. Army purchased 18 Model 1889 (serial No. 492-509), 17 Model 1891 (No. 510-527), and 18 Model 1892 (No. 530-547). These were the last .45/70 Gatling Guns ordered by the U.S. Government.

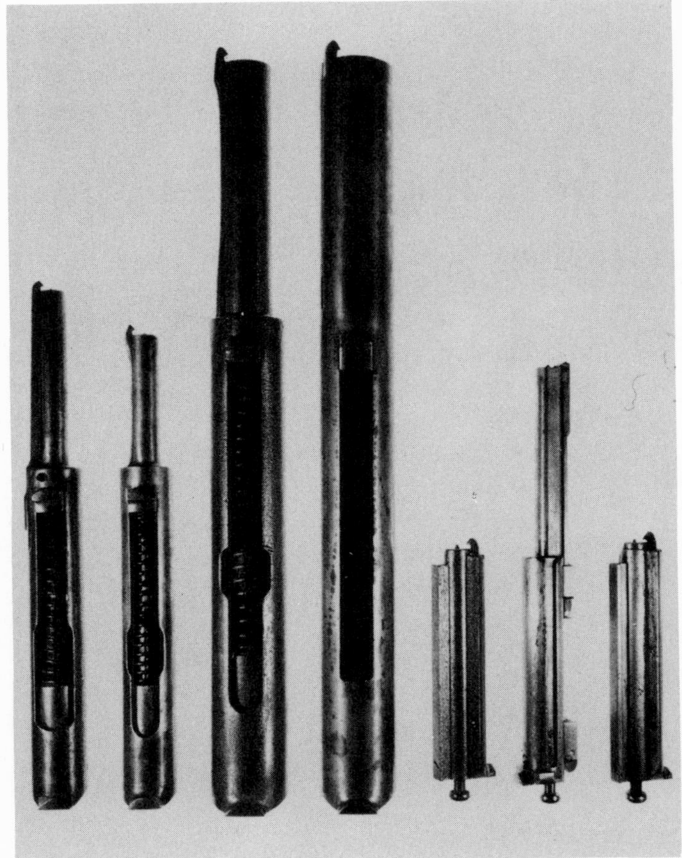

Evolution of the Gatling breech bolt: (left to right) Model 1865, .50 cal.; Model 1871, .50 cal.; Model 1865, 1″ cal.; Model 1871, 1″ cal.; Model 1874, .45-70 cal.; Model 1883, .45-70 cal.; Model 1893, .30-40 cal.

PRICE LIST

OF THE

GATLING GUN COMPANY.

GATLING GUNS.

(STRAIGHT FEED.)

1.00-inch caliber, ten barrels, . . .	$1,800.00
1.00 " " six " . .	1,600.00
.75, .65, and .55 caliber, ten long barrels,	1,600.00
Musket caliber (.50, .45, .43, .42, &c.), ten long barrels, ...	1,000.00
Musket caliber, ten short barrels, . .	850.00
Musket " five " " . .	750.00

(POSITIVE OR ACCLES' FEED.)

Musket caliber, ten long barrels and four feed magazines, ...	1,400.00
Musket caliber, six short barrels and four feed magazines, ...	1,000.00

GUN CARRIAGES, FEED CASES, ETC.

Carriage and Limber for Positive Feed Gun,	$400.00
Carriage and Limber for all other Guns,	300.00
Navy Carriage of steel, iron, and brass (no Limber required), ...	300.00
Tripod, ...	125.00
Pack Saddle, ...	110.00
Fixture for mounting Gun on gunwale of ship (not required when Navy Carriages are ordered), ...	100.00
Bed Plate for gunwale of ship, . . .	6.00
Straight Feed Cases, .55-inch caliber and larger, ...	2.80
Straight Feed Cases, .50-inch caliber and smaller, ...	2.25
Feed Magazines, ...	40.00

AMMUNITION.

1.00-inch caliber Cartridges, per thousand,	$200.00
.75 " " " " "	180.00
.65 " " " " "	170.00
.55 " " " " "	160.00
Musket " " " "	22.00

Cartridge shells of all sizes can be re-loaded and used fifty times and upwards.

The prices of Cartridges are subject to change without notice.

PACKING.

Guns of .55-inch caliber and larger, . .	$17.00
Guns of .50-inch caliber and smaller, . .	9.00
Carriage and Limber for Gun of 55-inch caliber and larger, ...	25.00
Carriage and Limber for Musket caliber Gun,	20.00
Tripods, ...	3.00

The Guns are packed in tin-lined boxes, and the packing-boxes for the Carriages and Limbers are hooped.

The above prices are in United States currency, and payment is required in all cases upon rendering the invoice.

All deliveries are made on cars or boat at Hartford, but if desired we will attend to placing the goods on board ship at New York, charging the actual cost therefor.

ALL PREVIOUS PRICES ARE HEREBY REVOKED.

Address,

THE GATLING GUN COMPANY,

HARTFORD, CONNECTICUT,

UNITED STATES OF AMERICA.

HARTFORD, Sept. 1, 1886.

THE LATTER YEARS OF THE GATLING GUN COMPANY

Among those listed as stockholders of the Gatling Gun Company, April 27, 1888, was Daniel Baird Wesson, whose shares amounted to 6 percent. Wesson was the famed American arms inventor and manufacturer, partner of Horace Smith in the Smith & Wesson Company, of Springfield, Massachusetts. At this time, D. B. Wesson was 63 years of age and a veteran of some 35 years in the gun business. The same report indicates that Richard Jordan Gatling, in the Spring of 1888, owned 10 percent of the company that bore his name.

On April 20, 1888, Frederick C. Penfield, of London, acquired from the Gatling Gun Company all of its European patent rights for the sum of $100,000. He also bought Gatling Gun Ltd., the European subsidiary—incorporated April 4, 1888—for $50,000. Terms of sale provided that Gatling Gun Ltd. would pay to Gatling Gun Company, of Hartford, Connecticut a royalty of $100 for every gun sold by the former in the Western Hemisphere. According to records of Gatling Gun Company, this agreement was violated in 1889 when Gatling Gun Ltd. sold guns to Chile without payment of the stipulated royalty. It is believed that the Gatlings sold to the Chilean Navy included eight guns aboard the French-built Chilean ram, *Don Arturo Prat.*

Gatling Gun Ltd. was liquidated late in 1890. Its successors were Grenfell & Accles Ltd., a firm in which J. G. Accles, a long-time associate of Gatling, was a partner. This firm manufactured a Gatling type gun at Holford Works, Parry Barr, Birmingham, England.

Penfield eventually sold the European Gatling patents to Continental interests. The Gatling firm had held a great many patents granted by Austria, Belgium, England, France, Italy, etc.; many were in the names of inventors who had patented some Gatling Gun improvement or accessory and made assignment to Gatling or his company. Because it was not uncommon for European nations to levy periodic taxes on patents, these were quite costly to maintain.

About 1890, the Gatling Arms & Ammunition Co., Ltd., was organized in Birmingham, England. It is presumed that this company sold and serviced Gatling Guns, as well as other firearms. The Toppel Collection once included a Gatling handgun—a Dimancea Revolver of the type Kynoch furnished Romania during World War I, this piece was stamped on the barrel rib "Gatling Arms & Ammn. Co. Ltd. Birmingham—Dimancea Patent." A letter, dated January 10, 1891, in the Gatling Gun Company files, indicates that the firm was awarded a judgment against Gatling Arms & Ammunition Co., Ltd., but does not reveal the nature of the litigation or other information.

As the nineteenth century drew nearer to its end, the intercompany relationship between Gatling Gun Company and Colt's Patent Fire Arms Mfg. Co. grew ever closer. While the Gatling Gun Company letterhead used in 1896 lists R. J. Gatling as president of the firm, the company was reorganized in 1897 with Colt executives John H. Hall and Lewis C. Grover in the offices of president and vice president respectively. In a letter dated December 14, 1897, Col. A. Mordecai advised the Chief of Ordnance that, following the reorganization of the Gatling Gun Company that year, it and Colt's Patent Fire Arms Mfg. Co. had become practically one. John H. Hall, who became president of Colt's in 1901, appears to have served also as president of Gatling until 1902, when Lewis C. Grover succeeded him in both posts. Grover was president of Colt's and, presumably, of Gatling Gun Company until 1909. Thus, it seems that, for several years prior to Gatling's death in 1903, the company which bore his name had been completely absorbed by Colt's Patent Fire Arms Mfg. Co.

THE ELECTRIFIED GATLING

On the front page of the November 15, 1890, issue of *Scientific American,* there appeared an illustration captioned "Firing Gatling Guns by Electricity" together with the following article:

ELECTRICALLY-FIRED GATLING GUN

We illustrate in the present issue a new application of the electric motor, in which it is caused to operate a Gatling gun. This well known type of mitrailleuse has been placed on many of the U.S. naval vessels, and represents a very powerful weapon for repelling attacks and for general fighting work at close quarters.

Hitherto the Gatling gun has not been automatic. The loading is effected by turning a crank attached to the breech mechanism of the piece. As this causes the barrels to rotate, they are discharged one at a time. Ten barrels are comprised in the piece, so that for each revolution ten shots are delivered. While one man turns the crank, a second man holding the tail stock or lever may be employed in directing and aiming the piece, if continual change of direction is needed. While this character of manipulation is often required, and is that by which rapid-firing guns should perform the greatest execution, it has attendant difficulties. The turning

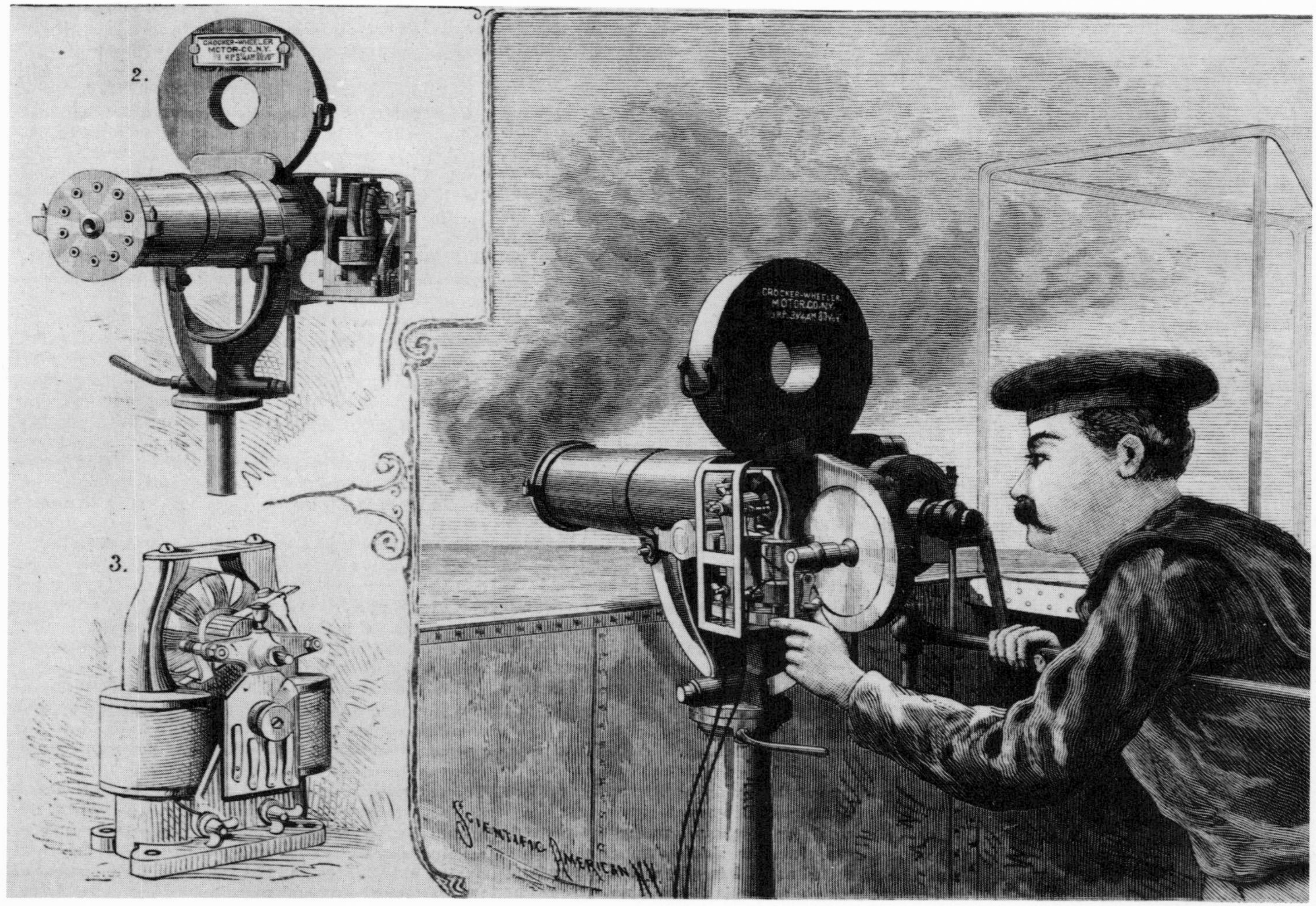

Firing the Gatling Gun by electricity: (1) gun in operation; (2) gun with electrical attachment; (3) Crocker-Wheeler motor.

of the crank inevitably causes the piece to oscillate and adds a second disturbing element to the vibration due to the recoil.

The Crocker-Wheeler Motor Company, of this city [New York], were invited by the U.S. Navy Department to arrange an electric firing mechanism for the Gatling gun. Several requirements had to be kept in mind in producing the design. The apparatus had to be attached to the barrel of the gun so as to move with it. It had to be out of the sighting line, and it was necessary to dispose of it so as not to interfere with elevation or depression of the gun. The motor finally had to be adapted for operation by the electric lighting plants as installed upon the ships of war. The drawings show clearly how the problem has been attacked.

Upon the left hand side of the breech of the gun an open frame of generally rectangular outline is secured. Within it is placed the motor. This is a specially wound motor, adapted for an electromotive force of 80 volts, and a current of 3 to 3½ amperes intensity. This, it will be seen, represents the absortion of a little over ⅓ electric horse power. The efficiency of the motor is placed at over 80 per cent. The spindle of the armature, which in general terms runs horizontally and at right angles to the axis of the gun, carries a pinion which engages a large gear wheel. The latter is inclosed in the cylindrical or disk-like case which is seen next to the motor by the side of the breech. The spindle of the large gear wheel is prolonged across the end of the gun barrel, and carries a worm at its end. This gears into a worm wheel on the working spindle of the gun.

This double reduction of speed causes the operation of the gun at about 150 revolutions per minute, giving 1,500 discharges. This rate is rather high for general practice and can be considerably reduced.

A small switch is provided for turning the current on and off. The artillerist, after starting the motor, is free to swing the piece in any direction. This he can do without interference from a second operator and the gun is undisturbed by the shaking due to the turning of the crank.

Between the motor and the large gear wheel is a clutch by which the motor can be connected or disconnected from the breech mechanism. The crank by which the piece is worked by hand under the former conditions is arranged for rapid disconnection or reconnection. This provides for injury to the electric apparatus. If the latter becomes disabled or if its connections are severed, the clutch can be thrown open and the handle connected, when the gun will be ready for operation by hand. This change takes only a few seconds. This application of electricity is of special interest as bringing the Gatling gun into the rank of automatically fired artillery.

THE POLICE GATLING

Use of machine guns in police work usually is associated with the famed "Tommy Gun"—Thompson Submachine Gun—of the Roaring Twenties, for many years manufactured by Colt's Patent Fire Arms Manufacturing Company for the Auto-Ordnance Corporation of America. Colt's also produced the first police machine gun almost 30 years earlier. This "Police Gatling" is described in the promotional booklet, *The Gatling Guns, For Service Ashore and Afloat,** published in England circa 1892:

> The most recent of the series of Gatling Guns is the Police Gatling, designed to fill the place in local troubles that the larger guns fill upon the field of war. For the clearing of mobs from streets, for use in revolts in penitentiaries, for the protection of buildings containing great amounts of money or other property, and for many similar emergencies, this little gun is a terrible engine of defence and destruction. It occupies a space only twenty inches long and six inches wide—a lilliputian battery, the little steel barrel of which, only a foot long, will land a bullet into a target at 1,000 yards and will

* This anonymous and undated publication is not to be confused with the earlier work of the same title, written by General Franklin of Colt's and published in 1874.

Gatling gun for police-patrol service.

Dr. Gatling with Model 1893 Bulldog.

kill a man a mile distant with its ounce missile and musket charge of seventy grains of powder. For police use in suppressing riots one or more of these guns may be placed in a police waggon mounted on pintles permanently attached to the waggon body. Or for use without any vehicle the gun, which weighs only seventy-eight pounds, may be carried by a strong man, a forty-pound tripod on which to mount it by another, while a third carries the ammunition. These three men with their little Gatling would have all the destructive force of a company of soldiers, for the gun with its latest improvements in lock and feed mechanism will discharge 900 shots per minute. Had these guns been available in some of the recent riots in America and England they would have saved in property losses their cost a thousand times over. One excellent feature is that all parts are interchangeable, so that if anything is broken the damaged parts may be supplied without any delay. It is believed that the Police Gatling will come into general use all over the world.

In 1892, *Scientific American,* for March 19, carried a front-page story, "The Gatling Gun for Police Patrol Service," with a half-page illustration made from a photograph of a Hartford (Conn.) Police Department patrol wagon mounted with a "Police Gatling." This article states:

The latest model of the Gatling gun, shown in the accompanying illustration, has been given the name of the "Police gun," from its admirable adaptation for police or mounted service, for guarding railway trains, banks, or safe deposit institutions, or for use on vessels, yachts or boats. Its weight is but 74 pounds, so that it can be carried if necessary by a single man, or, with all accessories for the field, on a single animal. It has six barrels, and the feed is positive, enabling it to be fired at the rate of 800 shots per minute at all angles of elevation and depression. When set up in the back part of a patrol wagon, and served by two or three men, it is designed to do more effective work in dealing with a mob or in dispersing rioters than could be accomplished by a whole company of infantry. In the patrol wagon is also carried a supply of ammunition, and a tripod on which the gun may be mounted for service out of the wagon.

The gun, in the "Police Patrol" picture, is said to have been given to the Hartford Police Department during the late '80's or early '90's. In 1893, Gatling posed for a photograph with a gun of this type. If the opinion of some gun experts is correct, only a few Police Gatlings were made.

GATLING MODELS OF 1893

Most of the differences between the Model 1893 Gatling and the types of 1889-1892 were slight: breech bolts were longer and the angles of the camming groove inside the breech casing were modified to speed up the action of the bolts; frame, main shaft, breech casing, and carrier block, all were lengthened slightly. Unlike its more immediate predecessors, which were .45/70 caliber, the Model 1893 was chambered for the recently adopted .30 U.S. Government (.30/40 Krag) cartridge, and a new feed was developed to handle it in this gun.

On September 5, 1893, C. M. Broderick and John Vankeirsbilck (assignors to the Gatling Gun Company) were granted U.S. Patent No. 504,516 for their strip feed. Stamped from sheet-metal, the feed strip had a series of V-shaped tabs cut in it and bent to form circular prongs to hold the cartridges. Construction of the strip was such that it could be inserted into the gun in only one way. The loaded strip entered a feed port on the left side of the hopper; as it passed through, a wedge inside the hopper stripped each round from its retaining prongs and allowed it to drop into a groove in the carrier block, from which the breech bolt pushed the cartridge forward into the chamber; the empty feed strip was ejected out of the right side of the hopper.

Although they could be reloaded, the feed strips were cheap to manufacture and might be considered as disposable. Much lighter and less bulky than any other Gatling feed, use of this system made possible carrying more ammunition in the same space. The strip feed had one—fatal—drawback: the strips regularly jammed in the guns. Ironically, the Gatling Gun Company had named this system its "Positive Feed"—another so-named, the Accles drum, also had proved unsatisfactory in service.

On June 19, 1893, the U.S. Ordnance Department, by Capt. Charles Shaler, Acting Chief, awarded the Gatling Gun Company a contract for 18 long ten-barreled Gatling Guns, U.S. Cal. .30, with positive feed, spare parts, 200 tin feed strips each, etc., at a unit price of $1,100, to be delivered by December 31, 1893. Apparently, the Ordnance Department was not completely sold on the new strip feed standard on the Model 1893—a clause in this contract provided that, at the option of the U.S. Government, the Gatling Gun Company would later convert these guns to the Bruce feed at $200 each. The strip feed proved unsatisfactory and, in 1897, Brig. Gen. D. W. Flagler, Chief of Ordnance, ordered all eighteen converted to Bruce feed. Serial numbers of these guns: 1001-1018.

At the time of the conversion of the Model 1893 Gatlings to Bruce feed, the headspace adjustment also was modified. Originally, headspace in this model was adjusted by screwing the cascabel knob

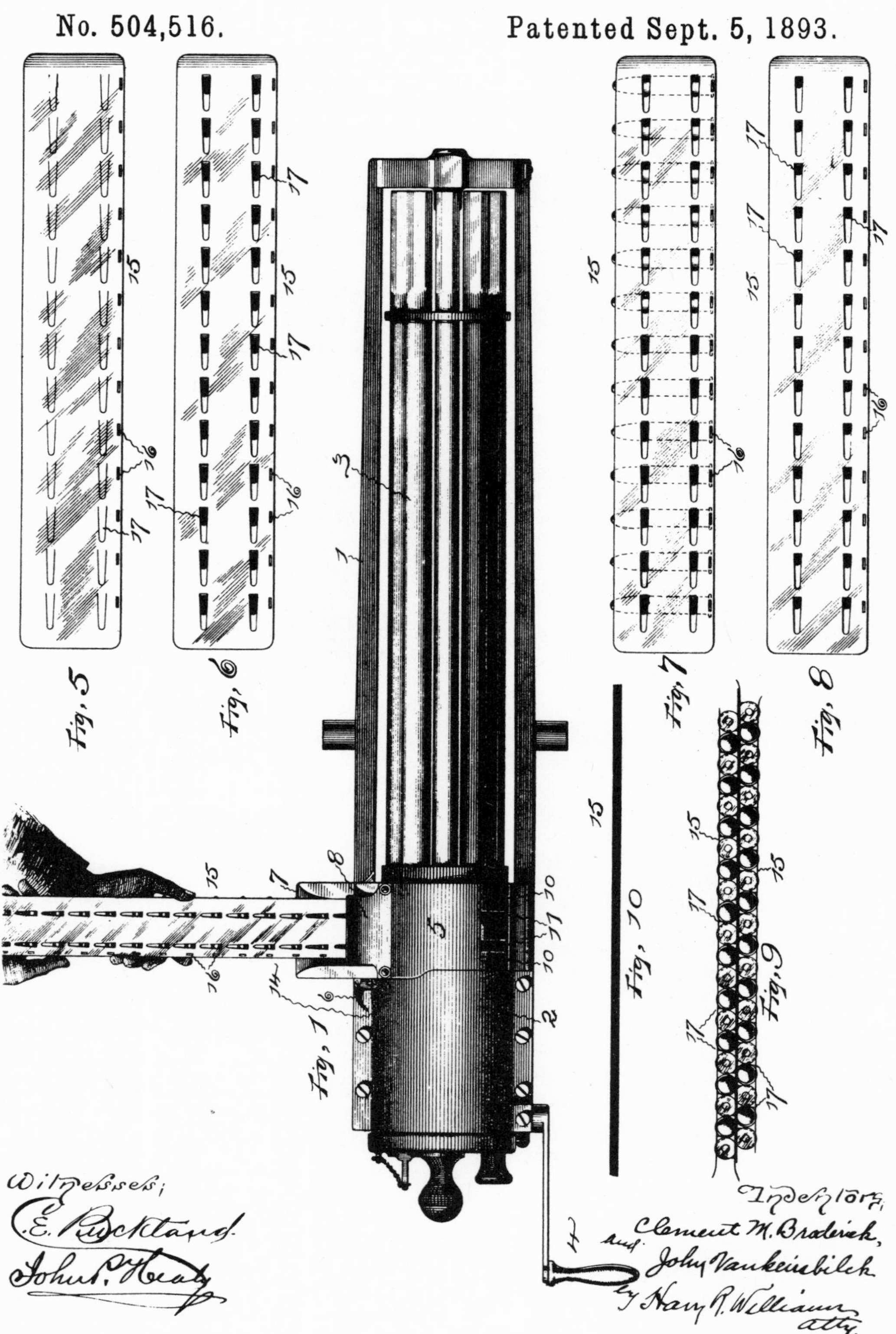

(No Model.)
2 Sheets—Sheet 1.
C. M. BRODERICK & J. VANKEIRSBILCK.
FEED FOR MACHINE GUNS.
No. 504,516.
Patented Sept. 5, 1893.
Fig, 5
Fig, 6
Fig, 7
Fig, 8
Fig, 10
Fig, 9
Fig, 1
Witnesses;
Inventors;

Strip feed.

(No Model.) 2 Sheets—Sheet 2.

C. M. BRODERICK & J. VANKEIRSBILCK.

FEED FOR MACHINE GUNS.

No. 504,516. Patented Sept. 5, 1893.

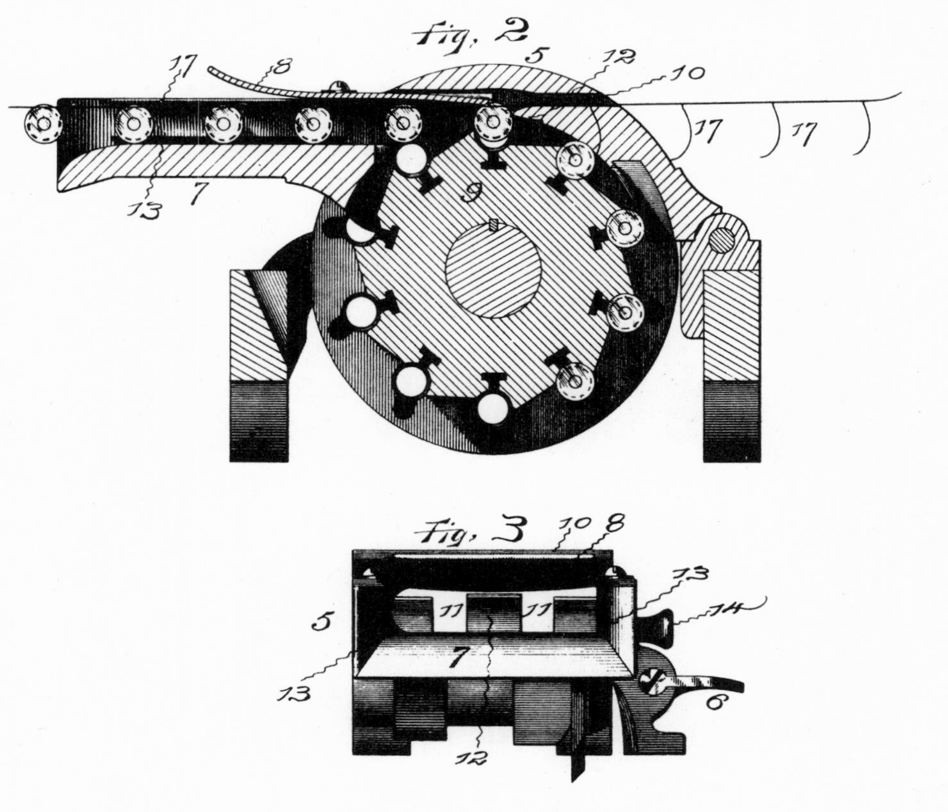

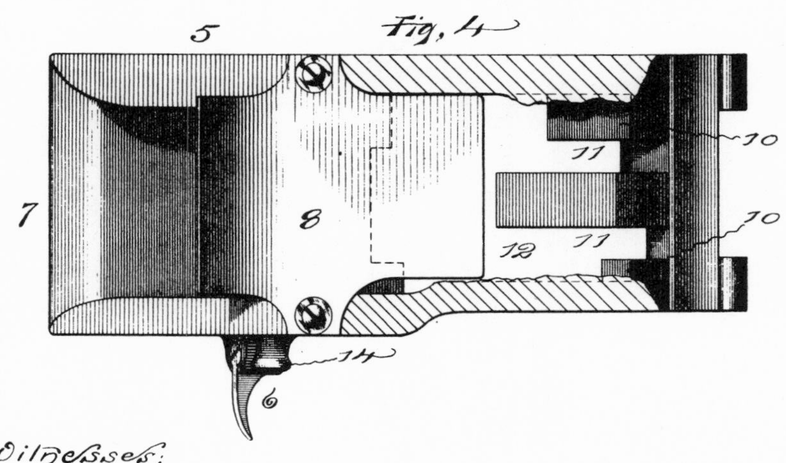

Witnesses;
E. Buckland.
John P. Healy

Inventors;
Clement M. Broderick
and John Vankeirsbilck.
by Harry R. Williams
Atty.

Feed hopper and mechanism, strip feed.

No Model.) 3 Sheets—Sheet 2.

R. J. GATLING.

MACHINE GUN.

No. 502,185. Patented July 25, 1893.

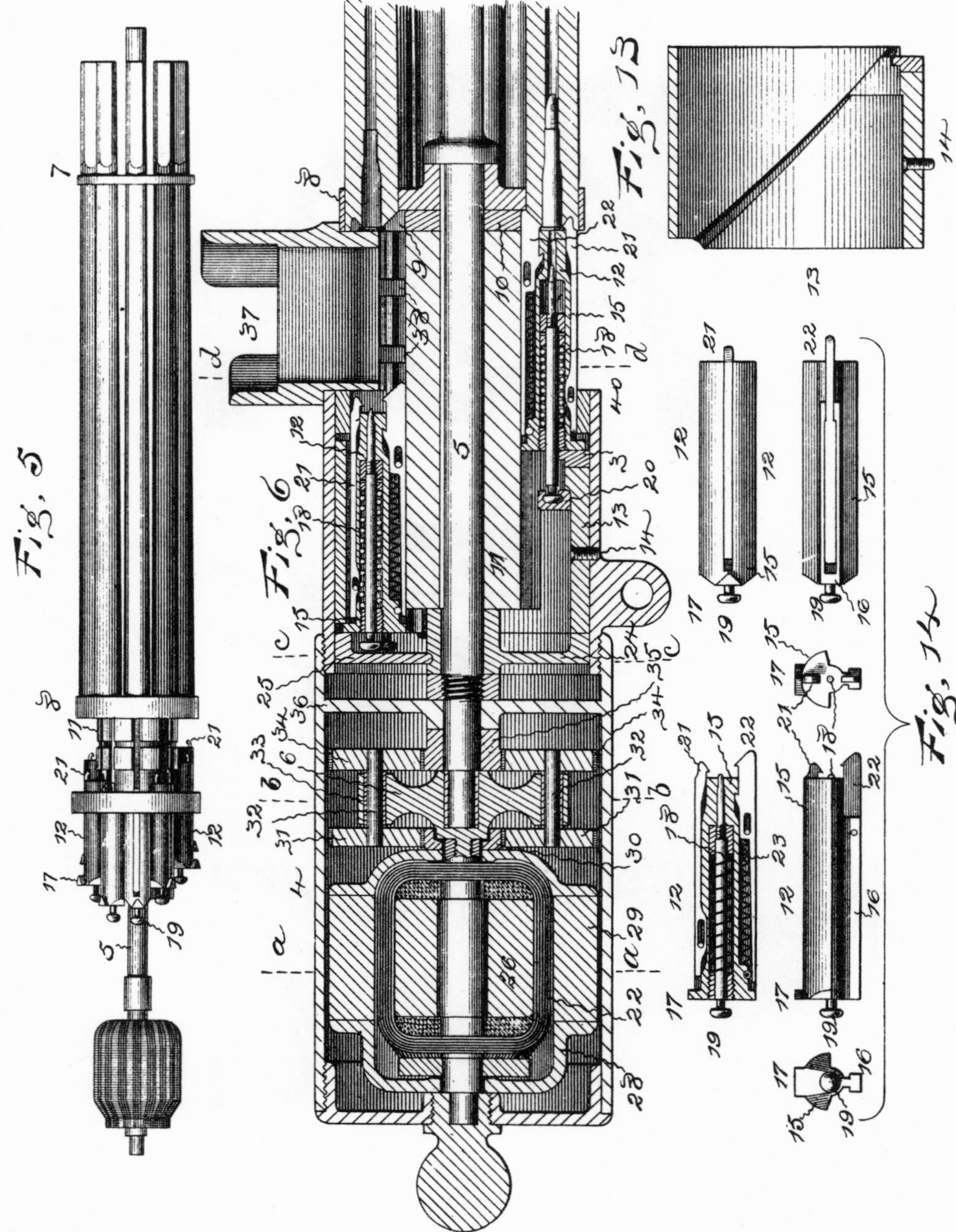

Witnesses:
Clarence E. Buckland.
P. A. Phelps.

Inventor:
Richard J Gatling by
Harry R. Williams
atty.

Electric Gatling—3,000 shots per minute!

Model 1893 Gatling, with strip feed, mounted on tripod.

in or out; setting was fixed by engaging a spring lock that held the knob at any point. This was found to provide too much latitude in adjustment and the cascabel knob was replaced with one having only five settings, in increments of .003 inch.

In 1893, the smallest of all Gatling Guns was introduced. Its six barrels were only 12 inches long. The patent illustration shows a ten-barreled gun, but none were ever manufactured. A few of these little Gatlings were made in caliber .45/70, intended for police sales. Actually an improved version of the Model 1877 Bulldog (or a scaled-down Model 1883), this gun was bronze-encased and rear-cranked, employed a miniature Accles drum feed. It incorporated a new extraction system with large, wide extractors, initially activated by cams within the breech casing, instead of by the direct action of the bolts. This system, it was claimed, minimized the chance of extractors tearing off cartridge heads, a chronic problem with Gatling guns.

On July 25, 1893, Gatling received U.S. Patent No. 502,185 for the Electric Gatling Gun. This is not to be confused with the earlier (1890) development by the Crocker-Wheeler Motor Company of an electric motor drive for Gatling Guns. The Model 1893 Electric Gatling was a large, bronze-encased, ten-barreled gun, with a motor housed within its breech casing. Driven by the electric motor, through gears, this model was capable of firing over *3,000* rounds per minute—faster than any machine gun before the current Vulcan, essentially an up-dated Gatling. Uniquely, the Electric Gatling was water-cooled; the bronze housing could be filled with water to keep the fast-fired barrels from overheating. Designed primarily for naval use, where ships' generators would afford a ready source of electric power, there was no provision for hand-cranked operation. Gatling also patented, during 1893, two new cartridge-feeding systems, neither of which ever got into production. The first was a hopper designed to handle loose ammunition. If kept clean, it was relatively jam-free, but it was impossible, under field conditions, to keep dirt out of the open trough that accepted the cartridges. The other was an improved Bruce-type feed, using oscillating metal strips to insure the smooth passage of the cartridges into the gun. With the adoption of the Broderick-Vankeirsbilck positive strip feed, the latter system seems to have been forgotten; how well it functioned is not known.

ACCLES "GATLING TYPE" MACHINE GUN

For many years a key member of the Gatling organization, James Accles not only served as the company's European representative, but also was responsible for a number of improvements in the design of the Gatling Gun. His inventions included the Accles Positive Feed, adopted in 1883.

No longer associated with Gatling, in 1891, James Accles founded the firm of Grenfell and Accles Ltd. to manufacture, at Holford Works, Parry Barr, Birmingham, England, a "Gatling type" machine gun of advanced design, that he had developed a few years earlier. In the United States, the Accles Machine Gun was produced by Driggs Ordnance Company, of Washington, D.C.

Although the Accles was much like the Model 1883 Gatling in appearance, it differed from the latter in several important mechanical details.

The barrels of this gun were fully encased, but not in bronze as in similar Gatlings. Aluminum was used for the jacket because of the light weight and corrosion-resistance of this metal.

Unlike the Gatling Gun, the Accles had a trigger. Located toward the rear of the underside of the breech casing, the trigger could be used only when the crank was fitted to the side crank shaft. Turning the crank revolved a worm gear, which in turn engaged a gear encircling the barrel unit, causing the latter to rotate. The trigger operated a clutch, which engaged or disengaged the two gears, thus controlling the fire of the gun. During firing, the gunner worked the trigger to discharge bursts at will, while another member of the gun crew turned the crank continuously. Some naval model Accles guns were equipped with electric motor drive, similar to that used on the motorized Model 1893 Gatlings.

Ordinarily, the crank of the Accles Gun was attached to a shaft that protruded from the right trunnion of the piece. When cranked, Gatling Guns typically whipped vertically, because of the rearward location of the side-mounted crank. This whipping was minimized in the Accles by positioning its crank at about the midpoint of the gun's side. Since the Accles Gun was chambered for modern, high-velocity cartridges, it was found necessary to limit the cyclic rate to 400 rounds per minute, to avoid overheating and undue wear and strain on the parts. Drive mechanism gear ratio was 3:1 and each revolu of the side crank discharged (provided that the trigger was held back) a number of shots equal to 1/3 the number of barrels—e.g., two shots for a six-barreled gun. For more rapid firing, the crank could be attached directly to the rear end of the barrel unit axle; trigger was not used and the gun fired by cranking like any Gatling.

Like all Gatlings, the Accles Gun had a switch to disengage the cocking arm, rendering the firing pins inoperative. Originally, in the Gatling Gun, the cocking switch was intended as a safety feature, to be applied during unloading or in dry runs, during training exercises, to avoid snapping the firing pins on empty chambers with the attendant danger of breakage. In the Accles Gun, the cocking switch was controlled by a special key, the idea being that, forced to abandon their gun to the enemy, the crew, before retreating, would lock the cocking switch in the nonfiring position and take the key.

The Accles Gun used no magazine. Cartridges were contained in long packets of carboard, varnished for increased strength and resistence to moisture, and stiffened by a fluted strip of tin. The packet was inserted downward into the mouth of the hopper; a toothed wheel transported it into the gun, cartridges being stripped from the packet during this passage; empty packet was automatically ejected out of the bottom of the hopper.

Mounts for the Accles Gun employed a yoke assembly similar to that of the Model 1883 Gatling, but having an elevation arc with adjustable stops to limit the range of elevation or depression of the gun to any desired degree. Purpose of this arc system is explained in the Accles Gun brochure:

> For night work, if defending a given point, the gun can be set in the day time and arranged to cover any required space. For instance, if it is necessary to cover a bridge (or landing) and part of the approach, say a space of 200 yards in length, at a distance of 1000 yards, the gun would be put into position while there was daylight, and aimed for 1000 yards, which would be the approximate center of the bridge. The stops on the arc would then be set and clamped so that the gun would elevate to 1150 yards and depress to 850. This would give a vertical oscillating movement which would cover 300 yards. The gun would also be given a slight horizontal movement.
>
> The gun is now ready for action. We will suppose that the alarm is given that the enemy is crossing the bridge; the gun would commence firing; the pointer (gunner) would move the gun up and down and sidewise between the stops while firing, which would cover the bridge with a stream of bullets. As a rapid fire would be more effectual, the gun would be fired with the crank at the rear.
>
> For street defense this gun has no equal. By setting the stops on the arc, the gun could be given a vertical oscillation that would take in the whole length of the street, or up to the extreme range of the gun.

The Accles mount for land forces was a heavy field carriage with protective shields that folded down to serve as seats for the gun crew while the piece was bing transported. This all-steel carriage had two ammunition chests, each holding 1,000 cartridges; the accompanying limber provided space for an additional 8,0000 rounds.

Zinc-lined, wooden chests were furnished to carry the cartridge packets for the Accles Gun. The chest was made ⅝" longer than the feed packets and this space filled with a board. When the chest was full and it was necessary to remove feed packets quickly, the filler board could be pulled out, leaving space in which to grasp the packets easily. At the top of the chest, there was a beeswax-filled groove in the zinc liner; when the corresponding flange of the cover was pressed down into this groove and sealed all around with more beeswax, the ammunition chest was made airtight.

Recognizing the potential of the Oriental market, Accles offered an unique Chinese wheelbarrow mount for his gun, designed to negotiate the narrow roads and trails of China and other Far East countries. Despite its odd appearance, this was a very practical mount—at the time, the wheelbarrow was probably the most common land vehicle in that part of the world.

A variety of Accles mounts were designed for naval service. A tall cone or pedestal, with a socket to accept the yoke, mounted the gun on a ship's bridge, while a lower cone—the boat mount—was intended for use in the bow of a longboat or other small craft. A rail socket, to be attached to the ship's rail, placed the gun for use against boarding parties or nearby small craft. Warships of this era often had "fighting tops"—a kind of oversized crow's-nest, up on the mast, from which fire could be directed down on the enemy's decks. The railing of the fighting top could be fitted with a track on which Accles Guns might ride on small wheeled carriages, to cover a 360° field of fire.

There was an effective turret mount designed for installation in armored ships' turrets or in blockhouses and other fortified land positions. This mount permitted the Accles Gun to be elevated or traversed independent of any movement of the turret, and a pair of tracks in the mount allowed the gun crew to run the piece in or out of the firing port, as required.

Accles offered a naval landing carriage, intended to be drawn by manpower. A team of six sailors, each wearing a wide leather belt with a ring at the back, were to be hitched to the carriage by ropes leading from it to their belt rings. This type of carriage by ropes leading from it to their belt rings. This type of carriage had four ammunition chests, each containing 1,000 rounds. Complete, this unit weighed 913 pounds. An accompanying, man-drawn limber carried additional ammunition and was fitted with racks to hold the rifles of the men pulling it and the landing carriage.

Another naval landing carriage offered for the Accles Gun looked like a big tricycle, the carriage being fitted with an additional wheel at the end of its trail. This carriage could be pushed, as well as pulled in the conventional manner; the gunner rode on a seat behind the gun, could fire while the carriage was moving. Of this type of mount, the Accles brochure said:

> The ability to fire while retreating or advancing is a very essential feature in machine guns, particularly when they are called upon to maintain a continuous fire in close contests. Oftentimes a change of base becomes necessary, but to stop firing might prove disastrous. With the gun mounted on this carriage an effective fire can be maintained while the carriage is being moved, so that no time is lost and no weak places are left exposed by the gun being thrown out of action.
>
> From the axle of the small wheel a rod is taken terminating in a cross bar. This serves to operate the guide wheel, and together with a drag rope hooked to the end of the trail, to pull the carriage along.
>
> The gun's crew should consist of an officer and ten men . . . stationed as follows: on the march, three at each drag rope, two at the heaving bar, and two as reliefs and to assist at the wheels over rough ground.

On this mount, the Accles Gun weighed 1,358 pounds.

Contrasting with this heavy mount, there also was a light (44 lb.) tripod for the Accles. Each leg was spiked at the end for firm footing; when used aboard ship, the ends were fitted with wooden "shoes," rubber-bottomed to avoid slipping or damage to decks. One of the hollow legs of this tripod unscrewed, providing storage for spare parts and tools.

SPECIFICATIONS

	6 barrel	*10 barrel*
Caliber	.30 Krag*	.30 Krag*
Number of barrels	6	10
Total length of gun	41.5″	43.5″
Diameter of gun at breech	6.75″	6.75″
Diameter of gun at muzzle	6.25″	6.25″
Length of barrels	28″	30″
Length of rifling	25.7″	27.7″
Number of grooves	4	4
Depth of grooves	.004″	.004″
Twist of rifling, one turn in	10″	10″
Diameter of each barrel at breech	1⅛″	1⅛″
Weight of barrel	5 lb.	5¼ lb.
Weight of gun complete	150 lb.	220 lb.
Weight of yoke	26 lb.	26 lb.
Extreme elevation	50°	50°
Extreme depression	50°	50°
Rate of fire per minute, crank at side	360 rds.	500 rds.
Rate of fire per minute, crank at rear	700 rds.	1200 rds.
Total length of cartridge	3.085″	3.085″
Total length of case	2.315″	2.315″
Total length of bullet	1.265″	1.265″
Weight of bullet	220 grs.	220 grs.
Charge of powder	40 grs.	40 grs.
Kind of powder	smokeless	smokeless
Initial velocity	2000 f.p.s.	2025 f.p.s.

The Accles Machine Gun was, admittedly, a copy of the Gatling—its inventor referred to it as a "Gatling type" weapon. Despite the fact that, in many respects, it was an improvement of the original, the Accles was doomed to early obsolescence. When it appeared, the era of crank-operated machine guns was already drawing to a close. At the turn of the century, the world armed forces, once almost universally equipped with Gatlings, were turning to the newly developed gas or recoil-operated automatic weapons, which were not only smaller and lighter, but less expensive to acquire and maintain.

---

* A few guns, ordered by the U.S. Navy, were chambered for the 6mm. (.236) Lee Navy cartridge, also used in that service's Lee straight-pull rifles.

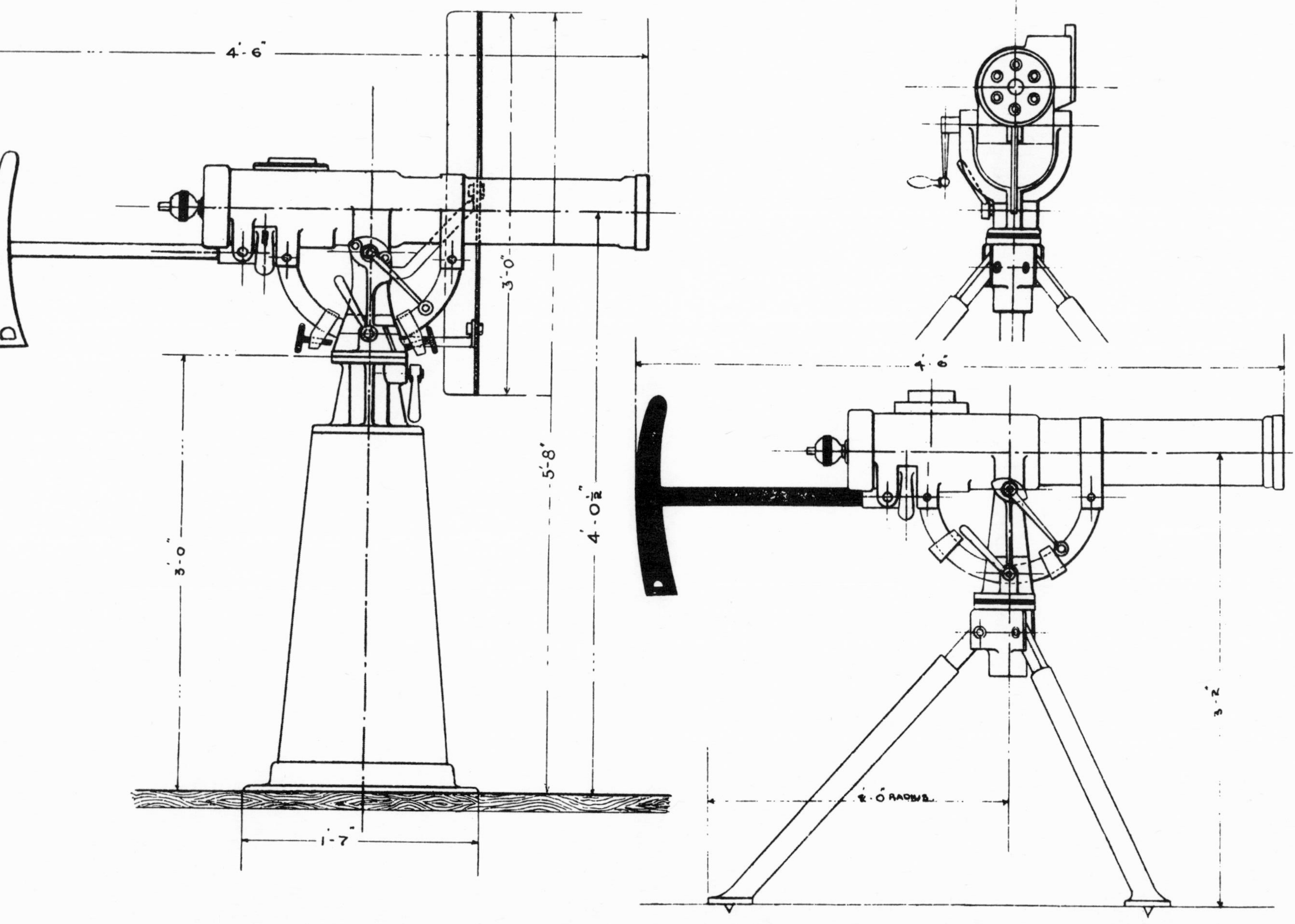

Accles machine gun, with shield, on deck, or bridge, pedestal.

Accles machine gun on tripod mount.

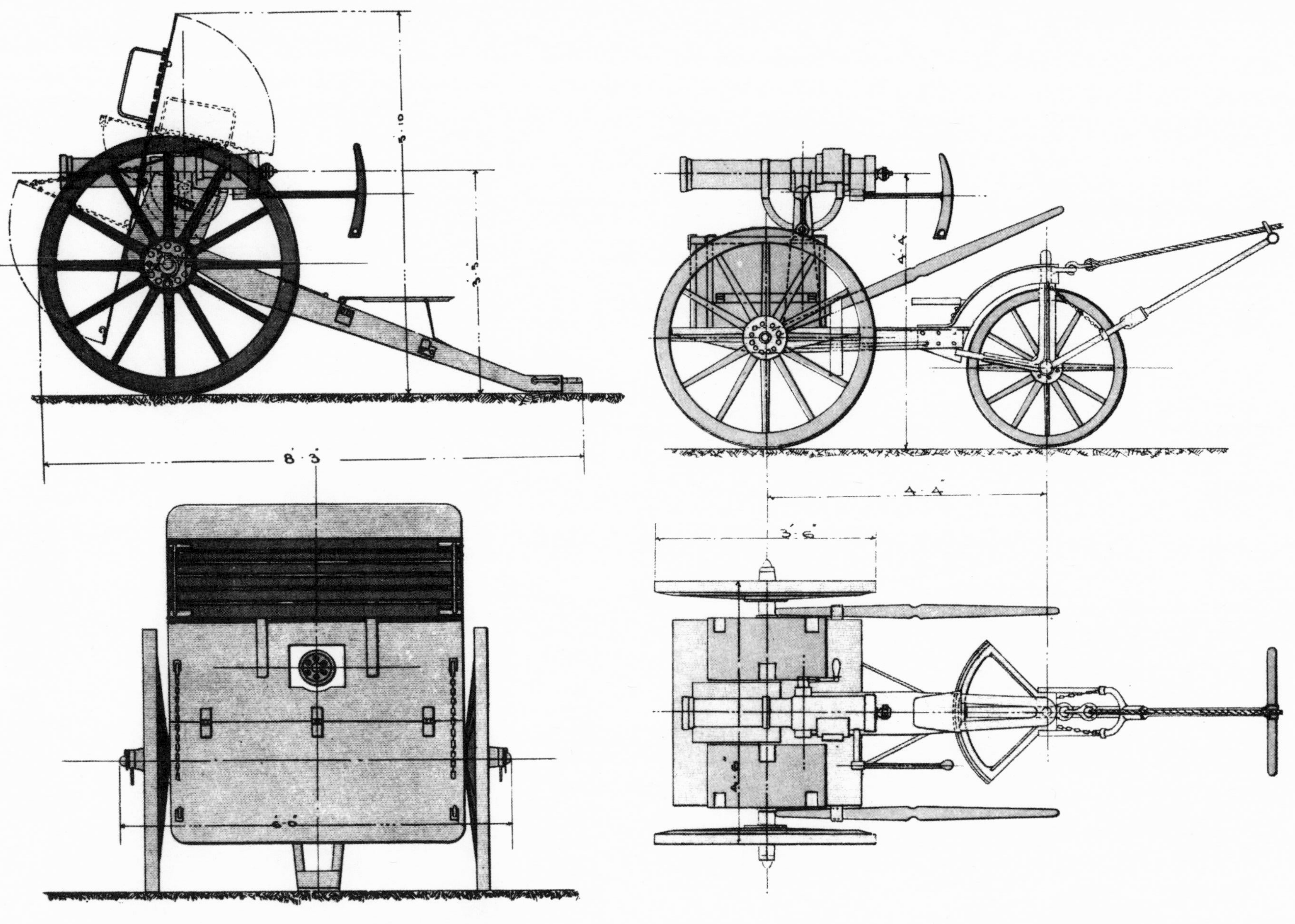

Accles machine gun on field carriage.

Accles machine gun on 3-wheeled naval landing carriage.

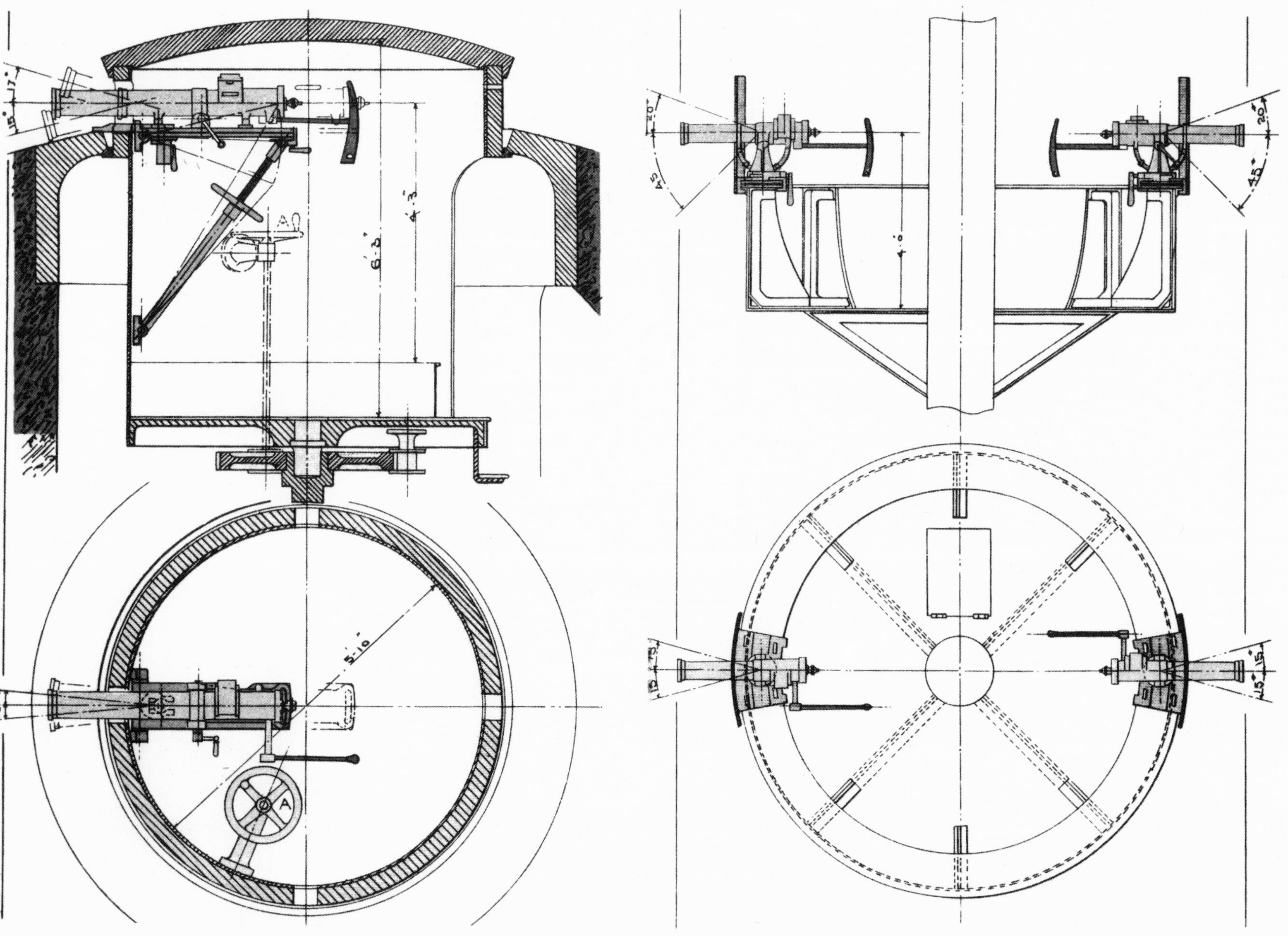

Accles machine gun on turret mount.

Ship's top with Accles machine guns mounted.

*Disassembly procedure for Accles Machine Gun:**

Place the gun horizontally or on its own mounting. When on its own mounting see that all clamps are tight, or the muzzle end of the gun will drop and damage the casing when the rear parts are removed. To remove the breech bolts turn the lock port door to the right and draw it to the rear. Turn the gun backwards with the crank until the breech bolt comes in line with the opening; then draw the bolt out by hand. Repeat the operation until all the bolts are removed.

Knock out the taper pin and remove the cascabel knob. Remove the rear sight bar by giving it a half turn. Take out the screw locking the cascabel plate, and remove plate by unscrewing to the left. Remove the camming sleeve out of the rear end of the cam case. Take care that the small round safety cam at the front end of the cocking device does not drop out and get lost. Should the cam, or cocking sleeve, stick in the barrel casing so that it can not be drawn out by hand, leave it until the barrels are drawn out at which time it will come away with them.

Remove the cocking device. Remove the hopper by turning up the locking pin at its right side, and drawing the hopper horizontally away from the gun.

Press down on the small spring on the trunnion box, and pull its cover to the rear. The worm and clutch will then drop out.

Push the barrel unit forward until the barrels project several inches out of the front of the barrel casing. Drive out the pin that holds on the muzzle plate; remove plate. Draw the barrel unit out of the rear end of the gun.

Knock out the taper pin and remove the cascabel knob. Remove the rear sight bar by giving it a half turn. Take out the screw locking the cascabel plate, and remove plate by unscrewing to the left. Remove the camming sleeve out of the rear end of the cam case. Take care that the small round safety cam at the front end of the cocking device does not drop out and get lost. Should the cam, or cocking sleeve, stick in the barrel casing so that it can not be drawn out by hand, leave it until the barrels are drawn out at which time it will come away with them.

Remove the cocking device. Remove the hopper by turning up the locking pin at its right side, and drawing the hopper horizontally away from the gun.

Knock out the small pin which passes through the trigger shaft; press the trigger shaft to the front and draw it out at the front of the trunion box. Catch the switch which will drop out of the trunion box; take out the screws and remove the trigger handle.

To remove the barrel casing from the yoke, give a quarter turn to the rear to the two pins which secure the ends of the elevating arc to the lugs on the underside of the gun; withdraw the pins, freeing the arc. Remove the trunion caps, and lift the barrel casing free of the yoke.

* Quoted from the Driggs Ordnance Company instruction manual.

LAST TRIALS BY THE U. S. NAVY

The last important trial, in which the Gatling Gun figured, was held by the Bureau of Ordnance, U.S. Navy, in 1894. In addition to the Gatling, five other machine guns were included in this competition: Accles, Gardner, Maxim, Robertson, and Skoda. The Accles Machine Gun was essentially a Gatling and, since it was advertised as an "improved Gatling type," Gatling was especially anxious that his gun outperform what he regarded as Accles' copy.

Comparatively poor performance put the Gardner, Robertson, and Skoda guns out of contention. The Accles Machine Gun's unusual feed system, using papier-mache chargers to hold the cartridges, was condemned by the trial board. In their opinion, if the charger became wet or otherwise lost its rigidity, the gun could not be fired. Furthermore, they reported, because of the considerable pressure needed to force the charger into the gun, because of a spring arrangement in the hopper, loading tended to disturb the aim of the piece. As the Accles grew hotter with prolonged firing, parts expanded and exerted such friction that cranking required much effort.

Both the Accles and the Gatling were faulted because of their great weight. The board also pointed out that, in the Gatling, the rearward location of the crank caused side motion, resulting in a marked derangement of aim.

The board recommended adoption of the Maxim for U.S. Navy use, citing its comparatively small size and light weight, as well as the small gun crew it required. Commander C. S. Sperry, U.S.N., filed a minority report in favor of the Gatling, based chiefly on the gun's superior rate of fire. In one test, a Gatling discharged 1,547 rounds in the time it took a Maxim to fire only 720 shots.

After the conclusion of the trials, Driggs Ordnance Company, of Washington, D.C., representing Accles in America, addessed a letter to the trial board, advising that their machine gun now had a new type of feed, replacing the cardboard charger system found unsatisfactory. The new feed employed tin strips, much like those used in early Hotchkiss guns. Although this was a considerable improvement, it came too late to affect the board's decision.

GATLING MODELS OF 1895-1903

The Model 1895 Gatling was much like the Model 1893 gun, although some minor changes were made. Breech bolts were fitted with rebounding hammers.

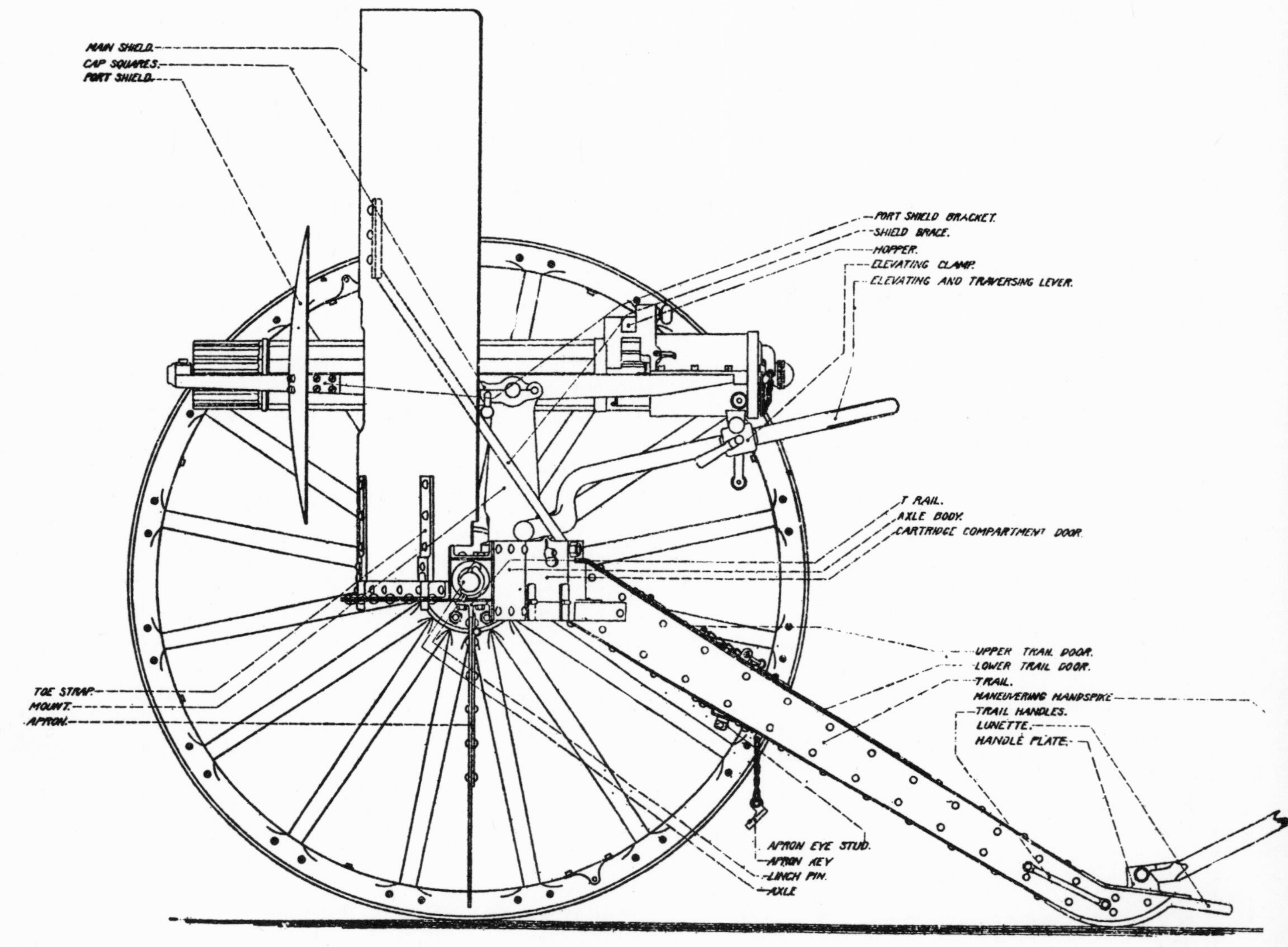

Model 1895 Gatling on armored field carriage.

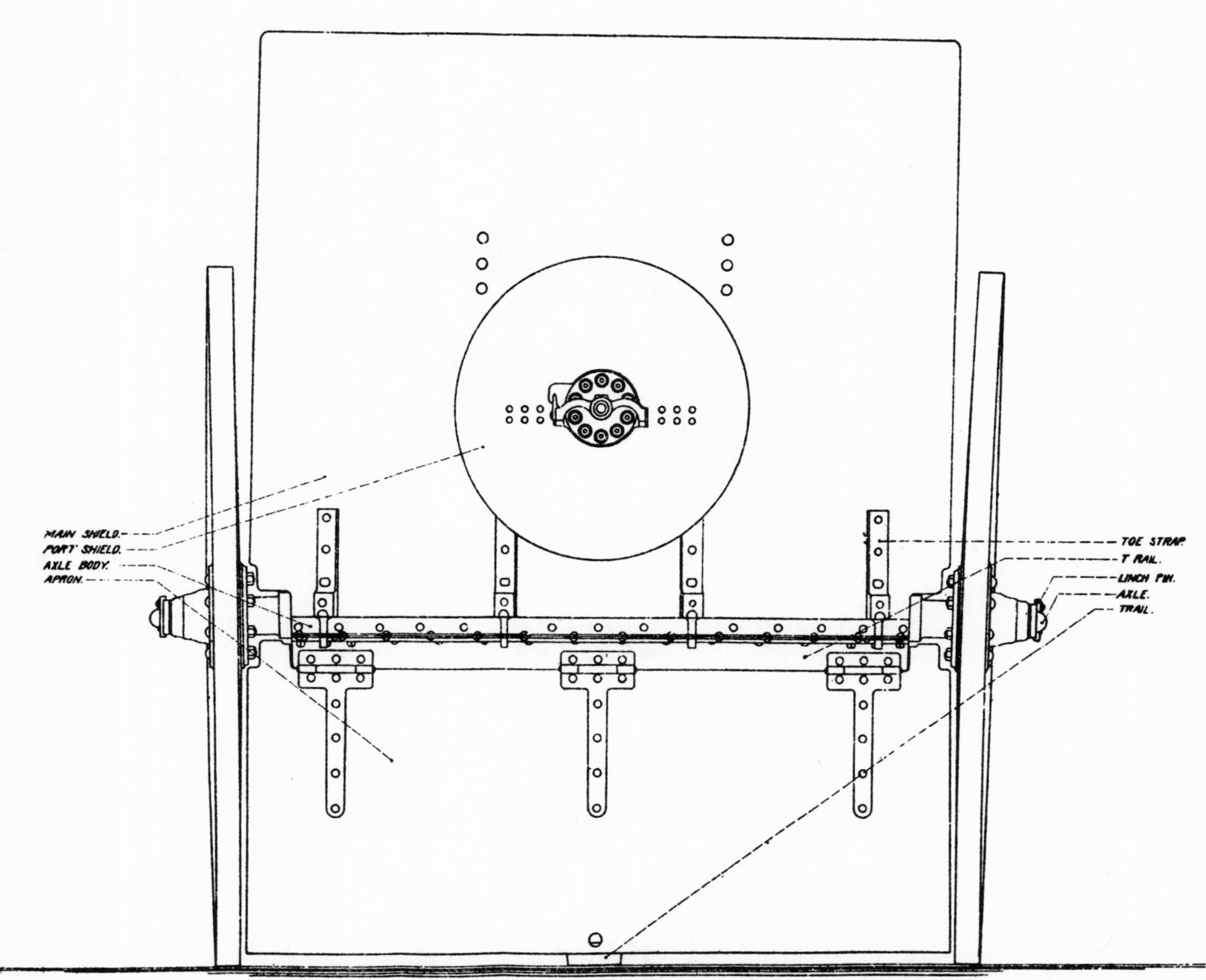

Models 1900 and 1903 were almost identical.

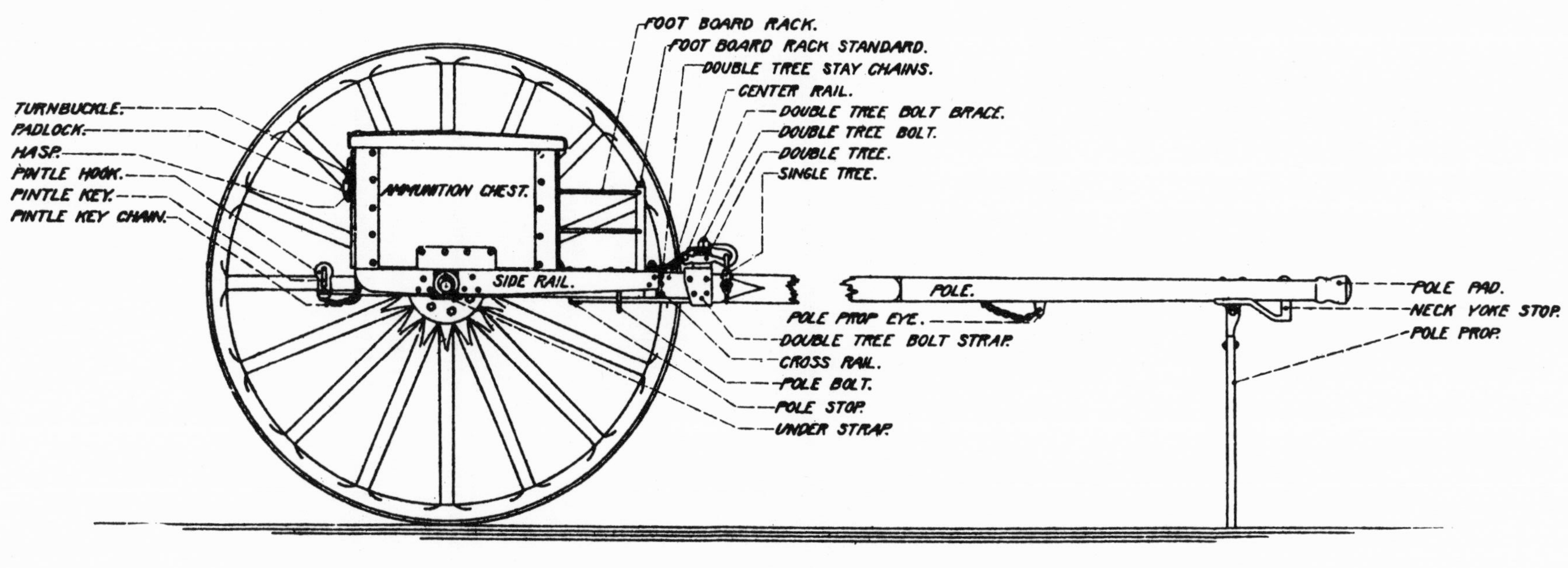

Iron-framed limber. This type of limber was furnished with most late-model Gatlings. For guns equipped with Bruce feed, ammunition was carried boxed instead of in magazines, greatly increasing carrying capacity of limber.

Hopper was designed to accept the Bruce feed only; to reduce wear, incident to the gun's high rate of fire, the hopper and carrier block were made of a harder phosphor bronze. While nearly all earlier Gatlings were furnished with metal parts "bright" —i.e., bare—in the Model 1895, bronze parts were painted olive drab, the frame was painted black or blued, and other steel parts, such as barrels and pointing bar, were blued. The awkward system of rotating discs, employed in the Model 1893 to protect the open gun port in the upper shield from enemy small arms fire, was replaced by a single, round shield—convex to deflect bullets—attached to the gun frame about 12 inches behind the muzzles; a small cutout on the right side of this shield permitted sighting. The former arrangement interfered with both aiming and traversing.

There were few differences between the Model 1900 Gatling and the preceding Models 1893 and 1895. Although specifications called for painting of bronze parts, as in the Model 1895, extant specimens of the Model 1900 have these parts bright and show no indication of having been painted; the Bruce feeds, however, have bronze frames painted olive drab. In this model, the hopper was machined from a solid block of phosphor bronze, instead being assembled from a number of separate pieces. This made for greater strength and more precise fitting.

As in all late Gatlings, headspace in the Model 1900 was adjusted by screwing the cascabel knob in or out. A large bronze washer, under the knob, had a spring lock, which engaged one of the five square notches on the knob, setting the headspace at 0.063″, 0.060″, 0.054″, or 0.051″; thus, setting could be maintained accurately instead of being determined more or less by "guesstimate," as formerly. By turning the knob to the right, headspace was reduced, the barrels being drawn to the rear and closer to the breech bolts.

All Gatling Guns had their barrels and breech bolts numbered 1 through 5, 6, or 10, corresponding numbers indicating the proper bolt for each barrel. These components of the Model 1900 were numbered in like manner, but closer tolerances permitted interchangeability and it was possible to put any bolt behind any barrel and still have the gun function properly.

Markings of the Models 1895 and 1900 are engraved on top of the bronze breech housing; in the Model 1900, the model designation appears on the right side of the frame.

On May 20, 1898, eighteen Model 1895 guns (serial No. 1032-1049) were delivered to the U.S. Army; August 29, 1898, thirty-one (No. 1050-1080); November 28, 1898, forty-five (No. 1081-1125). The U.S. Army also purchased many Model 1900 Gatlings.

U. S. Navy Gatling Model 1900 Mark II, caliber .30, tripod-mounted.

A number of fully bronze-encased Model 1900 guns were produced for the U.S. Navy; these resembled the Model 1883 in appearance. Designated "Model 1900 Mark II, Cal. .30," it was chambered, like the standard Model 1900 sold to the U.S. Army, for the .30/.40 Krag cartridge, and employed the well-proved Bruce feed exclusively. The crank could be attached to either the gear-reduced side shaft or directly to the rear end of the barrel-unit axle. Although higher rates of fire were possible with direct drive, the recommended maximum was 600 rounds per minute. The Navy Model 1900 had an 1883 style cocking-switch on the lower right side of its barrel casing. Unlike the dual-sighted Model 1883, this gun had only one set of sights, graduated to 2,000 yards elevation and adjustable for windage, mounted on the right side of the piece. Yoke was of the 1883 pattern, had an arc under the gun to govern elevation and depression. A stem in the base of the yoke adapted it to either the Navy cone mount or the wheeled carriage; both had sockets to accept this stem. The lightweight wheeled carriage afforded unique mobility. Its trail was fitted with a hand bar, permitting the piece to be pulled by men; a horse-drawn limber was available for towing the gun for long distances. To keep the weight down, only 1,320 rounds of ammunition were carried in the chests on the carriage; 12,000 rounds were accommodated by the limber (replacement of the tool box with an ammunition chest increased this capacity by 1,000 rounds).

Identifying markings were engraved on the top of the breech casing of the Navy Model 1900 Gatling; U.S.N. Bureau of Ordnance marks appeared on the top of the barrel casing, between the trunnions. Each gun had two sets of serial numbers, Colt's and the U.S. Navy's. Highest U.S.N. number observed was 17, indicating limited issue of this model. A few unmarked Navy Model 1900 Gatlings are known; however, these have experimental or non-standard features, and probably were never intended for sale.

In 1903, the Model 1900 was chambered for the .30-03 cartridge of the new U. S. Model 1903 Springfield Rifle; this gun was designated Gatling Model 1903. Subsequently, the U.S. Government officially adopted the .30-06 cartridge for the '03 Springfield, and it was decided that all .30 caliber Gatlings be converted to this caliber. In 1907, thirty-four Model 1903 Gatlings (serial No. 1128-1159) were thus altered by Colt's at a charge of $70 per gun. This figure was considered too high and all later conversions of this type were made at the Springfield Armory—by 1909, a total of 171 Gatlings, including 40 new Model 1903 guns in .30-03, were changed to .30-06. Rechambered guns are identified by the numbers "-06" added as a suffix to the serial number, and by their replacement sights, graduated for the .30-06 cartridge.

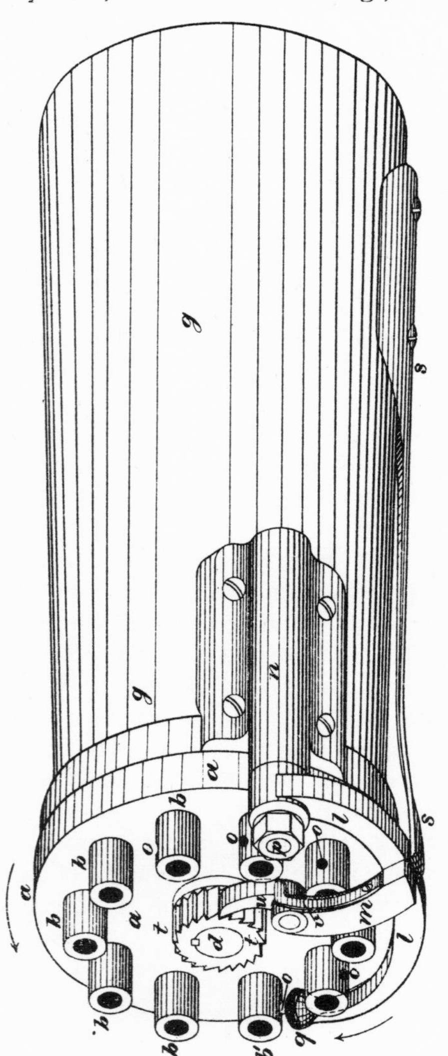

The Model 1903-06 was the last Gatling Gun produced by Colt's. It was manufactured until 1911, when the U.S. Government ceased to buy Gatlings. As late as World War I, instruction manuals for this gun were published by the U.S. Government.

Disassembly procedure for Gatling Model 1903:

1. Remove lock plug and breech bolts.
2. Unscrew cascabel knob. Remove latch and washer beneath it.
3. Pull out and lock cocking switch.
4. Remove hopper hinge screws and hopper.
5. Unscrew cascabel plate by turning to left.
6. Drive out lock pin in worm gear. Remove crank shaft and worm gear.
7. Remove drive gear at rear end of barrel axle.
8. Remove six action bolts holding bronze breech casing to frame.
9. Remove breech casing, being careful to support the barrels. Remove barrels from the frame.

(*Note:* The foregoing instructions apply to all exposed-barrel models with headspace adjustment in cascabel knob.)

GAS-OPERATED GATLING GUN

In 1895, Carl J. Ehbets patented a "Gas-operated Machine-gun," which actually was a device for application to the Gatling, designed to convert that gun into a gas-operated, fully automatic weapon. As shown in the patent illustration reproduced at left, the Ehbets system operated as follows:

The first shot was fired in the usual manner by turning the crank. Powder gas, generated by firing, escaped through port *o* in barrel *b′*, striking cap *q*, which covered the gas port. Pressure on the cap turned lever *l*, to which it was attached, against spring *s*. In the return travel of the lever, pawl *u* moved ratchet *t* on axle *d*, rotating the succeeding barrel into firing position with cap over its gas port. At this point, the cartridge in that barrel was discharged automatically and the operating sequence repeated as long as cartridges were fed into the chambers.

The patent was assigned to Colt's, but Ehbets' idea never got past the experimental stage. In 1894, the U.S. Navy adopted the Maxim machine gun and it was apparent, in the face of strong competition from smaller, lighter, automatic weapons, that the Gatling's days were numbered.

SPANISH-AMERICAN WAR IN CUBA

The nineteenth century saw repeated, abortive attempts by Cuban patriots to free their land from Spanish misrule. In 1895, insurrection was so widespread that the industry and commerce of the island were virtually paralyzed, and Spain landed 150,000 troops in Cuba to put down the revolt. Nevertheless, by 1896, more than half of the island was in the hands of the rebels under Generals Calixto García y Iñiguez* and Máximo Gómez y Báez, veterans of the Ten Years War for Cuban Independence of 1868-1878 and old hands at revolution and guerrilla warfare.

To counter the rebellion with terrorism, Spain sent a leading expert in the field, Gen. Valeriano Weyler y Nicolau, known as "The Butcher" because of his harsh reprisals against Cubans during the 1868-1878 revolution. Inmmediately upon assuming the dual role of governor and commander-in-chief, General Weyler implemented a program of reconcentration under which the rural population—noncombatant men, women, and children—were herded into concentration camps, where thousands starved to death. As Cuba was laid waste by the Spanish troops and stories of atrocities committed by them were played up heavily in the U. S. press, the cause of *Cuba Libre* found much support among the American public.

Early in 1898, the incident that served to trigger the Spanish-American War occurred. Since January 25, the battleship USS *Maine,* ostensibly on a goodwill tour, but actually sent at the request of the U.S. Consul General for protection of American nationals and property in Cuba, was anchored in the Havana harbor. On the evening of February 15, 1898, an explosion tore the *Maine* apart and it sank with a loss of 260 lives. An inquiry by the U.S. Navy resulted in the report that the ship had been sunk by a submarine mine, while a Spanish board of investigation claimed that the destruction of the *Maine* was caused by an accidental explosion in its forward magazine—the truth of the matter was never established. As far as American public opinion was concerned, Spain was guilty. The U.S. press headlined its demand for war with the battle cry "Remember the *Maine!*" On April 19, Congress passed a resolution proclaiming Cuba free and independent and authorizing the use of U.S. armed forces to expel the Spaniards from the island. The Spanish Government declared war on the United States on April 24 and Congress responded by stating that war had existed as of the 21st, when Admiral Sampson and the main squadron of the Atlantice Fleet sailed for Cuba.

June 23-25, 1898, Brig. Gen. William R. Shafter landed with 17,000 troops to undertake the capture of Santiago de Cuba. This contingent, which landed at Daiquiri, included the Gatling Gun Detachment, 5th Army Corps, commanded by John Henry Parker, first lieutenant of the 13th Infantry, graduate of West Point, Class of '88. Lieutenant Parker was responsible for the organization of the Gatling Gun Detachment sent to Cuba and for the effective use of machine guns in the assault and capture of San Juan Hill, July 1, 1898. In this battle, for the first time, the U.S. Army employed close-support machine guns in an attack. Parker tells the story in his book, *Tactical Organization and Uses of Machine Guns in the Field:*

> At the outbreak of war between the United States and Spain, April 26, 1898, there were about 150 Gatling guns and about half as many Gardner guns of the two-barreled type in the land service of the United States. The Government had some time before ordered from the makers, a private firm, 100 of the Gatling guns, to be of the .30 caliber adopted for the new magazine rifle, and to use the same ammunition. A consignment of 15 of these new guns reached Tampa while the expedition was being fitted out for the Santiago campaign. A detachment of four pieces was formed, under command of a lieutenant, as an independent organization, under the direct orders of the general commanding. The detachment was not decided on until the 14th of June, after the expedition had already embarked, and as one result of this delay, the men were imperfectly equipped, not having any revolvers, and being hampered by having to carry the rifle, which was more of a burden than otherwise. There was no time to look after the proper equipment of the guns in the matter of spare parts for repairs, etc., and the pieces were taken into the campaign without any tools for repair, or possibility of overhauling a disabled piece, unless the enemy should furnish such necessaries out of a rare spirit of generosity. The men to serve the guns were taken from infantry regiments, without special instruction of any kind until after they had been rushed to the extreme front of the lines, within 5,000 yards of the enemy. Even then only four days were available for special instruction, and it became necessary, after the pieces were on the skirmish-line, to instruct men in the art of feeding the guns.
>
> The guns were pushed right up in the hottest place there was in the battle-field, at "the bloody ford" of the San Juan, and put into action at the most critical moment of the battle, after part of the troops had already been forced back by the

---

* García achieved a kind of second-class immortailty in the U.S. because of Elbert Hubbard's inspirational essay (1899), which recounted the heroic journey of Lt. Andrew S. Rowan to meet the Cuban rebel leader during the Spanish-American War.

Gatlings to the assault. San Juan Hill, Santiago de Cuba, July 1, 1898.
U. S. Army's first use of close support machine guns in attack.

strong fire of the defenders, and so successfully subdued the Spanish fire that from that time to the capture of this practically impregnable position was only 8½ minutes. The expenditure of ammunition during this time, in which a continuous fire was kept up from three guns, was 6,000 rounds per gun. The remaining ammunition, with the guns, was pushed up at once on to the captured position, which enabled the now exhausted troops to hold it without reinforcements against two counterassaults of the Spaniards.

. . . .

General Shafter says in his official report, speaking of the assault on San Juan Hill: "In this part of the field most efficient service was rendered by . . . the Gatling Gun Detachment. . . . The fighting continued at intervals until nightfall, but our men held resolutely to the positions they had gained at the cost of so much blood and toil."

The commander of this detachment stated in his official report that during the counterattack of the enemy he had been assailed by a battery of 16-cm. guns, and had successfully resisted the fire of this battery at a range of 2,000 yards, driving the enemy's cannoneers from their pieces after they had fired three shells which were correctly ranged, and which exploded in the immediate vicinity of the Gatlings. This Spanish battery consisted of seven guns, as follows: one 16-cm. converted bronze rifled gun, four 3-inch bronze guns, and two mountain guns. The claim was made in his report, "This is probably the first time that such a piece was ever silenced in land fighting by machine gun fire."

During the siege of Santiago, which followed, the Gatlings were used in conjunction with two automatic guns and a dynamite gun, exemplifying perfectly all that has ever been claimed for either of these weapons, as far as opportunity offered. The machine guns were used in the most advanced trenches to hold down the enemy's fire; were used against heavy artillery; were used to resist a night attack, and on outpost duty. All that had ever been claimed by the most enthusiastic advocates of the weapons as to their effectiveness was here exemplified, and the result of the campaign was to place the machine gun beyond dispute as a weapon to be reckoned with in some form in all future wars.

In his preface to Parker's book, *The Gatlings at Santiago*, Theodore Roosevelt tells the story from his point of view:

On the morning of July 1st, the dismounted calvary, including my regiment, stormed Kettle Hill, driving the Spaniards from their trenches. After taking the crest, I made the men under me turn and begin volley-firing at the San Juan Blockhouse and intrenchments against which Hawkins' and Kent's Infantry were advancing. While thus firing, there suddenly smote on our ears a peculiar drumming sound. One or two of the men cried out, "The Spanish machine guns!" but, after listening a moment, I leaped to my feet and called, "It's the Gatlings, men! It's our Gatlings!" Immediately the troopers began to cheer lustily, for the sound was most inspiring. Whenever the drumming stopped, it was only to open again a little nearer the front. Our artillery, using black powder, had not been able to stand within range of the Spanish rifles, but it was perfectly evident that the Gatlings were troubled by no such consideration, for they were advancing all the while.

Soon the infantry took San Juan Hill, and, after one false start, we in turn rushed the next line of block-houses and intrenchments, and then swung to the left and took the chain of hills immediately fronting Santiago. Here I found myself on the extreme front, in command of the fragments of all six regiments of the cavalry division. I received orders to halt where I was, but to hold the hill at all hazards. The Spaniards were heavily reinforced and they opened a tremendous fire upon us from their batteries and trenches. We laid down just behind the gentle crest of the hill, firing as we got the chance, but, for the most part, taking the fire without responding. As the afternoon wore on, however, the Spaniards became bolder, and made an attack upon the position. They did not push it home, but they did advance, their firing being redoubled. We at once ran forward to the crest and opened on them, and, as we did so, the unmistakable drumming of the Gatlings opened abreast of us, to our right, and the men cheered again. As soon as the attack was definitely repulsed, I strolled over to find out about the Gatlings, and there I found Lieut. Parker with two of his guns right on our left, abreast of our men, who at that time were closer to the Spaniards than any others.

From thence on, Parker's Gatlings were our inseparable companions throughout the siege. They were eight up at the front. When we dug our trenches, he took off the wheels of his guns and put them in the trenches. His men and ours slept in the same bomb-proofs and shared with one another whenever either side got a supply of beans or coffee and sugar. At no hour of the day or night was Parker anywhere but where we wished him to be, in the event of an attack. If a troop of my regiment was sent off to guard some road or some break in the lines, we were almost certain to get Parker to send a Gatling along, and, whether the charge was made by day or by night, the Gatling went. Sometimes we took the initiative and started to quell the fire of the Spanish trenches; sometimes they opened upon us; but, at whatever hour of the twenty-four the fighting began, the drumming of the Gatlings was soon heard through the cracking of our own carbines.

I have had too little experience to make my judgment final; but certainly, if I were to command either a regiment or a brigade, whether of cavalry or infantry. I would try to get a Gatling battery—under a good man—with me. I feel sure that the greatest possible assistance would be rendered, under almost all circumstances, by such a Gatling battery, if well handled; for I believe that it could be pushed fairly to the front of the firing-line. At

Gatling guns in front of Santiago.

any rate, this is the way that Lieut. Parker used his battery when he went into action at San Juan, and when he kept it in the trenches beside the Rough Riders before Santiago.

With the destruction of the Spanish fleet July 3 and the surrender of Santiago de Cuba on July 17, 1898, the war in Cuba was virtually over, although the armistice was not signed until August 12. The peace treaty, signed in Paris on December 10, guaranteed Cuban independence.

The important role played in this conflict by the Gatling Gun Detachment and its commander, Lieut. John H. Parker, is reiterated in this statement by Theodore Roosevelt in his memoir of the Spanish-American War, *The Rough Riders:*

> . . . I think Parker deserved rather more credit than any other one man in the entire campaign. I do not allude especially to his courage and energy, great though they were, for there were hundreds of his fellow officers of the cavalry and infantry who possessed as much of the former quality, and scores who possessed as much of the latter; but he had the rare good judgement and foresight to see the possibilities of the machine guns, and, thanks to the aid of General Shafter, he was able to organize his battery. He then, by his own exertions, got it to the front and proved that it could do invaluable work on the field of battle, as much in attack as in defense.

At Santiago, Lieutenant Parker acquired the nickname that was his for the rest of his life—he was known thereafter as "Gatling" Parker. After the war, Parker wrote two books: *The Gatlings at Santiago* ("History of the Gatling Gun Detachment, Fifth Army Corps, at Santiago, With a Few Unvarnished Truths Concerning that Expedition"), published in 1898, and *Tactical Organization and Uses of Machine Guns in the Field,* published in 1899. The former set forth, in interesting narrative, the experiences of Lieutenant Parker and his command during the war in Cuba. The latter provided a definitive manual on machine gun tactics, based upon Parker's exhaustive study of the subject and his practical experience in the field. Unfortunately, Parker's ideas were too advanced at the time for adoption by the United States—or any other—army.

THE PHILIPPINE INSURRECTION

After the Spanish surrender of the City of Manila, August 14, 1898, to U.S. forces under Commodore George Dewey and Maj. Gen. Wesley Merritt, many Filipinos were under the mistaken impression that they would be given immediate independence. The revolutionist, Emilio Aguinaldo, exiled to Hong Kong after the unsuccessful insurrection of 1896, had been returned to the Philippines by Commodore Dewey, after the destruction of the Spanish Fleet in Manila Bay, to lead the Filipino insurgents in hemming in the Spanish on land until enough American troops arrived to invest the City of Manila. Peace between the United States and Spain was arranged by the Treaty of Paris, signed December 10, 1898, and ratified by the U.S. Senate on February 6, 1899; under the terms of this agreement, the Philippine Islands were transferred to the United States for a payment of $20,000,000. Thus, the Philippines became a possession of the United States of America. Aguinaldo, meanwhile, had established the Philippine Republic, with himself as president and the capital at Malolos, northwest of Manila, in Bulacan Province, Luzon.

Two days before the ratification of the treaty, hostilities broke out in the Manila area. Maj. Gen. Elwell S. Otis, who had succeeded Merritt, commanded a force of some 21,000 men, of which number there were only about 12,000 effectives, the others being volunteers scheduled for return to the States. U.S. control in the Philippines was limited, practically, to Manila; insurgent forces, numbering about 40,000, held a semicircle of blockhouses around the city. However, in the battle that followed the February 4 outbreak, the Filipino losses were 3,000 men, while the Americans lost only 250.

To meet the insurrectionist challenge to U.S. control of the islands, ten volunteer regiments were raised in the States and, within seven months, almost 35,000 men were on their way to reinforce the U.S. Army of Occupation in the Philippines.

Short of firearms, the Filipinos avoided open battle, resorting to guerrilla tactics, well-suited to the jungle country. Movement of troops was difficult because there were no roads; the terrain heightened the dangers of ambush and surprise attack, the advantage being with the Filipinos, fighting on familiar home ground. Many of the natives were equipped only with bolos, since rifles were scarce. Their attacks were met by the Americans with small-arms fire and bayonet charges. Although Gatling Guns had been used effectively against the Spanish, they were found too unwieldy for jungle fighting. However, Gatlings saw service on the water.

A converted gunboat was mounted with two six-pound cannon forward and four Gatling Guns, in an improvised turret, aft. This boat was used to keep Manila harbor free of insurgent craft, and also was employed against rebel forces ashore. On March 3, 1899, American outposts beyond San Pedro Macati were fired upon from the walls of the Guadalupe Church. The gunboat advanced 300 yards behind the lines, from which point its Gatling gunners wiped out the Filipino attackers. In another engagement, this boat, sweeping river banks with Gatling fire, ended the fighting careers of hundreds of guerrillas, who were hiding in the canebrakes along the shore. Later, 180 bodies were removed from the banks and a greater number left there.

According to two articles which appeared in the *Hartford Times*, the Gatling Guns sent to the Philippines in 1898 were of the Model of 1865:

> *August 30, 1898.* . . . A correspondent on the steamer, *China*, says, "For instance, the Gatling guns sent on board are of the type of 1865. The first one tried in practice the other day discharged with the barrels in every position but the right one, and the bullets struck against portions of the carriage [frame] and went flying about the deck. Several men were wounded slightly."

Gatling gun crew, USS "Alliance."

> *September 13, 1898.* Dr. Gatling said, "It was just as bad at Manila. I wish you would tell me why, with 80 new Gatling guns using smokeless powder on hand in our forts, they sent 16 of the 1865 pattern to the Philippines. It seems incredible. One wonders how a civilized government could do such thing, but they did. Some of the officials advanced the reason that the new guns needed carriages. But the carriages could have been supplied in a few weeks—long before General Merritt embarked."

It was this sort of logistics snafu that caused Maj. Gen. Joseph Wheeler, who commanded a brigade during the Philippine Insurrection, to state angrily that, on his return to the U.S., he would bring the situation to the attention of Congress, and also make every effort to secure passage of legislation providing for the purchase of more Gatling Guns of the latest type for the Army. General Wheeler, a West Point graduate, who had been a lieutenant general in the Confederate Army, was a member of the U.S. House of Representatives.

Organized resistance by the Filipinos ended early in 1900, but bitter fighting continued. During the period from May 1900 to June 1901, over a thousand engagements were fought. After that date, the insurrection was over—except for minor outbreaks which occurred spasmodically for years thereafter.

Emilio Aguinaldo, the Filipino commander, was captured March 14–25, 1901, in a daring feat by Brig. Gen. Frederick Funston. Born near Cavite, Luzon, c.1869, Aguinaldo had been a rebel leader for a number of years, first against Spain and then the United States. After his capture, he took an oath of allegiance to the United States and then, ostensibly, retired from public life. He later resumed his political activities and, in 1935, was an unsuccessful candidate for the presidency of the Commonwealth of the Philippines, being defeated by Manuel Quezon. Accused of collaboration with Japanese occupation forces during World War II, General Aguinaldo was taken into custody in 1945, but was not tried. He died February 6, 1964, in Manila; his age was given as 94.

GATLING'S LAST INVENTIONS

In the fifteen years preceding his death in 1903, Richard Jordan Gatling, 70 years old in 1888, busied himself with an amazing diversity of inventions from toilets to torpedo boats.

When the American Association of Inventors and Manufacturers was organized in 1891 at Washington, D.C., Richard Jordan Gatling was elected its first president; he held this office for six years, an honor of which he was justly proud.

On April 10, 1888, he was granted U.S. Patent No. 380,756 on an *Apparatus for Casting Ordnance.* The Gatling system for casting large cannon and other heavy ordnance involved a cast-iron mold with double walls separated by insulation. Molten metal was fed, through an arrangement of pipes, into the bottom of the mold. A core, in the center of the mold, rough-formed the bore of the gun.

A *Combined Torpedo and Gun Boat* was patented by Gatling March 12, 1889, U.S. Patent No. 399,516. This craft, designed to launch a spar torpedo and armed with a gun throwing high-explosive charges, was controlled by two operators riding on an outrigger extending back from the stern. Electric controls were to be provided for the directing of the torpedo-carrying spar, as well as the fire of the gun and the steering of the craft. The inventor explained the use of the outrigger for carrying the crew as intended to use the boat itself as a shield for the men. It would seem, however, that the crew were in a more exposed position on the outrigger and more vulnerable than if they were in the hull of the boat.

Gatling seems to have been very much interested in torpedo boats, although none of his designs appear to have been successful. On May 13, 1890, he received U.S. Patent No. 427,847 on a *Pneumatic Gun and Torpedo Boat.* Another *Torpedo and Gun Boat* was covered by U. S. Patent No. 424,288, March 25, 1890. Designed to carry an improved type of spar torpedo, this boat was provided with a means of automatically operating the torpedo and discharging a projectile from a pneumatic gun in the bow of the boat by a single action of the operator.

U.S. Patent No. 423,045, granted March 11, 1890, on a *Mold Core,* covers a system of venting and cooling cannon molds—an improvement to be applied to *Apparatus for Casting Ordnance,* patented by Gatling in 1888.

Doctor Gatling seems to have had a life-long interest in applications of the power of compressed air. It will be remembered that, in 1849, he devised a compressed air power distribution system, which the U.S. Patent Office ruled was a "discovery" not an "invention" and, therefore, could not be patented. Forty years later, he experimented with guns designed to discharge projectiles through the use of compressed air. His *Pneumatic Gun and Operating Mechanism* patented May 13, 1890, U. S. Patent No. 427,848, employed compressed air not only as a propellant but also to elevate and train the gun on its target. U.S. Patent No. 434,662, August 19, 1890, covered a *Pneumatic Gun Valve* providing an improved means of operating the air valve of a pneumatic gun and for conducting compressed air to such a gun mounted on a turntable.

Another of Gatling's great interests at this time was the casting of heavy ordnance. On June 9, 1891, he was granted U.S. Patent No. 453,833 on the *Art of Making Ordnance.* This omnibus title was given to an improvement in the method of gun casting, in which the inner and outer shells of the gun barrel were fabricated and then molten metal introduced between these walls, resulting in a laminated construction. The disastrous "Cast Steel Gun" episode of 1899 was the end result of Gatling's work in the field of casting ordnance.

An *Apparatus for Cleansing Wool or Other Material by the Use of Steam or Other Fluid,* was patented by Gatling on March 1, 1892, U.S. Patent No. 469,822. Dry cleaning originated in France about the middle of the nineteenth century and, for many years, the operations were carried out by hand in small plants. It was not until the perfection of specialized machinery that dry cleaning developed into a major industry. The Gatling cleaning apparatus was a pioneer effort in this field. As stated in the specification, the object of this invention was "to provide an apparatus by means of which wool or other raw fibrous material and also clothing or like fabrics may be cleansed with but little wear and tear in the operation." The material to be cleaned was placed in a tank into which steam or fluid was introduced with sufficient pressure to produce a washing action through the agitation of the material in the tank.

U.S. Patent No. 496,873 on a *Machine for Forging and Compacting Ingots,* issued to Richard J. Gatling on May 9, 1893, states:

> This invention relates to an improved mill for forging and compacting cylinders, tubes or shafts of malleable cast metal, the object being to condense the metal and change the crystalline structure thereof, which is the form assumed by all cast metal, into the homogeneous fibrous condition of forged metal.
>
> To this end the invention consists in a mill having a chamber in which an ingot may be heated, combined with rolls for compacting, condensing or forging the ingot . . .

Last of Gatling's metal-processing patents, this invention was a product of his absorbed interest in the foundry field.

A somewhat bizarre indication of the wide diversity of Gatling's interests—at 74 years of age—is his *Bicycle,* invented in 1892 and patented May 8, 1894, U.S. Patent No. 519,384. At first glance, this vehicle looks very much like a present-day bicycle; closer study, however, reveals a singular difference: it was designed for propulsion by either or both arm and leg power. Gatling's object was to provide exercise for the arm and chest muscles, as well as those of the legs and, by combining arm and leg power, to give greater speed for racing. In addition to pedals, this bicycle was equipped with a pair of hand-pulls; when the rider drew these handles toward himself, the cords to which they were attached, operating through an arrangement of drums, pulled on a pawl engaging the sprocket-chain and, thus, powered the rear wheel. When the cyclist's hands were occupied with the pulling operation, steering was provided for in an ingenious manner: the handlebars were connected by rods or cords to the front of the seat; the rider steered by swiveling his rump from side to side, moving the oscillating seat and, thereby, the handlebars and front wheel. In conventional use of the bicycle, the handlebars-to-seat connections were removed and the seat locked in a fixed position. It is not known whether or not any Gatling Bicycles were ever made; if so, under full hand and foot power, it really must have been a sight to see!

In 1895, Gatling invented a *Torch*—U.S. Patent No. 549,122, November 5, 1895—which, like the proverbial candle, could be burned at both ends. This was a simple device, consisting of a metal cylinder, open at both ends, with a central receptacle filled with granular material, such as gravel, and holding a quantity of coal-oil, kerosene, or other combustible fluid; the ends of the fluid chamber were perforated to permit flow of the combustible into the mineral wool or fibrous asbestos packing in both ends of the torch. Either end (or both!) could be lighted, providing a flame for kindling fires, destroying insects, tent caterpillars in trees and shrubs, etc., or for any purpose where a cheap torch-light was needed.

Reverting in 1896 to his original field of invention, agricultural machinery, Gatling devised an improved *Combined Cotton Thinner and Cultivator,* U.S. Patent No. 558,682, April 21, 1896. A half-century earlier, he had assisted his father, who patented the device in June, 1835, in the development of a cotton thinner. The patent specification of the 1896 machine states, in part:

> The object of the improvement is the production of a machine for thinning out young cotton-plants in the rows, and at the same time cultivating the ground on both sides of the rows. In raising cotton-plants it is customary to have the plants in rows which need to be thinned out when the plants are young, so as to leave intervals of free ground from one bunch of plants to another. This machine is intended for effecting that end, and also for cultivating the ground at the same time.

(No Model.) 2 Sheets—Sheet 1.

R. J. GATLING.

BICYCLE.

No. 519,384. Patented May 8, 1894.

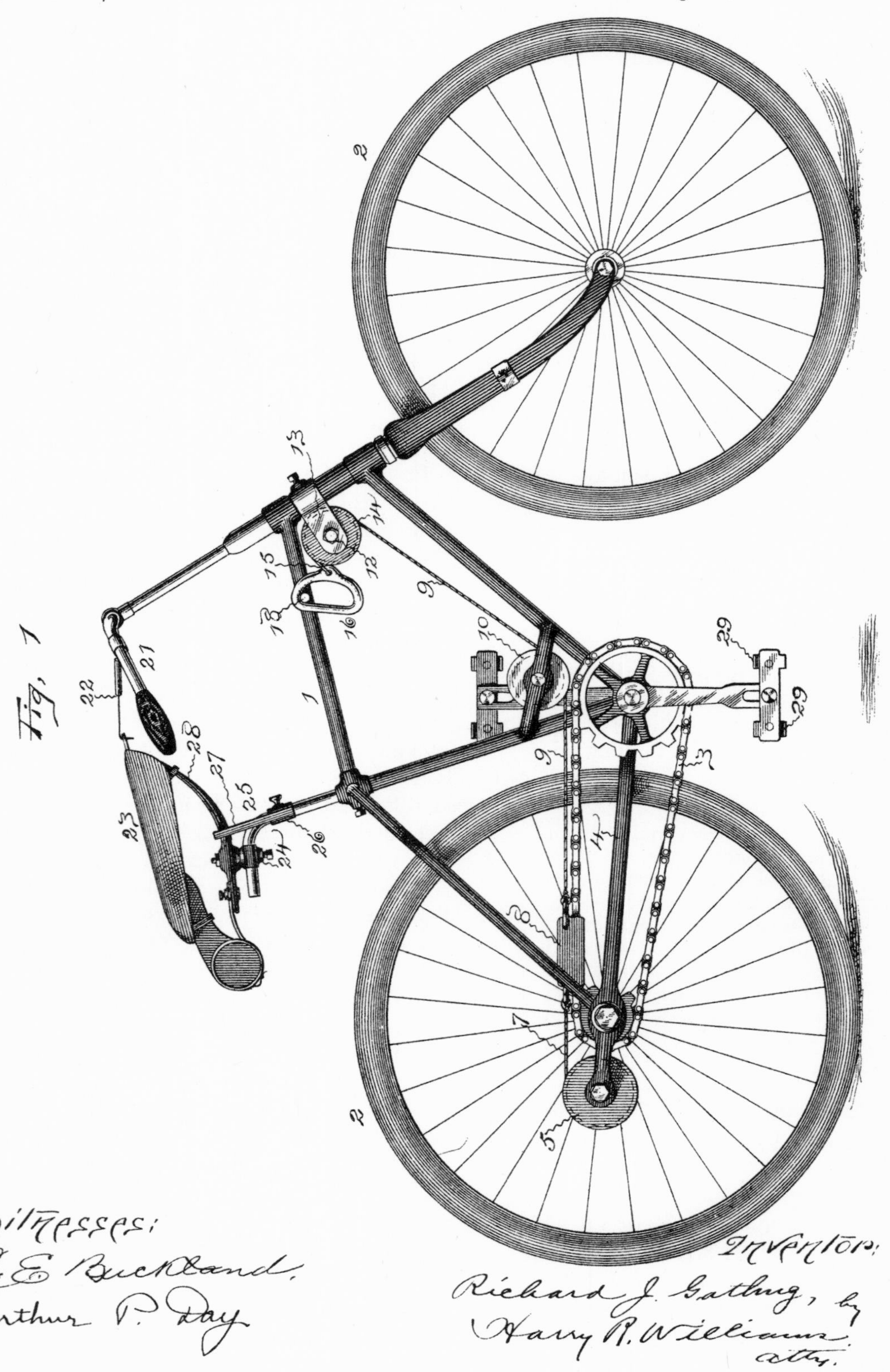

Witnesses:
C. E. Buckland.
Arthur P. Day

Inventor:
Richard J. Gatling, by
Harry R. Williams
atty.

The Combined Cotton Thinner and Cultivator performed its work by means of reciprocating hoes. Gatling designed both one- and two-horse models. On May 3, 1898, he patented an improved *Cotton Thinner,* U.S. Patent No. 603,271, employing a system of rotary knives to cut out unwanted plants; at the operator's discretion, the blades could be raised, sparing the plants to be retained.

Although, as the nineteenth century drew to a close, the horseless carriage was coming into evidence on the American scene, it still would be quite a few years before the horse became "obsolete" in transport and agriculture. On October 10, 1899, Doctor Gatling patented a Rein Controlling Means, U.S. Patent 634,451, to enable the driver to control a team without the use of his hands to hold the reins. This device consisted of a frame, to which the reins were attached, that rested on the driver's shoulders; by movement of the shoulders, a pull was exerted on either of the reins. In plowing, and other farming operations, it is necessary that the driver's hands be free; it long was the practice among plowmen to drape the reins over their shoulders while guiding the plow by handles held in each hand. This practice was dangerous in the event of a runaway; Gatling's rein-controller was equipped with provision for quick release in such instance. The patent specification suggests, as an ancillary benefit, that, by freeing the driver's hands from the task of holding the reins, it made it possible for him to better protect them from extreme cold.

On April 10, 1900, Gatling was granted U.S. Patent No. 646,977 for a *Machine for Thinning Out and Cultivating Cotton Plants,* a rather large affair embodying both thinning-out and cultivating instruments. This labor-saving device was intended to complete in one operation the tedious jobs of thinning or "blocking" out unwanted plants, by hand, with a weeding hoe and following up with a cultivator.

Later the same year, Gatling patented two other agricultural machines: a cultivator and a forerunner of the farm tractor. His *Cultivator,* Patent No. 651,659, of June 12, 1900, bears a marked resemblance to the smaller, somewhat simpler, garden cultivators offered for sale today in most suburban and rural hardware stores. Gatling's *Motor Driven Vehicle,* Patent No. 660,098, of October 23, 1900, was in effect a steam-powered tractor of great size. The power, generated by the steam engine, was transmitted to drive either or both of the rear wheels at the operator's option. Steam power was also used to provide a rudimentary form of power-steering; the massive front wheels of the vehicle, steered by a system of control-levers, were so heavy that ordinary muscle-power was inadequate to turn them.

Among Gatling's last patents was a *Flushing Apparatus for Water Closets,* covered by U.S. Patent No. 668,853, of February 26, 1901. This device consisted, simply stated, of a pitcher-like water vessel which, when the chain was pulled, tilted into the funnelled end of the flush-pipe, pouring the water therein, thus flushing the toilet. The patent drawings exhibit two styles of Gatling W.C.: a single unit and a three-seater, toilet-room installation. The latter provides a startling illustration of nineteenth century "togetherness."

As early as 1857, Gatling's inventions included a steam plow. This machine, which was not self-propelled like his later developments, was never exploited, because of the inventor's poor health at the time and a lack of receptiveness on the part of farmers. Forty-five years later, Gatling was granted two *Motor Plow* patents: the first, U.S. Patent No. 696,808, April 1, 1902, covered a steam tractor equipped with ganged plows, adjustable to control the width of ground plowed, the width and depth of furrow; the second, U.S. Patent No. 705,337, was concerned primarily with a motor-powered lift to raise and lower the heavy agricultural implements attached to the tractor.

Just before his death, on February 26, 1903, at the age of 84, Richard Jordan Gatling was engaged in the organization, in St. Louis, Missouri, of the Gatling Motor Plow Company to handle the exploitation of his motor plow patents.

To the very last day of his long life, Doctor Gatling was a very busy man—indeed, this may have hastened his end. Of all of his many inventions, perhaps only two can be declared eminently successful: the Gatling Gun and the wheat drill. These inventions made fortunes which Gatling largely dissipated in railroad and real estate speculations and in the fruitless promotion of his other inventions. Over the years, Gatling is said to have invested and lost over $2,000,000—a considerable sum today and fantastically great in Gatling's time—yet, when he died, he was still a wealthy man.

GATLING'S CAST-STEEL GUN

One of the great disappointments of Richard Jordan Gatling's latter years was the failure of his cast-steel gun. The story of this fiasco is told in the following quotations from the *Scientific American* of December 31, 1898, and January 14, 1899:

No. 668,853. Patented Feb. 26, 1901.

R. J. GATLING.

FLUSHING APPARATUS FOR WATER CLOSETS.

(Application filed Aug. 4, 1899.)

(No Model.) 2 Sheets—Sheet 2.

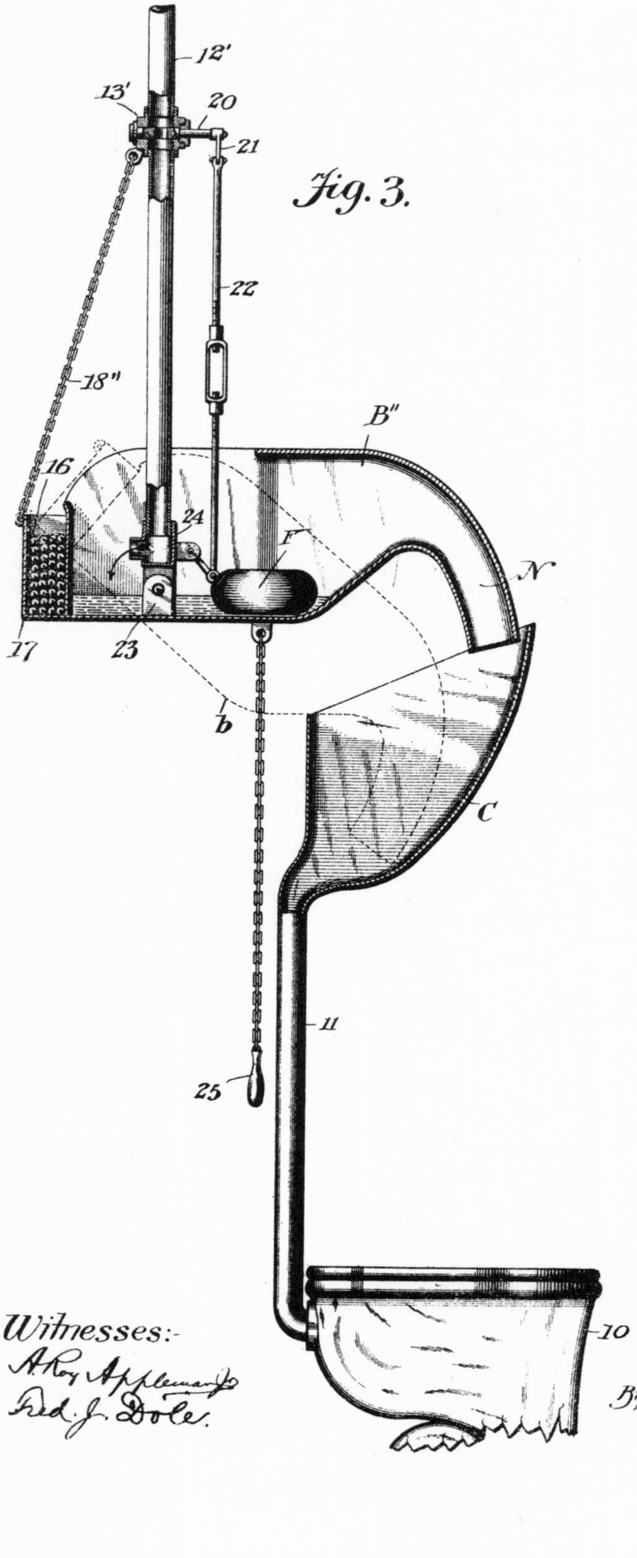

Fig. 3.

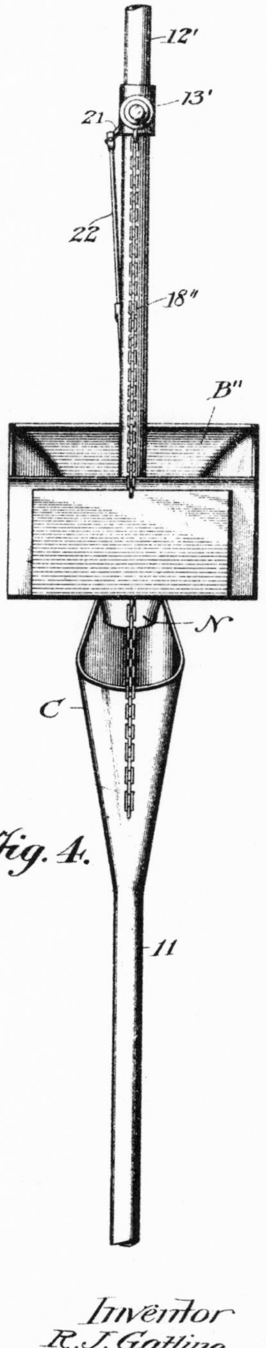

12'
13'
20
21
22
18"
B"
16
24
F
N
17
23
b
C
25
11
10

Fig. 4.

12'
13'
21
22
18"
B"
N
C
11

Witnesses:-
A. Roy Appleman Jr.
Fred. J. Dole.

Inventor
R. J. Gatling,
By his Attorney,
F. H. Richards.

Gatling's ill-fated cast-steel gun.

THE GATLING CAST-STEEL GUN

Great interest attaches to the government tests of the 8-inch cast-steel gun designed by Dr. Gatling of machine gun fame. It is the object of Dr. Gatling to produce a gun which shall possess all the ballistic qualities of the prevailing type of hooped or built-up gun without its excessive cost. The present built-up system is founded upon the method introduced by our General Rodman during the Civil War, who, in order to compress the interior metal of the gun, cooled the gun from the inside, thus causing the exterior layers to shrink with tremendous gripping effect upon the bore. The same effect is secured in forged steel guns by shrinking successive hoops of steel upon an interior tube. Rodman's method was cheap and rapid; the present method is slow and very costly.

Of late years several attempts have been made to dispense with the hooped construction and produce a steel gun of one integral forging or casting. In 1895 Maxim made a 5-inch gun of a single forging and cooled it from the inside by running a stream of coal oil through the bore. In the firing test his gun showed a velocity of 2,200 feet per second with a pressure of 33,600 pounds to the square inch, and withstood a maximum pressure of 50,400 pounds without injury. In January of this year a single-forging steel gun, designed by Capt. F. E. Hobbs, of the Ordnance Department, United States Army, was tested at Sandy Hook with excellent results, a velocity of 2,700 feet being attained with a pressure of 50,000 pounds to the square inch.

Dr. Gatling is endeavoring to go one step further and cheapen gun construction by dispensing as far as possible with forging processes and casting his gun direct from the cupola. It is evident that if a reliable cast steel gun can be manufactured, the cost and time consumed in heavy gun construction will be greatly reduced—according to Gatling, fully 50 per cent. The metal used is a special steel alloy, and the gun is cast in a vertical position, muzzle downward. An attempt is made to impart a fibrous character to the casting by giving a swirling motion to the steel as it enters the mould, and Dr. Gatling states that a certain amount of forging of the interior is affected by the use of a rotary mandrel when the gun is red hot in the annealing furnace. The desired compression and tension are secured by cooling from the interior. In the preliminary tests the gun has withstood a pressure of 37,000 pounds to the square inch. This is satisfactory as far as it goes, but with the records of 50,400 and 50,000 pounds pressure in the Maxim and Hobbs guns and 82,850 pounds pressure in the Brown wire gun ahead of it, the cast steel gun has a long road to travel before it eclipses its predecessors. If it equals these pressures and survives the 300 rounds to which the government officials will subject it. Dr. Gatling will have made an invaluable contribution to the science and art of heavy gun construction, and it will only remain to overcome the undoubted prejudice which modern artillerists entertain against cast as compared with forged or wire-wound ordnance. (December 31, 1898.)

FAILURE OF THE GATLING CAST-STEEL GUN

The idea that a cast-steel gun can be produced which will have the same ratio of energy to weight of gun as the hooped or wirewound gun, and stand the test of continued firing, dies hard. The latest attempt to work out a proposition which our artillery experts regard as, in the nature of things, impossible was embodied in the 8-inch cast-steel gun of Dr. Gatling, for the construction of which Congress appropriated $40,000. As we noted in a recent issue, the gun was duly constructed according to the inventor's specifications and sent to the Sandy Hook proving-ground to be tested. A sum of $18,600 was allotted by the Board of Ordnance and Fortification for this purpose, and it was the intention to subject the weapon to three hundred rounds in all. These tests are commenced at the standard firing pressure used in the army guns of 37,000 pounds to the square inch, but before they are over it frequently happens that the pressures rise far above this figure, in some cases exceeding it by over 100 per cent. When a gun has stood three hundred rounds, during which the pressure may have risen as high as 82,858 pounds, as actually occurred in the case of the Brown wire gun, the ordnance experts do not hesitate to pass it as being perfectly satisfactory, as far as danger of rupture is concerned.

The Gatling gun had already resisted five rounds with ordinary charges in its first trials. During the second series of trials, which took place on January 4, ten rounds were fired with the same charges and pressures of about 37,000 pounds. At the tenth round of the series, or the fifteenth round for the gun, it failed completely, and is described as flying into many fragments.

On being interviewed, Dr. Gatling stated that the failure did not surprise him, because he was aware that there was a mishap at one stage of the manufacture. He avers that tests of the metal of the gun showed that the breech was considerably weaker than the muzzle of the gun, the defect being due to the fact that the breech was subject to a high temperature for three days longer than it should have been. As a result, the strength of the breech compared with the muzzle was about as six to ten, the metal at the muzzle representing the strength which was designed to be secured for the whole gun.

If these are the facts, though we confess the statement needs elucidation, it is greatly to be regretted that the weapon was not rejected and another cast. Every one, and none more than ordnance officers, in anxious to know the exact possibilities of cast ordnance. The present failure, notwithstanding the alleged mishap in the manufacture, will tend to strengthen the prejudice which undoubtedly exists against the type. (January 14, 1899.

Another version of the cause of this failure, attributed to Gatling, appears in his obituary in *The New York Times* of February 27, 1903: "He maintained that the gun had been overcharged by enemies, who did not want the patent to substitute other Governmental guns."

In response to demands for an explanation of the unsuccessful conclusion of the Cast Steel Gun Project, in which the Government had invested nearly $60,000, Gatling engaged the services of John Nelson Stockwell to make an investigation and prepare a report on the causes of the failure of the gun. The choice of Stockwell for this assignment seems odd—he was a scientist and author (e.g., *Memoir on the Secular Variations of the Elements of the Orbits of the Eight Principal Planets*) best known for his work in the field of mathematics and astronomy. At any rate, the Stockwell Report, apparently a masterpiece of scientific gobbledygook, seems to have effected a complete obfuscation and, happily for Gatling, the whole affair was forgotten.

DEATH OF THE MAN AND THE GUN

On the morning of February 26, 1903, 84-year-old Richard Jordan Gatling awakened to his last day of life. Two weeks earlier, he and his wife, Jemina, had arrived in New York City for a visit with their daughter, Ida, and her husband, Hugh O. Pentecost, at the latter's home in the Aberdeen, 249 West 107th Street. Prior to the trip to New York, Gatling had spent some time in St. Louis, Missouri, location of the headquarters of his newly organized firm, the Gatling Motor Plow Company, which was to exploit his recently perfected motor plow; this company was capitalized for $500,000. Although suffering from a heart condition for the past three years, he still was very active as an inventor and in business. A recent bout with influenza had left the aged man in a weakened condition and it was decided that he would come to New York for a rest.

Feeling much better after two weeks at his daughter's home, Gatling had gained strength rapidly and it was with difficulty that his family restrained him from going out. He insisted, on the morning of February 26, that he felt fine and would go downtown to the offices of Munn & Co., publishers of *Scientific American*, at 361 Broadway, more than four miles distant. For years, it had been Gatling's practice, whenever he was in New York, to call upon the editor of *Scientific American* for a half hour or so of conversation. This visit, he told his family, was necessary as he had business to transact with Munn & Co. Incidentally, the Scientific American Patent Agency had long represented him in patent matters.

Gatling returned to his son-in-law's home about noon, badly tired from his trip downtown and back. Instead of joining his wife and daughter at luncheon, he lay down to rest awhile on the couch in a nearby room. While Mrs. Pentecost and her mother were lunching, the telephone rang in the room

R. J. Gatling

where her father was resting and she hurried there to answer it. The caller was her husband, telephoning from his law offices in the New York Life Building. Mrs. Pentecost had no more than picked up the receiver when she was distracted by the sound of her father's labored breathing. She asked her husband to wait a moment, went to her father's side and saw that he was very ill. Returning to the telephone, she told her husband of Gatling's condition, and was instructed to call a physician immediately and that Mr. Pentecost would return home at once. Hearing her daughter's excited tones, Mrs. Gatling came into the room to see what was the matter.

"See if you can do anything," Mrs. Pentecost said to her mother, "I'll get the doctor." She called a messenger boy in the apartment hall and sent him to get Dr. Charles P. Duffy, of 211 West 107th Street. Running back into the room, Mrs. Pentecost found her father's condition worse: he was gasping, hardly able to breathe. Thinking that it might help him, his daughter raised his head and shoulders, holding him in her arms, it taking all her strength to support him. Mrs. Gatling bent over them in helpless agony, watching her husband's last throes. The end came before Dr. Duffy arrived. Thus concluded the long and useful life of Richard Jordan Gatling, at the age of eighty-four years and six months. He had been active to the very end.

The remains arrived in Indianapolis; over the Big Four, at 11:45 in the morning of March 2 and were taken to the residence of John R. Wilson, 1308 Central Avenue. Funeral services, attended by family friends, were held that afternoon at 2 P.M. Mrs. Gatling, her daughter, Ida (Mrs. Pentecost), and son, Richard H. Gatling, had accompanied the remains from New York City. The pallbearers were John S. Duncan, John R. Wilson, David Wallace, Walter Golt, Robert P. Duncan, and Judge James Leathers. Gatling was interred, at private burial services, in the old Sanders (his father-in-law) lot in Crown Hill Cemetery.

Destroyer USS "Gatling".

Jemina and Richard Jordan Gatling had five children, of whom the two eldest, a boy and a girl, died in childhood; the surviving children were their daughter, Ida, and two sons, Richard Henry and Robert B. Gatling. Ida's husband, Hugh O. Pentecost, a New York attorney, was previously the pastor of the South Baptist Church, of Hartford, Connecticut; the Gatling family were members of this congregation during their long residence in Hartford. Richard H. Gatling was engaged in the real estate field, while his brother, Robert B. Gatling, was in the fire insurance business.

Although Gatling was still well-to-do at the time of his death, much of the fortunes he had made on the wheat drill and Gatling Gun had been lost in the unsuccessful exploitation of other of his many inventions and in heavy losses on investments in Western railroads. In his long life, he had been a millionaire more than once as the fruit of his inventive genius.

As one of the most prominent men of his era, Gatling was the subject of lengthy obituaries in all of the leading newspapers. Most of these dwelt at length on his achievements; a few spoke of Richard Jordan Gatling, the man:

> *New York Times:* ". . . His life was full of disappointments, but friends say that he merely laughed at disappointments. . . . Aside from his ability as an inventor, his friends speak of Dr. Gatling as a student and a philosopher. . . ."

> *Scientific American:* ". . . . Although best known as the inventor of a terrible death-dealing weapon, Dr. Gatling was the gentlest and kindliest of men. The sight of returning wounded soldiers early in the civil war led him to consider how war's horrors might be alleviated. By making war more terrible, it seemed to him nations would be less willing to resort to arms. He devoted himself to the study of ordnance and ballistics, and finally invented what may be considered the first modern machine gun. As the inventor of that gun his name will probably be handed down."

The development of the automatic machine gun was the beginning of the end for the Gatling and all other manually-operated, multi-firing weapons. In 1911, the U.S. Army officially declared the Gatling Gun obsolete after 45 years of service. Most other nations had taken this action years earlier. Thereafter, the gun and its inventor, once world-famous, faded into virtual oblivion.

During the "Roaring Twenties," a new word came into common usage from the argot of the underworld: *gat,* derived from "Gatling" and meaning a pistol or revolver. This seems a poor memorial for Richard Jordan Gatling, "the Father of the Machine Gun." Forty years after his death, he was given a more fitting one.

In 1943, during World War II, the United States Government remembered Gatling and honored him by giving his name to a new destroyer. Mrs. John W. Gatling, wife of the inventor's grandson, sponsored the ship on June 20, 1943. Serving in the Pacific Theater, the USS *Gatling* traveled approximately 175,000 miles, its 5-inch guns discharged over 77 tons of ammunition, and its 20mm. and 40mm. antiaircraft batteries fired uncounted thousands of rounds. The ship's operations were without the loss of one member of the crew to enemy action, sickness or accident—a remarkable record, especially in wartime. Honors awarded the *Gatling* were the American Defense Ribbon, the Asiatic-Pacific Theater Ribbon with eight combat stars, and the Philippine Liberation Ribbon with two combat stars. Surely, Richard Jordan Gatling would have been proud to have such a ship as his namesake.

EPILOGUE

THE GATLING COMES BACK

AFTER its late-in-life triumph at Santiago de Cuba in 1898, the Gatling Gun, like an old soldier, just faded away. By 1903, when Richard Jordan Gatling's long life came to its end, the day of the multibarreled, manually operated machine gun had passed. For the most part, the world's armed forces by then had converted to automatic weapons such as the recoil-operated Maxim, the gas-operated Colt-Browning and Hotchkiss. Surplus Gatlings were being sold at bargain-basement prices for service with the ragtag armies of the "Banana Republics" in their interminable revolutions and wars of liberation. Many of these guns were relegated to scrap heaps and eventual destruction, while a few found kinder oblivion in dusty storerooms, from whence some have been rescued for display in museums and private collections.

The fiftieth anniversary of the invention of the Gatling Gun, in 1911, was marked by the U.S. Army declaring the weapon officially obsolete. It is interesting to note that our military, who were so slow to adopt the Gatling, were among the last to discard it. Acording to official records, on June 30, 1915, of 1,236 machine guns in U.S. Army service, 131 were Gatlings; the others: 670 Benét-Mercié (Hotchkiss type), 287 Maxim, 148 Colt-Browning.

It took 45 years for the Gatling Gun to rise from the ashes of obsolescence. This phoenix-like comeback is virtually unparalleled in ordnance history.

As World War II drew to a close, U.S. ordnance experts began to direct their attention to the armament needs of future military aircraft. Aerial machine guns then in use were essentially adaptations of ground weapons, modified for use on airplanes. Chief drawback was the inability of such guns to deliver sufficient firepower in the split second during which a supersonic aircraft would be on target. The cyclic rate of the .50 caliber machine gun had been accelerated to what was believed to be the practical maximum attainable with a reciprocating firing mechanism in this caliber: 1,200 rounds per minute—the Model 1880 Gatling was capable of this rate of fire. Since a much higher firing rate was considered essential, it became evident that the quest for a firing mechanism which would deliver a more lethal projectile at a higher velocity, with greater accuracy, at longer range, must be headed in the direction of an externally powered machine gun. Historically, the most successful firing mechanism of this type was that of the Gatling Gun; as far back as 1893, an electric-motor-driven Gatling attained a cyclic rate of 3,000 rounds per minute.

In 1945, the problem of high-firing-rate aircraft machine guns was being given serious consideration by the U.S. Army Ordnance Research and Development Service, Small Arms Branch, whose chief was Col. Rene R. Studler. After a study of all types of machine guns, it was decided that the basic principles of the Gatling system offered the greatest potential for a modern aircraft weapon, because of the tremendous rate of fire possible and the reliability of a design incorporating a rotating cluster of barrels, externally powered. By using a number of barrels, the erosion and heat generation of high-cyclic-rate guns is reduced, permitting cooler, more reliable operation, with minimum chance of overheated ammunition exploding prematurely and wrecking the gun. The external power source—electric motor or hydraulic drive—permits each round to be fired independently of the previous cartridge; thus, any "duds" are automatically ejected. This is an outstanding advantage over gas-operated weapons, which are subject to jamming if a round does not fire. The importance of such improved reliability is easily understood in terms of combat effectiveness.

Based upon the preliminary findings of his research group, Colonel Studler recommended further investigation of the feasibility of a power-driven Gatling type gun as aircraft armament. A

Model 1883 Gatling fitted with electric-motor drive for study preliminary to Project Vulcan.

contract for this study was awarded to Johnson Automatics, Inc., of Providence, R.I., a firm headed by Col. Melvin M. Johnson, Jr., inventor of the Johnson Semi-automatic Rifle and the Johnson Light Machine Gun. Later in 1945, Johnson was ready to make the first firing tests. Some difficulty had been encountered in procuring a Gatling Gun in shooting condition, but finally one was obtained from F. Bannerman Sons, of New York City. This gun, now in the Winchester Gun Museum, is a Model 1883 ten-barrel Gatling, caliber .45/70, with Accles feed. It was fitted with an electric motor drive; during testing, it was found necessary to replace the original breechbolts with modern ones of harder steel. After several trials, a firing rate of *5,800* rounds per minute (for 50 rounds, firing electrically timed) was attained.* In 1946, Colonel Johnson submitted his feasibility report, together with recommendations for the adaptation of the power-driven Gatling system to aircraft cannon.

* How does a gun sound firing at the rate of about 6,000 rounds per minute? Best description was given by the late Colonel Johnson, who had listened to a lot of automatic weapons; he said: "Actually, it sounds like a high-speed outboard motor without a muffler." Thus updated is what Victorian journalists liked to call "Gatling music."

PROJECT VULCAN

General Electric Company, in June, 1946, was awarded the contract for "Project Vulcan," to be a joint undertaking of that company, the U.S. Air Force, and Army Ordnance. Specifications for the preliminary design of the Vulcan Gun included these requirements: caliber, .60; number of barrels, 5 to 10; barrel length, 60 inches; over-all length of gun, 80 inches; total weight, not to exceed 100 pounds per barrel; minimum rate of fire, 1,000 rounds per minute per barrel. The first model was completed in April, 1949. It had 779 parts and was capable of firing 4,000 rounds per minute (the current 20mm. M61 Vulcan has 224 components, is designed to fire at steady-state rate of 6,600 shots per minute). By the summer of 1950, design improvements resulted in increasing the firing rate to 5,000 and later to over 6,000 shots per minute. Ten of the Model "A" .60 caliber T-45 guns were produced and subjected to extensive testing to prove the feasibility and potential of such a weapon.

Based on the favorable results experienced with the T-45 guns, work was started in December, 1950, on a production prototype, Model "C." A total of 33 Model "C" guns were produced and shipped to

Vulcan gun and its famous ancestor, the Gatling (Model 1903).

Army Ordnance and Air Force installations for test and evaluation. These guns were made in three versions: .60 caliber, 20mm., and 27mm. Testing at Springfield Armory and Aberdeen Proving Ground established the complete reliability of the system. In May, 1952, seven of the new guns fired 75,000 rounds without malfunction.

After exhaustive—and successful—testing, the T-171 20mm. gun was selected for further refinement and development of a true production design. A contract was given General Electric Company for the manufacture of 27 of these guns for delivery commencing August 1952. The T-171 fired a 20mm. round 6⅝ inches long, had six barrels, was 72 inches over-all and about 11 inches in diameter; weight was approximately 290 to 300 pounds—about 50 pounds for each barrel, half the weight limit set by original specifications. It was capable of firing in excess of 6,000 rounds per minute. Power supply was either electric or hydraulic, depending upon the aircraft in which the gun was to be installed.

This development program resulted, in 1956, in the T-171 20mm. gun being standardized by the U.S. Air Force and Army as the *M61, 20mm. Vulcan Aircraft Gun* and ordered into production.

Subsequent to the design of the 20mm. M61, General Electric Company, under direction of the U.S. Air Force and Army, developed a 30mm. version of the Vulcan Gun, designated T-212, firing a round 50 percent larger and three times as powerful as the 20mm. Although larger in caliber, the 30mm. gun was much like the previous Vulcans—even in weight, through the use of shorter barrels. Over-all length of the T-212 was 64 inches, compared with 72 inches for the M61. Two of the 30mm. Vulcans were produced, but it was never standardized.

Six thousand 20mm shell cases—one minute's firing of the Vulcan gun.

M61, 20MM. VULCAN AIRCRAFT GUN

The M61, 20mm. Vulcan Gun is an externally powered, six-barrel, rotary-firing mechanism, capable of discharging up to 7,200 shots per minute. Length is 72 inches, weight 255 pounds. It fires standard, electrically primed, 20mm. ammunition such as M53A1 armor-piercing incendiary, M56A1 high-explosive incendiary, and M55A1 ball; muzzle velocity is 3,380 ft./sec.

This weapon is powered by a drive motor–electric, hydraulic, or ram-air turbine, for compatibility with aircraft systems–that rotates the barrels and applies voltage to the firing circuit. When the gun is triggered, the cartridge belt is pulled into the feed mechanism, which strips the links from the round and places it in front of the bolt, which moves forward, seating the cartridge in the chamber. Successively, the bolt is locked, the cartridge fired, the bolt unlocked, the spent shell extracted and ejected. This cycle is repeated at high speed; when the trigger is released, power is interrupted and the rotor is braked to a stop. In the Vulcan Gun, rotation of the barrels is counterclockwise. Feed is at 5 o'clock, firing at 12 o'clock, and ejection at 6:30 o'clock.

The six rotating barrels contribute to a long life (gun life, 100,000 rounds; barrel life, 15,000 rounds) by greatly reducing the problem of barrel erosion and heat generation, as only one barrel fires at a time. This method of operation eliminates erratic recoil associated with multiple gun installations. All barrels are rigidly clamped together, producing a minimum dispersion pattern. The gun easily meets the military requirement that 80 percent of its shots

Detachable pod houses M61 20mm Vulcan gun.

Modern bombers—B52 (left), B58 (right)—carry potent stingers in their tails: 20mm Vulcans.

Linkless ammunition feed system, Vulcan gun.

fall within an 8 mil ring at 1,000 inches. Low-temperature and high-altitude tests have proved that the 20mm. Vulcan Gun will function properly throughout the range of —67 to +260° F. and at altitudes of 60,000 feet, which is in the spectrum of manned aircraft performance.

Generally, the life of the gun is considered equal to that of the aircraft in terms of missions. A complete overhaul is not necessary until 45,000 rounds have been fired. Several features of the M61 Vulcan permit simplified installation and maintenance. The muzzle clamp is quickly detached by removing only one nut. The mid-barrel clamp can be removed by simply pulling it forward over the muzzles after three bolts have been loosened. Barrels are detached with a one-third turn. The feeder is detached from the gun housing by two quick-release pins. The hydraulic drive may be easily removed by taking off only one clamp. The gun bolts are accessible through a hinged cover on the housing. Periodic field stripping of the Vulcan for normal cleaning can be accomplished in only 8 minutes by personnel familiar with the weapon.

The M61 Vulcan has been installed on the U.S. Air Force F104 Starfighter, F105 Thunderchief, B52H, and B58 Hustler; it also arms the F104G of the Belgian, Dutch, German, and Italian Air Forces, and the F104J of the Japanese Air Force.

M61, 20MM. GUN POD

The M61 gun pod is a weapon for engagement of ground targets by high-performance, close-support aircraft. Over 12 seconds of fire with high-explosive and armor-piercing ammunition is available. The pod has a self-contained power supply (ram-air turbine) and weighs about 1,600 pounds, including ammunition. It measures 220 inches in length, 22 inches in diameter. Two or more pods can be carried on jet fighter aircraft, giving greater rates of

Gun pod, 20mm Vulcan gun, on F-100.

Three-barrel 20mm Vulcan gun mounted in helicopter.

fire or longer time of firing as desired. It is also possible to load the pods with different types of ammunition and thus select the type best suited for various targets encountered. Ammunition capacity is 1,200 rounds. The gun pod incorporates an M61-A1 20mm. Vulcan Gun, utilizes a linkless ammunition feed system; spent cartridge cases are ejected from the pod.

THREE-BARREL 20MM. VULCAN GUN (MODIFIED M61)

Tailored for U.S. Army use in helicopters, the three-barrel version of 20mm. Vulcan is a modification of the standard M61 six-barrel gun, accomplished by changing feeder and barrels. If necessary, these changes can be made in the field with standard hand tools. Firing rate is up to 3,000 shots per minute, depending upon power source used.

GENERAL ELECTRIC 7.62MM. MINIGUN

An evolution of the 20mm. Vulcan used in many modern high-performance fighter and bomber aircraft, the GAU-2/A Aircraft Machine Gun (Minigun) was designed to provide a fast-firing, lightweight armament package for helicopters and other light aircraft, where a very high rate of fire is needed against personnel and light, unarmored vehicle targets. The basic Vulcan mechanism has been simplified and redesigned to fire percussion-primed ammunition. Intended to handle the 7.62mm. NATO round, the gun design can be readily modified to fire other small caliber ammunition (e.g., 5.56mm.) by changes in the feeder, housing, bolts, and barrels. Variable firing rate combinations, up to about 7,000 shots per minute, are available to adapt the gun to a variety of missions.

The basic Minigun weighs approximately 35

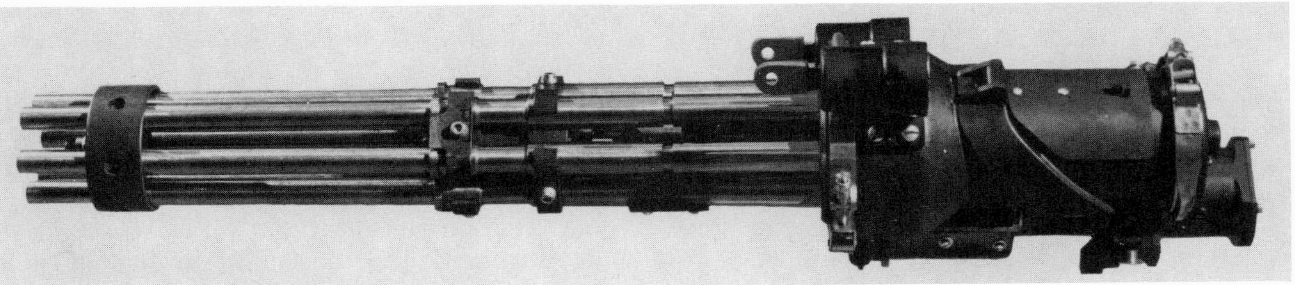

GE 7.62mm Minigun.

7.62mm Minigun pod.

pounds; feeder adds 5 or 8 pounds; motor and gear box, 9 pounds. Length, with 22-inch barrels, is 31½ inches. Design life is 100,000 rounds.

Applications of the Minigun include a pod configuration and a nose gun assembly for internal installation.

7.62MM. MINIGUN POD

General Electric's 7.62mm. Minigun Pod (SUU-11/A) is a weapon for engagement of ground targets by both high- and low-performance aircraft and for applications requiring highly accurate, concentrated firepower with minimum weight and maximum reliability.

The pod utilizes the GE 7.62mm. Minigun and Linkless Feed System, externally powered. Battery-powered electric motor drive is completely self-contained, so that only control power is required from the aircraft. An alternate drive, using gas from firing, is available for specific applications. The Minigun Pod is 85 inches long, 12 inches in diameter, weighs 250 pounds when fully loaded. Ammunition capacity is 1,500 rounds. Firing rate is variable, up to 6,000 shots per minute. Maximum length of burst is 1,500 rounds.

Although originally designed for caliber 7.62mm. NATO, the Minigun Pod may be adapted to other small calibers. In .22 caliber, a pod of the same dimensions and weight would have an ammunition capacity of 3,000 rounds. Such a weapon, chambered for the 5.56mm., M193 cartridge (used in the M16 and XM16E1 rifles), is entirely feasible for antipersonnel use.

THE MACHINE GUN IN MODERN AIR WARFARE

To say that these latter-day "Gatlings" represent the ultimate in aircraft machine guns may be temerarious, since the use of the word "ultimate" always involves a degree of risk; however, the Vulcans most certainly are the highest development of the power-driven machine gun. In these days of nuclear warheads, missiles, and rockets, military hardware as unsophisticated as a machine gun may seem to many as almost an anachronism. The Vulcan Gun well may be the last weapon of its type, but the need for aircraft machine guns will continue to exist for many years to come. With the Vulcan, aircraft can engage targets that might be impractical for missiles because of such conditions as target nature, range, adverse weather, evasive action, or electronic countermeasures. Capable of greater target saturation, at 6,000+ shots per minute, than any other known production weapon during the split seconds of time-on-target, the Vulcan Gun complements aircraft missile armament, providing a more versatile weapons array.

Thus, as the Vulcan Gun, the old Gatling has come full circle, after a century, from a mule-drawn carriage to a bulge on the hip of a supersonic jet fighter.

F-100 can fire 12,000 rounds per minute from its twin 20mm Vulcan pods.

BIBLIOGRAPHY

Accles Machine Gun. Washington: Driggs Ordnance Co., n.d. Beach, Alfred E. (ed.). *The Science Record for 1872.* New York: Munn & Co., 1872.

Beresford, Charles W. D. "Machine-guns," *Journal of the Royal United Service Institution,* Vol. XXVI (1884), pp. 601–628.

________. "Machine Guns in the Field," *Journal of the Royal United Service Institution,* Vol. XVIII (1885), pp. 941–963.

Board of Officers Gillmore, Treadwell, and Lorain. *Ordnance Memoranda No. 17:* Report of the Board of Officers; Appointed by Special Orders No. 108, A.G.O., May 31, 1873, on Gatling Guns of Large Caliber for Flank-defense. Washington: Government Printing Office, 1874.

Chinn, George M. *The Machine Gun,* Vol. I. Washington: Government Printing Office, 1951.

Dyer, A. B. *Handbook for Light Artillery.* New York: John Wiley & Sons, 1898.

Fletcher, H. C. "The Employment of Mitrailleurs During the Recent War, and Their Use in Future Wars," *Journal of the Royal United Service Institution,* Vol. XVI (1873), pp. 28–55.

Fosbery, G. V. "On Mitrailleurs, and Their Place in the Wars of the Future," *Journal of the Royal United Service Institution,* Vol. XIII (1870), pp. 539–563.

Foster, Charles H. "The Modern Vulcan," *Potter's American Monthly,* Vol. XII, No. 89 (May 1879), pp. 321–333.

Franklin, William B. *The Gatling Gun, For Service Ashore and Afloat.* Hartford: Case, Lockwood & Brainard Co., 1874.

________. *Manual of the Gatling Battery Gun.* Hartford: privately printed, 1872.

Fullam, William F., and Hart, Thomas C. *Text-book of Ordnance and Gunnery* (2nd ed.). Annapolis: U.S. Naval Institute, 1905.

Gatling, R. J. "Machine Guns: the Gatling Battery—the Agar and Claxton Guns—the French and Montigny Mitrailleurs," *Journal of the Royal United Service Institution,* Vol. XIV (1871), pp. 504–528.

The Gatling Guns (With Positive Feed) for Service Ashore and Afloat. London: Sheppard & St. John, n.d.

Gatling's Battery Gun. Hartford: Case, Lockwood & Co., 1867.

Goddard, Calvin. "The Machine Gun—Its Early Applications," *Army Ordnance,* Vol. XXII, No. 128 (Sept.-Oct. 1941), pp. 235–237; No. 129 (Nov.-Dec. 1941), pp. 405–407; No. 130 (Jan.-Feb. 1942), p. 579; No. 131 (Mar.-Apr. 1942), pp. 767-768.

________. "The Machine Gun—A Period of Evolution," *Army Ordnance,* No. 132 (May-June 1942), pp. 976–978; Vol. XXIII, No. 133 (July-Aug. 1942), p. 109; No. 134 (Sept.-Oct. 1942), pp. 314–316; No. 135 (Nov.-Dec. 1942), p. 514; Vol. XXIV, No. 136 (Jan.-Feb. 1943), pp. 107–109.

________. *The Machine Gun—The Period of Recognition.* Washington: Army Ordnance Association, n.d. (reprinted from the Mar.-Apr., May-June, July-Aug., Sept.-Oct., Nov.-Dec. 1943, and Jan.-Feb. 1944 issues of *Army Ordnance*).

Handbook of the Gatling Gun, .30 Caliber; Models 1895, 1900, 1903. Washington: Government Printing Office, 1917.

Hatcher, Julian S.; Wilhelm, Glenn P.; Malony, Harry J. *Machine Guns* (2nd ed.) Menasha, Wis.: George Banta Publishing Co., 1917.

Lewis, B. R. *Machine Guns of the U.S., 1895–1944:* An Authentic Account of All Official Models of That Period. Washington: Army Ordnance Association, n.d. (reprinted from the July-Aug., Sept.-Oct., Nov.-Dec. 1945, Jan.-Feb. and Mar.-Apr. 1946 issues of *Army Ordnance*).

Longstaff, F. V., and Atteridge, A. Hilliard. *The Book of the Machine Gun.* London: Hugh Rees Ltd., 1917.

McCarty, Arthur Clayton. "Dr. Richard Jordan Gatling (1818–1903)," *Annals of Medical History,* 3rd Series, Vol. II (Sept. 1940), pp. 359–365.

Marvin, J. D. *Instructions for Use and Care of Gatling Guns.* Washington: U.S. Bureau of Ordnance, 1875.

Nomenclature and Description of the Gatling Gun, .30 Caliber; Models 1895 and 1900. Washington: Government Printing Office, 1908.

Norton, Charles B. *American Breech-Loading Small Arms.* New York: F. W. Chistern, 1872.

________. *American Inventions and Improvements in Breech-Loading Small Arms* (2nd ed.) Boston: James R. Osgood & Co., 1882.

Norton, Charles B., and Valentine, W. J. *Report to the Government of the United States on the Munitions of War Exhibited at the Paris Universal Exhibition, 1867.* New York: Office of the Army and Navy Journal, 1868.

Parker, John H. *The Gatlings at Santiago:* History of the Gatling Gun Detachment, Fifth Army Corps, at Santiago, With a Few Unvarnished Truths Concerning that Expedition. Kansas City: Hudson-Kimberly Publishing Co., 1898.

________. *Tactical Organization and Uses of Machine Guns in the Field.* Kansas City: Hudson-Kimberly Publishing Co., 1899.

Pridham, C. H. B. *Superiority of Fire:* A Short History of Rifles and Machine-guns. London: Hutchinson's Scientific and Technical Publications, 1945.

Rogers, E. "The Gatling Gun; Its Place in Tactics," *Journal of the Royal United Service Institution,* Vol. XIX (1876), pp. 419–445.

Schofield, John M. *Modern Guns and Mortars.* Washington: Government Printing Office, 1895.

Tschappat, William H. *Text-book of Ordnance and Gunnery.* New York: John Wiley & Sons, 1917.

Winborne, B. B. *The Colonial and State History of Hertford County, North Carolina.* Privately printed, 1906.

INDEX